The Manual of Photography

The Manual of Photography

formerly The Ilford Manual of Photography

Edited by ALAN HORDER, CGIA, FRPS

FOCAL PRESS
London and New York

Distributed in the U.S.A. by
AMPHOTO
915 Broadway, New York, N.Y. 10010

The Ilford Manual of Photography
First published 1890

Fifth edition
Published in May 1958
Reprinted eight times

The Manual of Photography

Sixth edition
Published in April 1971
Reprinted December 1971

Reprinted September 1972

ISBN 0–8174–0798–7
Library of Congress Catalog Card No. 70–155805

REPRODUCED AND PRINTED BY PHOTOLITHOGRAPHY AND BOUND IN
GREAT BRITAIN AT THE PITMAN PRESS, BATH

Contents

Preface to the Sixth Edition

PHOTOGRAPHY, as a generally available process, is usually considered to date from 1839, in which year both L. J. M. Daguerre in France and W. H. Fox Talbot in Britain made public details of processes on which they had independently been working for some years.

The early photographic processes were, however, complex and the light-sensitive photographic materials required for their practice had very largely to be prepared by the photographer himself. Consequently, the practice of photography at this period was largely confined to the professional worker. Photography, as we know it today, with a wide variety of sensitised photographic materials readily available to professionals and amateurs alike, had to wait for the introduction of the gelatin "dry" plate.

The invention of this may be traced back to 1871, just 100 years ago, when R. L. Maddox published an account of an experiment in which he had made a photographic emulsion using gelatin as binding agent, instead of the collodion used in the normal "wet" plates of the time. From the experiments of Maddox, and of others who quickly followed him, stemmed the photographic manufacturing industry, which, by the end of the decade, was established in the major countries of the world.

Among the early manufacturers was Alfred Harman, who, in 1879, began making gelatin dry plates in the basement of a house in Ilford, in East London. From this small beginning grew the company that we now know as Ilford Limited.

The early photographic manufacturers were concerned, as are their successors today, not only to produce materials of the highest quality, but to ensure that they were handled by the user to the best advantage. With the latter aim in mind, several manufacturers published "handbooks" or "manuals" of photography, in which were outlined the essential steps in the taking of a photograph and the developing and printing of the result.

Outstanding among these manuals, and possibly the only one to survive to the present day, was the *Ilford Manual of Photography*, first published in about 1890, only a few years after the founding of the business that grew to become Ilford Limited. Since that date the book has been revised and reprinted many times, under successive editors, and has come to be valued by many generations of photographers for the straightforward account it gives of the theory and practice of photography.

In the present edition, the first to bear the imprint of the Focal Press, the name Ilford has been dropped from the title, but the aim of the manual remains unchanged: to provide the reader, whatever his or her interest in photography, with a clear account of the basic principles of the subject.

In the new edition the material on the camera has been almost completely rewritten and considerably enlarged, and two completely new chapters outlining the basic principles of colour photography have been added. In keeping with a policy, in recent years, of directing the emphasis of the book more towards the principles than the practice of photography, a number of chapters in the previous edition, dealing largely with craft and aesthetic aspects of the subject, have been omitted. Much of the remaining text, having stood the test of time, has been retained, with revision where necessary.

Technical information on specific Ilford products is not now included in the manual. For information of this type, whether on Ilford or on other manufacturers' materials, reference should be made to the instructions provided with the product concerned, or to the manufacturers' published data sheets.

In view of the change to the metric system taking place in the United Kingdom, SI units, the modern form of metric units, are now used throughout the book. Conversions between commonly used SI units and British units are given in the Appendix.

My thanks are due to colleagues in the Department of Photography, The Polytechnic of Central London, and in particular to Mr. S. Ray for Chapters 11, 12 and 13 on the camera and Mr. G. G. Attridge for Chapters 27 and 28 on colour photography.

London, January 1971   Alan Horder

CHAPTER 1

The Photographic Process

ALTHOUGH, today, the photographic process finds a host of applications, we still consider photography primarily as a method of making pictures. It is, in fact, a means of making pictures by the agency of light, the word photography having its origin in two Greek words meaning "light" and "writing".

We take a photograph by pressing a button on a camera. When we do this we are opening a shutter which permits light to pass through a lens to form an image on a light-sensitive film. The film records an impression of the image. This impression, which is invisible, is termed a latent ("hidden") image.

We obtain photographs from an exposed film by processing it. The processing of a film comprises several chemical operations, the purpose of which is to convert the invisible image on the film into a permanent visible image. The most characteristic operation in processing is development. The essential steps of the whole photographic process in its simplest (black-and-white, negative–positive) form are summarized in Table 1.1.

Exposure	Latent image formed
Processing:	
Development	Visible image formed
Rinsing	Development checked
Fixing	Unused sensitive material converted into soluble chemicals
Washing	Soluble chemicals removed
Drying	

Table 1.1 – The photographic process

The image formed when a film is processed in this way is a negative, and to obtain positive prints the negative is "printed". This involves a repetition of the photographic process using a further light-sensitive material – this time usually in the form of a sheet of paper – on which

I

an image of the negative is formed by passing light through the negative. This paper is processed in a similar manner to the film to produce a black-and-white print of the familiar kind.

The production of photographs

For success in the production of a photograph we must give proper consideration to each of the following four essential factors:

Composition

By composition we mean the choice and arrangement of the subject matter within the confines of the finished picture. The camera can only record what it sees, and we must control what the camera sees. We can do this, for example, by choice of viewpoint – its angle and distance from the subject, by controlling the placing of the subject within the picture space, and, sometimes, by suitable arrangement of the elements of the picture.

Illumination

Photographs are taken by light travelling from the subject towards the camera lens. Although some objects are self-luminous – e.g., firework displays – most objects are viewed and photographed by diffusely reflected light. The appearance of an object, both visually and photographically, thus depends not only on the object itself but also upon the light that illuminates it.

Our main sources of illumination in the day are the sun, the clear sky and clouds. Our "control" of the lighting of our pictures in day-time consists largely in selecting (or waiting for) the time of day or season of the year when the natural lighting produces the effect that we desire.

Our sources of artificial light are many, but all share, in varying degree, the advantage that, unlike daylight, they can be controlled at will. We can, therefore, obtain a wide variety of effects with artificial light. It is, however, good practice with most subjects to aim at producing a lighting effect similar to natural lighting on a sunny day, i.e., to use a main light in the role of the sun – casting shadows – and subsidiary lighting to lighten these shadows as required.

Image formation

To produce a photograph, as we normally understand it, light from the subject must be collected upon a light-sensitive surface, and must illuminate it in a pattern or image which resembles the subject. The faithfulness of the resemblance will depend upon the optical system employed, in particular upon the lens used and the relation of the lens to the sensitive surface.

Image perpetuation

Finally, the image-forming light must produce changes in the light-sensitive material in the camera so that there is implanted in this material an impression of the image, and this impression must be rendered permanent. This fourth factor is the one generally recognised as most characteristic of photography.

Each of the above factors plays an important role in the production of the finished picture, and the photographer should be familiar with the part played by each, and the rules governing it. The first factor, composition, is much less amenable to rules and regulations than the others, and it is primarily in the control of this – coupled with the second factor, illumination – that the personality of the individual photographer has greatest room for expression. For this reason, the most successful photographer is frequently one whose mastery of camera technique is so complete that he can give his whole attention to the subject that he is photographing.

Characteristic features of the photographic process

Photography is only one of a number of methods of making pictures. Others include pencil sketching, water-colour painting, oil painting, etching, charcoal drawing, etc. Each method has certain advantages and limitations both as regards its technique and its results.

An outstanding characteristic peculiar to the photographic method of making pictures is that the photographer usually has to wait for an appreciable period after "taking" the photograph before seeing the result. This has several consequences. On one hand it leads to the remark frequently made by the inexpert camera user – "I will let you have a copy … if it comes out!" – whereas, in fact, the performance of photographic materials and equipment has for many decades been such that total failure is most unlikely – unless the camera is handled with a complete lack of understanding of its operation.

The delay between exposure and the production of the actual print also means that great care must be taken in the selection of the subject and in choosing the right moment for exposure. The successful photographer trains himself to work very quickly when necessary, and to form in his mind a mental picture of the subject at the moment of exposure that usually enables him, without seeing the final print, to decide whether he has been successful or whether a retake is required. The ability to do this is indispensable to the professional photographer, for with many of the subjects which he is called upon to photograph there is no opportunity for a retake at a later date. (If, for any reason, he cannot be sure of his results he duplicates his shots.)

Among other features characteristic of the photographic process are the following:

(1) A real subject is necessary.

(2) Perspective is governed by optical laws.

(3) Colour may be recorded in colour, or in black-and-white, according to the type of film used.

(4) Gradation of tone is usually very fully recorded.

(5) Detail is recorded quickly and with comparative ease.

Perspective in photographs

The term "perspective" is applied to the apparent relation between the position and size of objects. In a scene examined visually, the perspective depends upon the viewpoint of the observer. The same principle holds good when a scene is photographed, the only difference being that the camera lens takes the place of the eye. Control of perspective in photography is therefore achieved by control of viewpoint.

A painter is not limited in this way; he can place objects in his picture anywhere he pleases, and alter their relative sizes at will. If, for example, he is depicting a building and is forced by the presence of other buildings to work close up to it, he can nevertheless produce a picture which – as far as perspective is concerned – appears to have been painted at a distance. The photographer cannot do this. Selection of viewpoint is thus seen to be of great importance to the photographer if a given perspective is to be achieved.

Reproduction of colour

As far as colour is concerned, photographs are of two main types: colour and monochrome (black-and-white). Colour photography did not become a practicable proposition for the average photographer until nearly 100 years after the invention of photography, but in recent years its use has gained rapidly over black-and-white photography, and in many fields now predominates. However, a great deal of photographic work – especially professional photography – is still done in monochrome, and it is with this type of work that this book is principally concerned. Colour photography is essentially a development of black-and-white photography, so that a study of the principles of the latter will provide a sound basis for a consideration of colour photography – the subject of the last two Chapters of the book.

Monochrome reproduction is not peculiar to black-and-white photography alone, but is shared by processes such as pencil sketching, charcoal drawing and etching. In all these processes we are attempting to reproduce in two dimensions and one colour, an original subject which is in three dimensions and in many different colours. This is a task to which we must bring all the help given us by the nature of the particular process which we are using. We can, for example, in a photographic print, obtain a fair impression of solidity by intelligent use of perspective, differential focusing, haze and receding planes, and, although we have only shades of grey from white to black in which to reproduce colours, we can, by reproducing them as greys similar in tone to the original colours, obtain an acceptable rendering of colours in monochrome. Fortunately, in the representation both of solidity and of colour we have the forces of convention and habit on our side.

Reproduction of tone

Various ways of achieving gradation of tone are employed in the graphic arts. In etchings and drawings in pen and ink – which consist of lines varying principally in width rather than in density – the effects of light and shade are obtained largely by controlling the width or the spacing of the lines. For example, several lines placed close together, in what is termed "hatching", produce an area of shade. Such pictures are referred to as *line* reproductions. In photographs, on the other hand, the effects of light and shade are obtained by variation of the tone of the print. Thus, a highlight of uniform brightness in the subject appears as a uniform area of very light grey, almost white, in the print. A shadow of uniform depth appears as a uniform area of dark grey, or black, in the print. Between these extremes all shades of grey may be present. Photographs are therefore referred to as *continuous-tone* reproductions. (When, of course, photography is used to record originals which are themselves confined to two tones, as for instance when a line original – e.g., an engineering drawing – is copied, the photographic process is then employed to produce a line, not a continuous-tone copy.)

It should be noted that in black-and-white photography we have only one variant in the print, that of tone, to reproduce all variations in the subject, whether of luminance or of colour.

Reproduction of detail

For the reproduction of detail the photographic process is without equal. Whereas a detailed drawing demands far more in time and energy from an artist than a simple sketch, the camera can record a wealth of detail just as easily and just as quickly as it can a simple object. Thus it is that the reproduction of texture – essentially fine detail – by the camera is the envy of the artist.

Negatives and positives

As we have already noted, most photographs are produced by exposing a film first, following this by a further exposure to produce a print on paper. This procedure is followed because, with most of the light-sensitive materials that have proved suitable for photography, increasing brightness of the subject produces increasing blackness on the photographic material. The film record therefore has the tones of the subject in reverse – black where the original is light, clear where the original is dark, with the intermediate tones similarly reversed. The original film is therefore referred to as a *negative*, while a print, in which by a further use of the photographic process the tones of the original are re-reversed, is termed a *positive*. Any photographic process by which a negative is made first and employed for the subsequent preparation of prints is referred to as a *negative-positive process*.

It should be noted here that, although the eye will accept a two-dimensional monochrome print as a fair representation of a three-dimensional coloured object, it will not accept a negative as an objective picture. Negative records are thus not acceptable for pictorial purposes – except for stunt effects – although they are acceptable in certain technical applications of photography, as for instance in some types of document copying.

It is possible to obtain positive photographs directly on the material exposed in the camera, but the procedure for doing this is usually more complex than the preparation of negatives. The first widely used photographic process – that due to Daguerre – did in fact produce positives directly. The first negative-positive process, due to Fox Talbot, although announced at about the same time as that of Daguerre, gained ground rather more slowly, but today negative-positive processes are used for the greater part of black-and-white photography. Although processes giving positive photographs in a single operation appear attractive, in practice, negative-positive processes are more generally useful – especially in professional work – by virtue of the very fact that two stages are required. In the first place, the negative provides a master which can be stored away for safe keeping. Then, it is easier to make copies from a transparent master than from a positive photograph – which is usually required to be on an opaque paper base. Again, the printing stage of a two-stage process gives an additional and valuable opportunity for control of the finished picture.

Negatives are usually made on a transparent base – film or glass – and positives on paper, though there are important exceptions to this. (For example, negatives are sometimes made on paper for reasons of economy, as in document copying and in some forms of commercial portraiture. Positives are sometimes made on film or glass for projection purposes, as in the case of lantern slides, filmstrips and cine films. Such positives are termed *diapositives* or *transparencies*.) It should be noted, however, that the action of light in producing an image on negative materials and positive materials is essentially the same in the two cases.

CHAPTER 2

The Nature of Light

PHOTOGRAPHY, as far as the photographer is concerned, starts with light. Light radiating from the sun – or whatever other source we are employing – travels through space and impinges upon the surface of our subject. According to the way in which it is received or rejected – in whole or in part – a complex pattern of light, shade and colour originates, which, appearing in the visual field, is interpreted by us from past experience in terms of three-dimensional solidity. The picture made by the camera is a more-or-less faithful representation of what a single eye sees, and, from the patches of light and shade in the positive photographic print, the eyes and the mind working together can arrive at a reasonably accurate interpretation of the form and nature of the objects portrayed. Thus, light makes it possible for us to be well-informed about the shapes, sizes, and textures of things – whether we can handle them or not.

The nature of light has been the subject of much speculation. In Newton's view it was corpuscular, i.e., consisted of separate particles, but this theory could not be made to fit all the known facts, and the *wave theory* of Huygens and Young took its place. Later still, Planck found that many facts could be explained only on the assumption that energy is always emitted in discrete amounts, or quanta. Planck's *quantum theory* might appear at first sight to be a revival of Newton's corpuscular theory, but there is only a superficial similarity. Nowadays, physicists make their interpretations in terms of both the wave and quantum theories.

Optics
The study of the behaviour of light is termed *optics*. It is customary to group the problems that confront us in this study in three different classes, and to formulate for each a different set of rules as to how light behaves. The science of optics is thus divided into three branches:

8

Physical optics

This is the study of light on the assumption that it behaves as waves. A stone dropped into a pond of still water causes a train of waves to spread out in all directions on the surface of the water. Such waves are almost completely confined to the surface of the water, the advancing wave-front being *circular* in form. A point source of light, however, is assumed to emit energy in the form of waves which spread out in all directions, and hence, with light, the wave-front forms a *spherical* surface of ever-increasing size. This wave-front may be deviated from its original direction by obstacles situated in its path, the form which the deviation takes depending on the shape and nature of the obstacle.

Geometrical optics

The path of any single point on the wave-front referred to above is a straight line with direction perpendicular to the wave-front. Hence we say that light travels in straight lines. In geometrical optics we postulate the existence of *light rays* represented by such straight lines along which light-energy flows. By means of these lines, change of direction of travel of a wave-front can be shown easily. The concept of light rays is therefore helpful in studying the formation of an image by a lens.

Quantum optics

This branch of modern physics, which assumes that light consists essentially of quanta of energy, is employed when studying in detail the effects that take place when light is absorbed by matter, e.g., on striking an emulsion or a photo-electric cell.

Light waves

As already stated, many of the properties of light are readily explained if we suppose that it takes the form of waves. Unlike sound waves, which require for their propagation air or some other material medium, light waves travel freely in a vacuum. In a vacuum, e.g., in free space, light travels at almost exactly 3×10^8 metres per second (300 000 kilometres per second). In air, its velocity is very nearly as great, but in water it is reduced to three-quarters and in glass to about two-thirds of its value in space.

Many forms of wave besides light travel in space at the same speed as light; they are termed *the family of electromagnetic waves*. All electromagnetic waves are considered to vibrate at right angles to their direction of travel. As such, they are described as *transverse* waves, as opposed to *longitudinal* waves – such as sound waves – in which the direction of vibration is along the line of travel.

The distance in the direction of travel from a point on one wave to the corresponding point on the next is called the *wavelength* of the radiation. Wavelength is usually denoted by the Greek letter lambda (λ). The number of waves passing any given point per second is termed the *frequency* of vibration. Different kinds of electromagnetic waves are distinguished by their wavelength or frequency. The amount of movement of a light wave in a lateral direction is termed its *amplitude*. Amplitude is a measure of the intensity of the light, but is a term rarely used in photography.

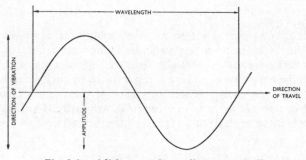

Fig. 2.1 – A light wave shown diagrammatically

Figure 2.1 shows a light wave diagramatically, and illustrates the terms wavelength and amplitude. In the figure, the ray of light is shown as vibrating in one plane only – the plane of the paper. It should, however; be considered as vibrating in all directions simultaneously, i.e., at right-angles to the paper as well as in its plane.

The product of wavelength and frequency equals the velocity of propagation of the radiation.

The electromagnetic spectrum

Of the other waves besides light travelling in space, some have wavelengths shorter than that of light and others have longer wavelengths. The complete series of waves, arranged in order of wavelengths, is referred to as the *electromagnetic spectrum*. This is illustrated in Figure 2.2. There is no sharp, clear-cut line between one wave and another, or between one type of radiation and another – the series of waves is continuous.

The various types of radiation forming the family of electromagnetic rays differ very widely in what they can do. Waves of very long wavelength such as wireless waves, for example, have no effect on the body – they cannot be seen or felt – although they can readily be detected by means of special apparatus. As we move down the spectrum, however, and wavelength diminishes, we reach waves which we feel as heat, and then come to waves which the eye sees as light. We call the last-named waves the *visible spectrum*. Proceeding to shorter wavelengths still, we reach radiation such as x-rays, which can penetrate the human body, and gamma-rays, which can penetrate several inches of steel. Both x-rays and gamma-rays, unless properly controlled, are dangerous to human beings.

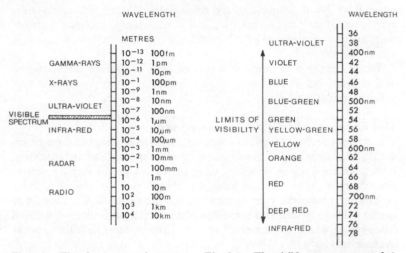

Fig. 2.2 – The electromagnetic spectrum   Fig. 2.3 – The visible spectrum expanded

The visible spectrum

In photography, we are principally interested in visible radiation, although other electromagnetic rays have important applications in specialized branches of photography. The visible spectrum occupies only a minute part of the total range of electromagnetic radiation, comprising wavelengths within the limits of approximately 400 and 700 nanometres*. Within these limits, the human eye sees change of wavelength as a change of colour. The change from one colour to another is not a sharp one, but the spectrum may be divided up roughly as shown in Figure 2.3. (See also Chapter 17.)

---

* I nanometre (nm) = 10^{-9} metre (m). The nanometre was formerly known as the millimicron (mμ).

The eye has a very slight sensitivity beyond this region – to 390nm at the short-wave end and 760nm at the long-wave end – but for most photographic purposes this can be ignored. Shorter wavelengths than 390nm, invisible to the eye, are referred to as *ultra-violet* (u.v.), and longer wavelengths than 760nm, also invisible to the eye, are referred to as *infra-red* (i.r.).

It will be noted from Figure 2.3 that the visible spectrum contains the colours of the rainbow in their familiar unvarying order, from violet at the short wavelength end to red at long wavelengths. For many photographic purposes we can usefully consider the visible spectrum to consist of three bands only: blue-violet from 400 to 500nm, green from 500 to 600nm and red from 600 to 700nm. This division is only an approach to the truth, but it is sufficiently accurate to be of help in solving many practical problems and has the virtue that it is readily memorized.

White light is a mixture of waves of light of various wavelengths, and contains all the colours of the spectrum – violet, blue, green, yellow, orange and red.

Use of the word "light" in photography

The various forms of waves comprising the electromagnetic spectrum are referred to generally as *radiation*, or *radiant flux*. Strictly speaking, only radiation capable of stimulating the eye to produce visual sensation should be referred to as light. For the purposes of photography it is, however, frequently convenient to use the term "light" to include both visible radiation and the near-visible radiation – ultra-violet and infra-red – which (as we shall see in Chapter 16) can affect photographic materials.

CHAPTER 3

Light Sources

WE take photographs by the agency of light travelling from the subject to the camera. This light usually originates at a source outside the picture and is reflected by the subject. Light comes from both natural and artificial sources. The natural sources of importance in photography are the sun, the clear sky and clouds. The artificial light sources employed in photography are more varied. For convenience, we may classify them in four main groups, in terms of the method used to produce the light, as follows:

(1) *By burning*, e.g., candles, oil-lamps, matches, magnesium ribbon, flash powder, flashbulbs.

(2) *By heating*, e.g., incandescent tungsten filament electric lamps.

(3) *By electric spark or arc*, e.g., carbon arcs.

(4) *By passing an electric current through a metallic vapour, or rare gas*, e.g., mercury vapour discharge lamps, electronic flash tubes.

Characteristics of light sources

Light sources differ in many ways, and it will help us in the selection of sources for various purposes if we study these differences in some detail. The important characteristics from a photographic point of view are:

(1) Spectral quality.

(2) Light output.

(3) Size.

(4) Efficiency.

(5) Cost.

(6) Constancy of output.

(7) Convenience.

We shall examine each of these factors in detail and then see how specific light sources perform in various respects. We shall consider both daylight and artificial light sources, although certain of the factors that we have listed above are applicable only to artificial sources.

The order of importance of these factors will depend upon circumstances and, in selecting a light source for a particular purpose, one factor must frequently be weighed against another.

(1) Spectral quality

The radiation from most light sources comprises a mixture of light of various wavelengths. The *colour* of the light from a source, or its *spectral quality*, may vary widely, depending on how the light is distributed in the spectrum, i.e., on the proportion of energy due to each wavelength. Practically all sources of light in common use for photographic work – with the exception of discharge lamps – give what is usually described as "white" light. This term is used in rather a loose way to describe light which is not very noticeably deficient in any particular colour, but it does not imply any very definite colour quality. In actual fact, the quality of so-called "white" light from artificial light sources is usually quite different from that of daylight, and different artificial light sources vary greatly among themselves. In everyday life these differences are of little importance, but they can be *very* important in photography – especially in colour photography. It is, therefore, desirable that we should be able to describe light quality in precise terms.

From the physical standpoint, light, in common with other forms of electromagnetic radiation, is a form of energy, and the colour quality of light can therefore be defined in terms of the way in which the energy is distributed throughout the spectrum. This can be expressed, with varying degrees of precision, in three ways:

(1) By means of a graph – called a spectral energy distribution curve – in which the energy of the light source is plotted against wavelength.

(2) By quoting the percentages of radiation present in the main regions of the spectrum, i.e., blue-violet, green and red.

(3) By the concept known as "colour temperature".

Each of these three methods has its own advantages, but not all methods are applicable to every light source.

Spectral energy distribution curve

Given a suitable instrument, it is possible to measure the way in which energy in the form of light is distributed through the spectrum, wavelength by wavelength. The information thus obtained can be usefully displayed in the form of a curve in which energy is plotted against wavelength. Such a curve is termed a *spectral energy distribution curve*. Curves of this type for sunlight, a clear blue sky and a tungsten lamp are given in Figure 3.1.

Spectral energy distribution curves bring out clearly small differences between various forms of light. For example, we should probably describe light from each of the sources illustrated in Figure 3.1, seen separately, as "white", because of chromatic adaptation by the eye (page 285), yet the three curves are seen to be quite different. Light from a blue sky is shown by its curve to be – as would be expected – particularly rich in blue radiation, while light from a tungsten lamp is shown to have a very high red content, although this is not normally obvious.

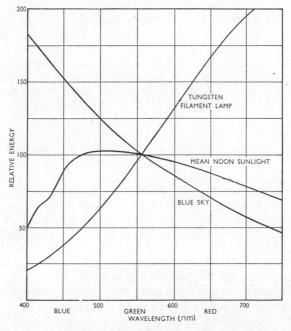

Fig. 3.1 – Spectral energy distribution curves of sunlight, light from a blue sky and light from a tungsten lamp

There are two main types of spectra. The three sources depicted in Figure 3.1 have what are termed *continuous* spectra, because energy is present at all wavelengths and the change in the energy present from one wavelength to the next is a gradual one. Most light sources – including all electric lamps in which light is obtained from an incandescent filament – have spectra of this type. In some sources, however, the energy is confined to a few, very narrow regions of the spectrum. At these wavelengths the energy is intense, but at other wavelengths it is almost or entirely nil. These sources are said to have *discontinuous*, or *line*, spectra. When an electric current is passed through a vapour at low pressure, the spectrum of the resulting radiation is of this type. Figure 3.2 shows the line spectrum of a low-pressure mercury vapour discharge lamp.

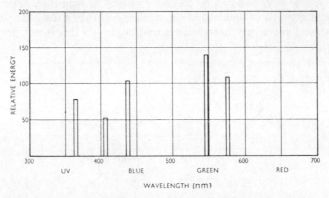

Fig. 3.2 – Spectral distribution of light from a low-pressure mercury vapour discharge lamp

When an electric current is passed through a vapour at *high* pressure, the lines comprising the spectrum broaden into bands, and are accompanied by a continuous background spectrum which becomes increasingly prominent as the pressure is raised. Thus, light from a high-pressure mercury vapour lamp takes the form of a band spectrum with a continuous background.

A spectral energy distribution curve provides a precise form of expressing the quality of light from any source – continuous or discontinuous. For practical photographic purposes, however, it is not the most convenient way of expressing the quality of light, the curves being laborious to produce and often difficult to apply.

Percentage content of the primary colours
Since, for many photographic purposes, the spectrum can be considered as consisting of three main bands – blue-violet, green and red – the quality of light from a source having a continuous spectrum can be approximately expressed in terms of the percentages in which light of these three colours is present. This method is not very precise, but is of interest because it is the basis of some instruments used for measuring the quality of light. (See page 42.)

Colour temperature
The most commonly employed method of defining the quality of light from an incandescent source is by means of its *colour temperature*. The

colour temperature of a light source is the temperature of a full radiator* which would emit radiation of substantially the same spectral distribution in the visible region as the radiation from the light source, and which would have the same colour. Colour temperatures are measured on the thermodynamic, or Kelvin, scale, which has a unit of temperature interval identical to that of the Celsius (centigrade) scale, but with its zero at $-273 \cdot 15°C$.

The idea of colour temperature can be appreciated by considering what happens when a poker is left in a fire. At first, it is a dull black, then it glows a deep red, then bright red and finally becomes "white" hot. Quite obviously, the quality of the light emitted changes with the temperature of the poker. Initially, the light consists almost entirely of red light but, as the poker becomes hotter, the proportion of other colours increases until all are present in approximately equal amounts, giving white light.

Luminous sources of low colour temperature are characterized by an energy distribution relatively rich in red radiation, giving what is commonly described as "warm" light. As we proceed up the colour temperature scale the emission of energy becomes more evenly distributed and the light becomes whiter. At the highest colour temperatures, the energy distribution is rich in blue radiation and the light is then commonly described as "cold". (The possibility of confusion in terminology here should be noted and guarded against.)

The concept of colour temperature is strictly applicable only to sources acting as full ("black-body") radiators, but its use can be extended without objection to any source having a spectral energy distribution closely matching that from a full radiator, e.g., a tungsten filament lamp. The term colour temperature is convenient, though improperly used, for classifying fluorescent lamps whose spectra, and hence photographic effects, are very different from those of full radiators.

Approximate colour temperatures of some light sources used in photography are given in Table 3.1.

Instead of colour temperature, the term *correlated colour temperature* is sometimes used to describe the quantity of light from sources whose spectra differ from those of full radiators. These figures, however, must be used with care when considering the photographic effect of such sources.

---

* I.e., a light source emitting radiation, the spectral distribution of which is dependent on the temperature only and not on the material and nature of the source. Sometimes termed a "black-body" radiator.

Light source	Approximate colour temperature
Standard candle	1930K
Dawn sunlight	2000K
Vacuum tungsten lamp	2400K
Acetylene lamp (used in early sensitometric work)	2415K
Gas-filled tungsten lamp (general service)	2760 to 2960K
Warm-white fluorescent lamp	3000K
"Photographic" lamp	3200K
Photoflood lamp	3400K
Clear flashbulb	3800K
Plain carbon arc	3800K
Daylight fluorescent lamp	4500K
White-flame arc	5000K
"Mean noon sunlight"	5400K
Blue flashbulb	6000K
H.I. carbon arc (sun arc)	6000K
Electronic flash tube	6000K
Average daylight (sunlight and skylight combined)	6500K
Colour matching fluorescent lamp	6500K
Enclosed arc	10 000K
Blue sky	12 000 to 18 000K

Table 3.1 – Colour temperatures of some common light sources

In black-and-white photography, the colour or quality of light is only of limited importance for the practical photographer, although it must be taken into account in sensitometry. In colour photography, however, light quality is of the utmost practical importance, and colour temperature then serves as a useful way of defining it. The measurement and control of colour temperature, in particular for colour photography, are discussed on page 41.

The mired scale

Any colour temperature can have assigned to it a value on the *mired scale*, the name of which is derived from the contraction of the words: micro reciprocal degrees. The relation between the mired scale and colour temperature is:

$$\text{Mired value} = \frac{1\,000\,000}{\text{Colour temperature in kelvins}}$$

Conversion from one scale to the other may be achieved by reference to Figure 3.3.

The main advantage of the mired scale is that equal intervals in it correspond to equal variations in colour. As a result, photometric filters (page 298) can be allotted *mired shift values*, which indicate at once the change in colour quality which the filter will effect, with whatever source it is used. Yellowish photometric filters, for raising the mired value of the light (lowering the colour temperature in kelvins), are given positive mired shift values; bluish photometric filters, for lowering the mired value (raising the colour temperature in kelvins), are given negative values.

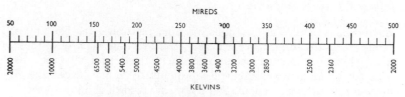

Fig. 3.3 – The mired and kelvin scales

Example: A certain bluish photometric filter is known to be suitable for converting tungsten light at 2360K (424 mireds) to 2850K (351 mireds). The mired shift value of the filter is therefore $424 - 351 = 73$, and, since the filter is bluish, the sign of this value is negative.

The filter is therefore suitable for making other conversions as follows:

2850K (351 mireds) to 3600K (278 mireds)
3400K (294 mireds) to 4500K (222 mireds)
3900K (256 mireds) to 5480K (183 mireds)
etc. etc.

(2) Light output

The output, or power, of a source is obviously one of its more important characteristics. Three related units are used to define it. They are: luminous intensity, luminance and luminous flux.

Luminous intensity is expressed numerically in relation to the output of a standard light source. This was originally a special form of wax candle. Oil lamps and acetylene lamps were later used as standards; then, for many years, the "international candle" was maintained by means of carbon and tungsten filament electric lamps, until in recent years a primary standard – the *candela* – was adopted. The magnitude of the candela, the unit of luminous intensity, is by definition the luminous intensity, in the direction of the normal, of a full radiator

surface 1/600 000 square metre in area at the temperature of solidification of platinum. While this definition puts the unit on a more
fundamental basis than formerly, for practical purposes in photography the unit can be regarded as unchanged from the more familiar
"candle".

The light-radiating capacity of a source in terms of the luminous
intensity expressed in candelas is termed its *candle-power*. The
candle-power of a source is not necessarily the same in all directions.
It is, therefore, common practice to specify a source in terms of the
average value of its candle-power in all directions. This is properly
referred to as *mean spherical candle-power*.

Luminance is defined as luminous intensity per unit area. The unit of
luminance is the candela per square metre. The luminance of a source,
like its luminous intensity, is not necessarily the same in all directions.
The term luminance is applicable equally to light sources and to
illuminated surfaces. In photography, we are recording luminances.

It follows from the definition of the candela given above, that the
luminance of a full radiator at the temperature of solidification of
platinum is 600 000 candelas per square metre.

Luminous flux. The amount of light emitted in unit solid angle* by a
point source having a uniform intensity in all directions of one candela
is defined as the unit of luminous flux, termed the *lumen*. Since a
sphere subtends 4π steradians at its centre (area of surface of sphere=
$4\pi r^2$), a light source of 1 candle-power radiating uniformly in all directions emits a total of 4π=approximately 12·5 lumens. (The conversion: 1 candela=12·5 lumens is only approximately applicable to
most practical light sources, as these do not radiate uniformly in all
directions. See page 38.)

The lumen provides a useful measure when considering the output
of a source in a reflector or other housing, or when considering the
amount of light passing through an optical system.

(3) Size

In ordinary photography, the size of a light source is important principally because it controls the nature of the shadows cast by the source.

---

* The unit solid angle, or steradian, is the angle subtended at the centre of a
sphere of unit radius by a surface of unit area on the sphere. Thus, an area of
1 square metre on the surface of a sphere of 1 metre radius subtends at its
centre a solid angle of 1 steradian.

Small light sources give shadows with hard edges; large sources give soft edges.† Small sources are therefore very valuable for the rendering of texture – which consists of light and shade in very small areas – where the essence of recording is to obtain sharply defined shadows. A spotlight (page 37) is essentially a means for controlling and using efficiently the light from a small source.

A small source is desirable whenever it is required to employ a light source in an optical system, as, for example, in photomicrography. Small light sources finding application in photography include projector-type tungsten filament lamps, car headlamp bulbs and carbon arc lamps.

(4) Efficiency

The *efficiency* of a light source is the ratio of the luminous flux emitted to the power consumed by the source. In the case of an electric lamp it is expressed in lumens per watt. A theoretically perfect lamp emitting white light of daylight quality would have an efficiency of about 220 lumens per watt. Values obtained in practice for some common light sources are given in Table 3.2.

Light source	Approximate efficiency
	lumens per watt
Carbon filament lamp	3·5
Tungsten filament lamps	
Vacuum	7
Gas-filled, single coil	10
Gas-filled, coiled coil	12
"Photographic" lamp	20
Photoflood lamp	30
Fluorescent lamp	50 or higher

Table 3.2 – Efficiencies of some light sources used in photography

The term "half-watt", often applied to ordinary domestic (general service) lamps, presumes an efficiency of 1 candle-power per half-watt, i.e., 2 candle-power per watt. This corresponds roughly with 25 lumens per watt. The term is thus seen to be rather optimistic. It originated, however, at a time when the introduction of the gas-filled lamp did mark a real advance in efficiency over the vacuum lamp.

In considering the efficiency of a light source for photographic work, both the spectral distribution of the source and the spectral

† The *size* and the *shape* of the shadows produced by a source are governed by the positioning of the source.

response of the photographic material (Chapter 16) must be taken into account. The photographic effectiveness of a light source, relative to a reference source, for a given film sensitivity, is termed its *actinity*.

(5) Cost

The initial cost, useful life, running cost and replacement cost are all factors to be considered in the choice of a light source. The initial cost of the source and its associated equipment may be very heavy, and is frequently the deciding factor in its choice.

Tungsten filament lamps are a relatively cheap source as regards initial cost of lamps, wiring and fittings and as regards replacement of lamps. Fluorescent lamps, on the other hand, require more expensive electrical fittings and the tubes themselves are dearer than tungsten filament lamps, watt for watt. Against this, the fluorescent lamp has a higher efficiency than the tungsten filament lamp, and running costs are therefore less.

(6) Constancy of output

Constancy of light intensity and quality are obviously desirable characteristics of any light source to be used in photography. Although, for black-and-white work, constancy of output makes primarily for convenience, in colour work it is an essential.

Daylight, although an intense and cheap form of lighting, is not constant as regards intensity or quality, and, because of this, is not used from choice when working against time. Electric light sources, which in one form or another are used almost universally when artificial light sources are required, are far more reliable than daylight. However, even these sources require a constant power supply in order to yield constant light output, and if the frequency and/or voltage of the mains supply fluctuates as the load applied by consumers changes, appreciable variation in light intensity and quality may result (page 25). For colour work, therefore, some form of voltage control is often desirable. Light quality may also change as bulbs age, and for colour work this may mean that bulbs have to be replaced by new ones before their useful life is ended, the old bulbs being then employed for black-and-white work only.

One of the advantages attending the use of flashbulbs and electronic flash is the constancy of light output and quality that can be obtained.

The control of light intensity and quality, in particular for colour photography, is discussed on page 42.

(7) Convenience

Under this heading we can group a number of factors:

Degree of heating which accompanies operation of the lamp.

Presence of fumes.

Need for high operating voltage and corresponding need for special safety precautions.

Need for unusual supply, e.g., a three-phase supply or very high current.

Ease of operation – initially and on re-starting after use.

Weight and bulk of source and associated gear.

These factors, which are more-or-less self-explanatory, all have their bearing on the suitability of a light source for a particular task.

Characteristics of some light sources used in photography

So far we have discussed the characteristics of light sources in general terms only. In the following pages, the characteristics of some specific sources used in photography – both daylight and artificial sources – are described in detail.

Daylight

A great deal of photographic work is done out of doors in ordinary daylight. Daylight includes light from the sun, from the sky and from clouds. It has a continuous spectrum, although it is not exactly represented by any single colour temperature. However, in the visual region – though not beyond it – colour temperature does give a close approximation to its quality. The quality of daylight varies through the day. Its colour temperature is low at dawn – in the region of 2000K if the sun is unobscured. It then rises quickly to a maximum and remains fairly constant through the middle part of the day. It tails off slowly through the afternoon, and finally falls rapidly at sunset to a value which is again below that of a tungsten filament lamp. The quality of daylight also varies from place to place and according to whether the sun is shining in a clear sky or is obscured by cloud.

The reddening of daylight at sunrise and at sunset arises from the absorption and scattering of sunlight by the atmosphere (page 305). These are greatest when the sun is low, because the path of the light through the earth's atmosphere is then longest. As the degree of scattering is most marked with the shorter wavelengths, the light which continues to the earth unscattered contains a preponderance of the longer wavelengths and thus appears reddish.

Fluctuations such as have been described prohibit the use of ordinary daylight for the testing of photographic materials in the sensitometric laboratory. Here, it is essential to use light sources of fixed colour quality. For many photographic purposes, especially in sensitometry, the average quality of sunlight at noon at Washington, D.C., is used as the standard. ("Sunlight" in this connexion means what it says; i.e., excludes skylight.) This is referred to as *mean noon sunlight* and approximates in quality to light at a colour temperature of 5400K. Sunlight at Washington was chosen for the standard because the U.S. National Bureau of Standards had made an extensive series of measurements of its quality. "Mean" noon sunlight was obtained by averaging readings taken at the summer and winter solstices (June 21st and December 21st). Light of this quality is sometimes referred to as "photographic daylight". It is achieved in the laboratory by operating a tungsten lamp under controlled conditions so that it emits light of a given colour temperature, and screening this by a Davis-Gibson liquid filter. Sunlight distribution is of importance in photographic sensitometry, not because it may approximately represent a standard white, but because it represents, perhaps better than any other single energy distribution, the average condition under which the great majority of photographic negative materials are exposed.

The combination of light from sun, sky and clouds usually has, near noon, a colour temperature in the region of 6500K. An overcast (cloudy) sky has a sllghtly higher colour temperature, while that of a blue sky may rise to as high as 12000 to 18000K. The colour temperature of the light from the sky and the clouds is of interest independently of that of sunlight, because it is skylight alone which illuminates shadows.

Tungsten filament lamps
One of the best known types of artificial light source is the incandescent lamp, in which light is produced by heating a filament by passing an electric current through it. Early incandescent lamps were made using carbon filaments in evacuated bulbs, but the efficiency was low and the light reddish in colour. The filament temperature in these lamps was limited to about 2080K, above which temperature the life of the filament was rapidly reduced. After considerable research, lamp designers found that by making the filament of tungsten – which has a melting point of 3650K – lamps could be made having much greater luminous efficiency and giving a whiter light. In the early tungsten lamps, the filament was in a vacuum and its temperature could not exceed 2400K, as above this figure extensive evaporation occurred, causing rapid blackening of the bulb and reducing the life of the filament. Later, it was found that by filling the bulb with a mixture

of argon and nitrogen gases the operating temperature could be raised to as high as 3400K. Other things being equal, an increase in the operating temperature of a tungsten lamp gives increased efficiency but a decrease in life. Some tungsten lamps have been designed to give very high efficiency at the expense of working life; these are termed *overrun* lamps. Photoflood lamps, described below, are in this category.

Types of tungsten filament lamp

Many different types of tungsten lamp are now made. Lamps used for photographic lighting purposes are of three main types, as follows:

(1) *General service lamps.* These are of the type used for normal domestic purposes. They are made in a range of sizes from 15W to 1500W, and may be supplied with clear, pearl or opal glass envelopes. The smallest lamps, rated at 15W, are vacuum lamps, with a colour temperature of about 2400K. Lamps from 25W and upwards are gas-filled and have greater efficiency. The colour temperatures of these lamps range from about 2760 to 2960K. General service lamps have a life of about 1000 hours.

(2) *"Photographic" lamps.* The term "photographic lamp" is applied to 500W lamps specially made for photographic purposes. This classification includes "Photographic Series B" lamps, "Photographic Pearl" lamps and "Argaphoto" lamps. These lamps have a slightly greater efficiency than general service lamps, the increase having been obtained at the expense of a reduction in life to 100 hours. The colour temperature of the light produced by "photographic" lamps is about 3200K.

(3) *Photoflood lamps.* Photoflood lamps were developed in an endeavour to obtain a large amount of highly actinic light from household circuits. The lamps operate at a colour temperature of about 3400K – only about 200K below the melting point of tungsten – and have an efficiency of about $2\frac{1}{2}$ times that of general service lamps of the same wattage.

Two types of Photoflood lamps are in general use. The smaller (No. 1) type is rated at 275W and has a life of 2 to 3 hours. The larger (No. 2) type is rated at 500W with a life of 6 to 10 hours. 1000W Photoflood lamps are also available.

Characteristics of the tungsten filament lamp

A tungsten filament lamp is designed to operate at a specified voltage, and its performance will be affected if this voltage is departed from, either through supply fluctuation or through selection of the wrong

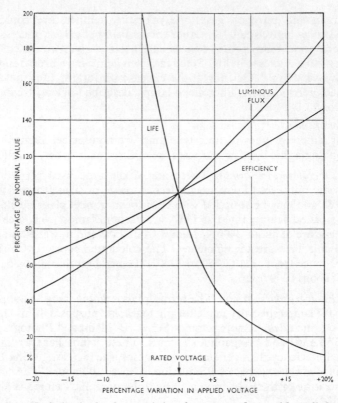

Fig. 3.4 – Variation in the characteristics of a tungsten lamp with applied voltage

lamp for the supply in use. Figure 3.4 shows how the luminous flux, efficiency and life of a lamp are affected by departure from the normal voltage. It will be noted from this figure that a 1 per cent. excess voltage results in a 4 per cent. increase in luminous flux, a 2 per cent. increase in efficiency, and a 12 per cent. decrease in life.

A further characteristic of the tungsten lamp which changes with supply voltage is colour temperature; this rises with the operating voltage. The colour temperature quoted for a given lamp, e.g., 3200K for a "photographic" lamp, is achieved only when the lamp is run at its rated voltage. This is illustrated in Figure 3.5. With a lamp having a nominal colour temperature in the region of 3200 or 3400K, a 1 per cent. excess voltage results in a 10K increase in colour temperature.

Type of cap and angle of burning

Tungsten lamps are supplied with a number of different types of cap. These are described by recognized abbreviations: e.g., B.C. (Bayonet Cap), E.S. (Edison Screw), G.E.S. (Goliath Edison Screw), S.C.C. (Small Centre Contact), etc. Details of standard caps are given in lamp manufacturers' catalogues. It is important when ordering lamps to ensure that the required type of cap is specified.

Certain types of lamp, in particular projection lamps, are designed

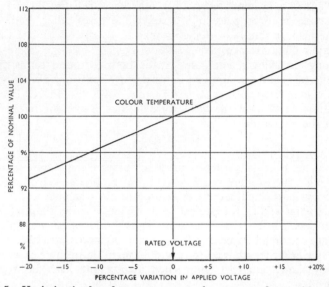

Fig. 3.5 – Variation in the colour temperature of a tungsten lamp with applied voltage

to operate in one position only, or in only a limited range of positions. If these lamps are used in other positions, the filament may break. Again, reference should be made to lamp manufacturers' catalogues for details. In such catalogues, the correct position of burning is normally specified by reference to the position of the cap.

Tungsten halogen lamps

The tungsten halogen lamp is a special form of tungsten lamp in which a trace of halogen is added to the filling gas. The halogen in a tungsten halogen lamp sets up a regenerative cycle by which evaporated tungsten is removed from the bulb wall and returned to the filament, thus eliminating blackening of the bulb wall and lengthening the life of the filament. The complex tungsten halogen cycle will function only when the temperature of the bulb wall exceeds 250°C, and this is achieved by using a bulb of small diameter made of quartz. This makes it possible to produce smaller sized lamps with higher light output and longer life than traditional tungsten lamps of the same wattage.

In the early lamps of this type, the halogen used was iodine and the lamps were commonly termed "quartz iodine" lamps. With new developments in lamp technology other heat-resisting materials are sometimes used in place of quartz, while gases other than iodine in the halogen family of elements may be used, and have advantage in certain circumstances.

Tungsten halogen lamps are made both as round bulbs and in tubular form and are supplied in a range of sizes from 50W to 2000W, with colour temperatures ranging from 2500K to 3400K. Tungsten halogen lamps have the advantage of constant colour temperature throughout their life.

Carbon arc lamps

Carbon arc lamps are still sometimes employed where light sources of very high intensity are required, e.g., in the photomechanical trades for copyboard illumination, in photoprinting machines and in cinematography – both for projection work and for the illumination of studio sets. The light from an arc lamp is produced by an electric discharge occurring between two carbon rods connected to a D.C. supply. To "strike" the arc, the rods are brought into contact and then rapidly drawn apart, a flame then maintaining itself between the electrodes.

There are two main classes of carbon arc: the low intensity (L.I.) arc and the high intensity (H.I.) arc. The H.I. arc operates at a current density of about double the L.I. type, but has a brightness of about six times as great.

Light from a carbon arc originates both from the glowing crater of the positive electrode and from the flame. The spectrum consists of lines, or bands, with a continuous background. In an ordinary low intensity arc employing plain carbons most of the light is emitted by the crater of the positive electrode. Light from this type of arc has a colour temperature of about 3800K. On the other hand, with the enclosed arc – a form of low intensity arc employed in process work – the majority of light is produced by the flame, which with this type of arc is very long. To prevent the flame from blowing about, the arc is enclosed in a cylinder of heat-resisting glass – hence its name.

The colour temperature of the light from an enclosed arc is about 10,000K.

The carbons employed in high intensity arcs usually contain a core of a metallic salt. The use of cored carbons allows control of the spectral distribution of the light emitted by the arc. A typical high intensity arc has a colour temperature of about 6000K.

The "white-flame arc" or "open arc" employed for photographic process work has characteristics intermediate between the L.I. and H.I. arc. Cored carbons are employed, and, while the arc gives an ultra-violet output similar to that of an ordinary L.I. arc of the same rating, the output in the visible spectrum is higher. The colour temperature of the white-flame arc is about 5000K.

Mercury vapour discharge lamps

A discharge lamp consists essentially of a tube filled with a gas or vapour containing two electrodes between which an electric discharge passes. A mercury vapour discharge lamp contains mercury (a liquid) which vaporizes when the lamp is operated. The method of light production in such a lamp is quite different from that in an incandescent filament lamp.

Mercury vapour discharge lamps are used to a considerable extent to provide large extended sources in enlargers, and in certain types of printing equipment. Their use has also been suggested for studio lighting, but, in general, the discontinuous nature of the spectrum of the light emitted has been a serious disadvantage. Attempts have been made with some success, however, to supply the missing radiation by using the tubes in conjunction with metal filament lamps or with sodium vapour discharge lamps, by including other metals, e.g., cadmium, in the tube, and also by coating the interior surfaces of the tubes with suitable fluorescent materials. (See below.) In high-pressure mercury vapour lamps the spectral lines are broadened somewhat and are superimposed upon a continuous spectrum of lower intensity, so that the deficiency is not so great.

The advantages of mercury vapour lamps are high efficiency – with consequent economy in current consumption – and relatively low heat emission. The early mercury vapour lamps were extended in size, but more compact sources have now been developed.

Fluorescent lamps

A fluorescent lamp consists of a low-pressure mercury vapour lamp with an envelope coated internally with a fluorescent powder. Fluorescent substances have the property of converting short-wave radiation into radiation of longer wavelength. The fluorescent powders (phosphors) used in lamps absorb ultra-violet radiation and emit visible radiation, the colour of which depends on the powder used. By coating tubes with such powders it is possible to obtain a light quality which is much more acceptable for photographic purposes than the light from ordinary low-pressure mercury vapour lamps. Fluorescent lamps are, in fact, available yielding light in a range of colours, including close matches for daylight and artificial light as represented by the tungsten lamp.

Fluorescent lamps are supplied as tubes, which, for electrical reasons, are usually several feet long. They are, therefore, useful for studio use where a flood of soft light for general illumination is wanted. Fluorescent lamps such as are used for office lighting, etc., employ what is termed a hot cathode and operate at normal mains voltage. By working at a very much higher voltage lamps can be made to operate with a cold cathode, which makes it possible to switch them on and off without any delay. Normal hot cathode fluorescent tubes can, with a suitable circuit arrangement, also be made to give an "instant start". Cold cathode fluorescent lamps in which the tube is in the form of a grid or spiral, are widely used as light sources in enlargers (page 377).

Fluorescent lamps emit a line spectrum with a strong continuous background. Because of the presence of this background, the quality of light from such lamps can be *approximately* expressed in terms of colour temperature. Thus "daylight" lamps may be described as operating at about 4500K, "warm-white" lamps at about 3000K, and "colour matching" lamps at 6500K. (*Note.* There is no international agreement on the naming of colours of fluorescent lamps, and lamps described by the same name do not always emit the same colour.)

Sodium vapour discharge lamps

Sodium vapour discharge lamps emit an intense yellow line spectrum, 95 per cent. of the energy of which is emitted at a wavelength of 589nm. Sodium lamps are sometimes used in high-intensity viewing lanterns and also for the illumination of photofinishers' printing rooms. As the spectrum shows some weak lines and a weak continuum outside the yellow band, for use in safelights the lamp must be screened by a yellow filter which absorbs wavelengths less than about 550nm.

Flash powder

Flash powders, consisting usually of a mixture of aluminium or magnesium powder with a suitable oxidizing agent, were used for many years by press photographers and others who required to make pictures in circumstances where the normal lighting was insufficient for their purpose. Such powders were effective, but the smoke produced was a great disadvantage. Flashbulbs – which are perfectly clean in action – have almost entirely displaced the use of flash powder.

Flashbulbs

Most flashbulbs contain shredded foil or fine metal wire in an atmosphere of oxygen at low pressure. The foil, used in the smaller bulbs, is of zirconium while the wire, used in the larger bulbs, is of an aluminium-magnesium alloy which allows it to be drawn more thinly than is possible with pure aluminium. The spectrum of a flashbulb is continuous, with a colour temperature of about 3800K. The duration of the flash ranges from about 1/100th to 1/50th of a second, the larger bulbs emitting the longer flash.

Flashbulbs – which are available in a range of sizes – are designed to be operated from dry-batteries with a voltage range of, typically, 3 to 30V. In the usual battery-capacitor (B.C.) system of firing, a battery is used to charge – through a high resistance – a capacitor from which the bulb is subsequently fired. A small 15V or 22½V battery is commonly employed. This system makes for greater reliability in firing than when using a circuit with a 3V or 4·5V battery directly across the bulb. (A 15V or 22½V battery cannot be used directly across a flashbulb, i.e., without capacitor and resistor, because the high internal resistance of the battery prevents the bulb firing.)

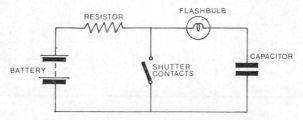

Fig. 3.6–Preferred battery-capacitor circuit for firing flashbulbs

If a battery-capacitor system is employed it should preferably use the circuit shown in Figure 3.6. This has the advantage that the capacitor is charged only when a bulb is fitted in the socket. Hence, provided the flashgun is stored without a bulb in the socket, the leakage current of the capacitor cannot continuously discharge the battery. In this circuit the resistor must be of sufficiently high value to ensure that the capacitor charging current is insufficient to fire the flashbulb, but low enough to ensure that the capacitor is adequately charged by the time the user is ready to take the photograph.

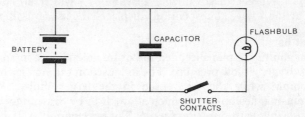

Fig. 3.7 – Alternative battery-capacitor circuit for firing flashbulbs

If the alternative battery-capacitor circuit shown in Figure 3.7 is used, the leakage current in the capacitor must be low enough to ensure that the battery does not become prematurely discharged.

Flashbulb characteristics
The performance of a flashbulb is best illustrated by a curve in which the luminous flux emitted by the bulb is plotted against time, as in Figure 3.8. The following information can be gained from such a curve:

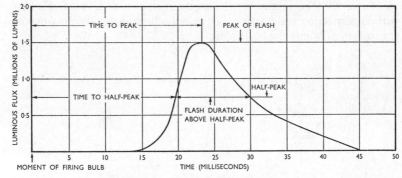

Fig. 3.8 – Flashbulb light output curve

(1) *Effective flash duration.* This indicates the motion-stopping power of the bulb when the whole flash is used. For most purposes it may be measured from the time when the rising intensity of the bulb reaches a value equal to half its peak value to the time when the intensity falls to "half-peak" again (i.e., "flash duration above half-peak").

(2) *Time to half-peak*. The shutter blades must be fully open at half-peak if use is to be made of the whole flash.

(3) *Time to peak*. The shutter blades must be fully open just before the peak of the flash for synchronization at high shutter speeds.

(4) *Total light output*. This indicates the power of the bulb as a light source. It is expressed in lumen seconds, and is represented on the graph by the total area below the light output curve.

(5) *Maximum luminous flux*. When very fast shutter speeds are employed – using only the peak of the flash – the total light output is not the best guide to the power of a bulb. A more useful figure is the maximum luminous flux, i.e., the luminous flux at the peak of the flash. This is expressed in lumens.

Bulb types
There are four main classes of flashbulbs, as follows:

(1) *Class MF* (*"medium-fast"*). These are small bulbs. They have an effective flash duration of about 12 milliseconds and a time to peak of 10 to 16 milliseconds.

(2) *Class M* (*"medium"*). These bulbs have a time to peak of 15 to 25 milliseconds. The useful duration of the flash is about 15 milliseconds.

(3) *Class S* (*"slow"*). These have a time to peak of 27 to 33 milliseconds. They have a very large total light output and a duration above half-peak of about 20 milliseconds.

   Note. In the classification of the above three types of bulb, the words "medium-fast", "medium" and "slow" refer to the time taken by the bulb to reach its peak.

(4) *Class FP* (*"focal-plane"*). Synchronization of focal-plane shutters and flashbulbs (at speeds other than those when the blind opens fully) requires a bulb whose light output is constant for the time that it takes for the shutter blind to travel from one end of the film frame to the other. This may range from about 10 milliseconds to 30 milliseconds, depending on the size and design of the shutter. Slow-burning "focal-plane" bulbs, with a duration above half-peak of 25 milliseconds or more, have been specially produced for this purpose. They have a time to half-peak of 9 to 21 milliseconds. ("Focal-plane" bulbs similar in other respects to Class FP bulbs, but with a time to half-peak of 6 to 14 milliseconds, are sometimes distinguished as Class FP+ bulbs.)

   In Figure 3.9 are shown light output curves for typical bulbs of each of the above four classes.

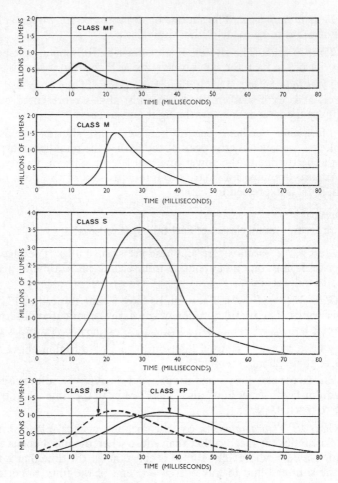

Fig. 3.9 – Typical flashbulb characteristics

Most types of flashbulb are supplied with the glass envelope coated with transparent blue lacquer. This blue filter layer adjusts the colour balance of the light given out by the bulb to give an approximate match for daylight. Such blue-coated flashbulbs were originally designed for use with daylight-type colour films, but they are quite suitable for use with black-and-white materials, and, in fact, the smaller flashbulbs are supplied only in the blue-coated form.

Electronic flash tubes

In an electronic flash tube, an electrical discharge takes place in a rare gas – usually xenon, krypton or argon or a mixture of these gases. There is no foil or wire to be consumed by the flash – in contrast to expendable flashbulbs – and the tube can therefore be flashed repeatedly. Electronic flash tubes are designed to give flashes of extremely short duration. Xenon filled tubes are used for ordinary photography and give flash exposures which range from about 1/500th to 1/10,000th of a second, depending on the design of the tube and the associated electrical circuit. There is no appreciable delay when these tubes are fired, the flash occurring practically instantaneously. The spectrum is a line one, with a very strong continuous background, and the light has a colour temperature of about 6000K. Electronic flash tubes used in specialized scientific applications are sometimes designed to give flashes of a few microseconds' duration only. Such tubes are commonly filled with argon and produce a spectrum in which blue predominates.

The essentials of an electronic flash circuit are shown in Figure 3.10. The capacitor C, from which the flash tube is operated, is charged from a source of high voltage V – usually between 500 and 2000 volts – through a current-limiting resistor R. The pressure of the gas in the tube is such that at the voltage to which the capacitor is charged no flow of current takes place, but by applying to an external electrode a triggering voltage – a momentary pulse of very high voltage – the gas in the tube is ionized and permits the capacitor to discharge rapidly through it, with the accompaniment of a vivid flash.

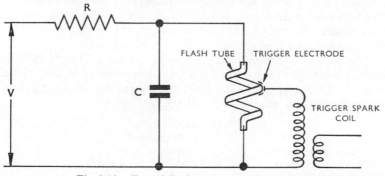

Fig. 3.10 – Essentials of an electronic flash circuit

The amount of light given by an electronic flash tube is normally quoted in terms of the electrical power expended in producing the flash, i.e., in joules (=watt seconds). An average tube is rated at 100 joules, but both smaller and larger tubes are available. A typical 100 joule tube has a luminous efficiency of about 45 lumens per watt, giving a total light output of about 4500 lumen seconds. This is equal to the output of one of the smaller expendable flashbulbs.

Making flash exposures

With flash *powder* it is the practice to fire off the flash with the camera shutter left open. This method was also followed with flash-bulbs when these were first introduced, and is referred to as the "open-flash" technique. Improved reliability of flashbulbs, has, how-ever, made it possible for devices to be employed which enable shutter and flash to be "synchronized". Using a suitable synchronizer, it is possible either to employ the whole of the flash, by using a sufficiently long shutter speed, or to limit the exposure to a very short period of time coincident with the peak of the flash, and thus to take pictures of subjects in very rapid motion. The synchronization both of flashbulbs and of electronic flash tubes is dealt with in Chapter 11.

Reflectors

Most light sources are used in *reflectors*. The reflector may be an integral part of the lamp or it may be a separate item. A reflector affects the emission from a light source considerably as regards distri-bution of illumination and also as regards colour.

Reflectors differ widely in size, shape and nature of surface. Some are flat or very shallow, others deeply curved, e.g., of spherical or para-boloidal form. The surface finishes of reflectors range from a mirror-like finish to a matt or satin finish. The majority of reflectors used for photographic purposes have the latter type of surface, giving a mixture of direct and diffuse reflection.

The ratio of the illumination provided on the subject by a light source in reflector to that provided by the bare source is termed the *reflector factor*. Approximate reflector factors for three types of flashgun reflectors are given in Table 3.3.

Type of reflector	Approximate reflector factor
Shallow, matt or satin	2
Deep, matt or satin (average)	4
Deep, polished	6

Table 3.3 – Typical flashgun reflector factors

Spotlights

A *spotlight* (Figure 3.11) consists essentially of a lamp housing at the front of which is mounted a condenser lens. A concave mirror is mounted behind the lamp, the filament of which is at the centre of curvature of the mirror. The distance of the lamp from the condenser

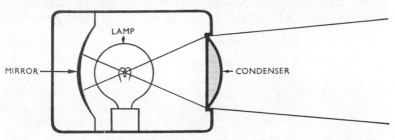

Fig. 3.11 – Principle of the spotlight

is usually adjustable, to enable the size of the spot to be varied at will. For a parallel beam, the lamp is adjusted to bring it to the focus of the condenser.

A spotlight provides a high level of illumination over a relatively small area, and normally yields shadows with hard edges. If softer-edged shadows are required, a diffusing screen may be fitted over the condenser lens. The illumination at the edges of the area illuminated by a spotlight falls off more-or-less rapidly. A harder edge to the area than usual may be obtained by fitting to the spot a "snoot" – a hood in the form of a cylinder open at both ends.

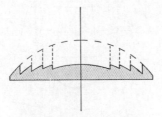

Fig. 3.12 – Fresnel lens

To reduce the mass of the condenser in a spotlight, a *Fresnel lens* is frequently employed. This is a lens which is "collapsed" in a series of small steps, as shown in Figure 3.12. With this construction, there is less weight and less risk of internal stress on heating in use than with an ordinary condenser.

Polar distribution curves

It was stated earlier, in connexion with the definition of luminous intensity, that most practical light sources do not radiate uniformly in all directions. An effective way of showing the distribution of light from a source, is to plot the luminous intensity in each direction in a given plane through the source as a curve in polar co-ordinates, as shown in Figure 3.13. In this figure, the source is at the origin and the

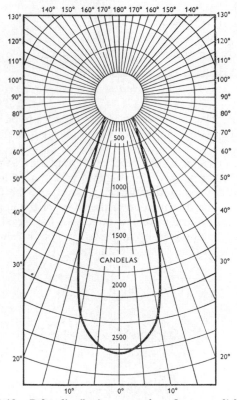

Fig. 3.13 – Polar distribution curve of a reflector spotlight lamp

length of the radius from the centre to any point on the curve gives the luminous intensity, in candelas, in that particular direction. A curve drawn in this way is called a *polar distribution curve*.

Illumination

The term *illumination* is applied to light falling on a surface. Illumination is defined as the ratio of the luminous flux falling on a surface to its area. The unit of illumination is the *lux*, an illumination of one lumen per square metre.

The illumination produced by a lamp at any distance from it depends on the power of the lamp, and, inversely, on the square of the distance from the lamp. This relation between illumination and the distance from the source is referred to as *the inverse square law*. The reason for the relationship is illustrated in Figure 3.14.

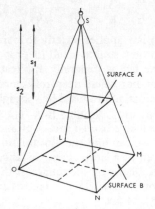

Fig. 3.14 – Demonstration of the inverse square law

We have already stated that for many purposes we can assume that light travels in straight lines. In Figure 3.14, therefore, all the light in the pyramid bounded by the four lines, *SL*, *SM*, *SN* and *SO*, must pass both through surface *A* and through surface *B*, and each surface will therefore receive the same total amount of light. The area of *B* is obviously greater than *A*, so that when the light falls on *B* it will be spread over a greater area. The illumination on *B*, will, therefore, be less than on *A*, the two illuminations being inversely proportional to the areas of the two surfaces. Now it can be shown, by similar triangles, that the areas of *A* and *B* are proportional to the squares of their distances from the light source, so that the illuminations will be inversely proportional to the squares of these distances. In the example shown, surface *B* is actually twice as far from the source as surface *A*, so that the illumination on *B* will be only one-quarter of that on A. The inverse square law can be expressed mathematically by the equation:

$$\frac{I_1}{I_2} = \frac{s_2^{\,2}}{s_1^{\,2}}$$

where I_1 and I_2 are the illuminations corresponding to the source-to-subject distances s_1 and s_2 respectively.

Example: A subject is lit with a single lamp at 12 feet. The lamp is then brought in to 8 feet. By how much is the illumination increased?

$$\text{Answer:} \quad \frac{I_2}{I_1} = \frac{s_1^{\,2}}{s_2^{\,2}} = \frac{12^2}{8^2} = \frac{144}{64} = 2\tfrac{1}{4} \text{ times}$$

The inverse square law applies strictly to point sources only. It is *approximately* true for any source small in proportion to its distance from the subject. The law is generally applicable to lamps used in shallow reflectors, but not when deep reflectors are used. It is not applicable to the illumination provided by spotlights.

Since, by definition, the luminous flux falling upon each square metre of a surface one metre from a source of one candle-power is one lumen, it follows that we can find the illumination, in lux (lumens per square metre) produced by a lamp at any distance from it, by dividing the candle-power of the lamp by the square of the distance in metres. Thus, the illumination on a surface 5 metres from a source of 100 candle-power is $100/5^2 = 4$ lux.

In Table 3.4 are listed values of illumination typical of those likely to be encountered in different areas.

Purpose	Illumination in lux (lm/m²)
Underground station	25
Lounge	100
Well-lit restaurant	100
General office	400
Drawing office (over drawing board)	600

Table 3.4 – Illumination values for some different activities

Figure 3.15 illustrates the relation between some of the photometric units to which reference has been made in this Chapter.

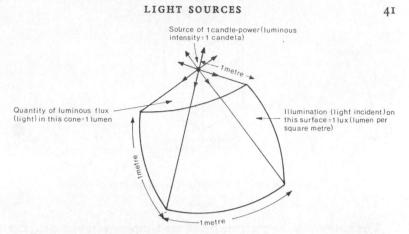

Fig. 3.15 – Relation between luminous intensity of a source, luminous flux and illumination on a surface

Measurement and control of colour temperature

In colour photography, the colour temperature of the light emitted by all the lamps on a set must agree with that for which the process being used is balanced. This applies equally to the use of integral tripacks, where the three emulsion layers are balanced for a certain colour temperature, and to the making of separation negatives, where the filter factors required vary with the colour temperature.

The tolerance permissible depends on the process employed and to some extent on the subject. A departure by all the lamps of 100K from the specified value (which may arise from a 10 per cent. variation in supply voltage), is probably the maximum which can be tolerated in any integral tripack process balanced for a colour temperature of around 3400K. In the final photograph, a difference between one lamp and another will be more noticeable than a difference between all the lamps and the specified colour temperature. A difference of 50K between lamps, for instance, may be more noticeable than a difference of 100K between all the lamps and the specified value. Differences between lamps are most noticeable in mid-tones – a sheet of crinkled white paper will soon reveal any differences.

Comparing the quality of two lamps
The quality of two lamps can readily be compared by the following procedure. A piece of white blotting paper is folded to form a V and placed so that each side is illuminated by one of the lamps only, as shown in Figure 3.16.

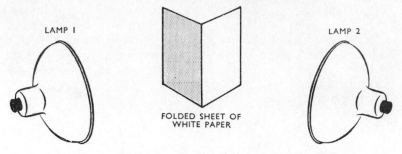

LAMP 1

LAMP 2

FOLDED SHEET OF
WHITE PAPER

Fig. 3.16 – Comparing the quality of the light from two lamps

The position of the paper between the lamps is adjusted until the two halves are equally illuminated, and the colours of the two halves are then compared. Any difference in colour temperature between the two lamps will be visible as a difference in colour between the two halves of the paper. In general, it will be safe to assume that a difference which is visible to the eye will be noticeable in the photograph and must be corrected. (See below.)

Measurement of colour temperature

If an *absolute* value of the colour temperature of a lamp is required, the lamp may be matched with a standard lamp by means of photometric filters (page 297). A more convenient method for practical use is to employ a *colour temperature meter*. Several commercial instruments have been marketed for this purpose from time to time. Most of these incorporate a photo-electric cell and two colour filters passing different regions of the spectrum, e.g., a tricolour blue filter and a tricolour red filter. The two readings are compared on a table or calculating device, and can yield quite a close indication of colour temperature. A good meter may read to within $\pm$ 25K at 3400K. Colour temperature meters may generally be used successfully in daylight and in tungsten filament lighting, but with artificial light sources with marked line spectra, meter readings can be very misleading.

Control of colour temperature

The colour temperature for which a colour film is balanced and the colour temperature of a lamp are specified by the manufacturers of film and lamp respectively. The colour temperature of a lamp may be affected by the reflector used, and will change with variations in the power supply and with the age of the bulb.

To obtain light of the correct quality, the following steps should be taken:

(1) The film should be exposed with lamps of the colour temperature with which it is intended to be exposed. Other lamps may be used only if an appropriate photometric filter is available to make the necessary colour correction. In general, it is desirable to avoid the need for such filters, because, whenever a photometric filter is employed, film speed is lost, whether the change in colour temperature is up or down.

(2) All lamps must be operated at the specified voltage.

(3) All the reflectors and diffusers employed must be as near to neutral in colour as possible.

(4) Voltage control must be employed if supply fluctuations are likely. Control may be achieved by inserting a variable resistance in series with each lamp, with a variable transformer (Variac) and meter controlling the complete supply. If, for example, the mains supply is a nominal 240V, 200V lamps may be used and the variable transformer used to keep the meter reading at 200V. The lamp rheostats should be used to bring the colours of all lamps into agreement. If available, a voltage stabilizer may be used in place of manual control of the variable transformer.

(5) As an alternative to individual rheostats, coloured gelatin or Cellophane photometric filters may be placed over each lamp to raise or lower the colour temperature as required. Pale yellow filters will lower the colour temperature; pale blue ones will raise it.

(6) As soon as a bulb envelope begins to darken it should be replaced. When one bulb requires to be replaced all the bulbs on the set should be replaced. To assist in achieving uniform ageing of bulbs, they may be moved from lamp to lamp periodically.

CHAPTER 4

Image Formation

In Chapters 2 and 3 we have considered the nature of light and the characteristics of light sources. In the present Chapter we shall consider the way in which light forms images.

When light falls on matter, any, or all, of the following five things may happen:
(1) Absorption.
(2) Direct reflection.
(3) Diffuse reflection.
(4) Direct transmission.
(5) Diffuse transmission.
Of these, (1) and (2) and/or (3) always happen to some extent; in very many cases, all five occur together. No single effect happens alone.

Absorption
When light is absorbed, it disappears as light and reappears in some other form, usually as heat. Hence, because they absorb more light, lantern slides with large dark areas get hotter than clear ones. Light may produce other effects besides heat when it is absorbed. Thus, in a silver bromide emulsion, it produces chemical changes, while, when light falls upon a photo-electric cell, it produces electricity.

Direct reflection
The term *direct reflection* is applied to reflection without scatter, i.e., reflection as in a mirror. When light is reflected directly, it reappears in a definite direction on the same side of the object as it originated. This is illustrated in Figure 4.1 The angle of incidence *i* is equal to the angle of reflection *r*.

Direct reflection – sometimes referred to as regular reflection or specular reflection – is, in photography, usually the less important of the two forms of reflection. Its chief importance probably lies in the trouble it causes when not wanted!

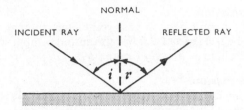

Fig. 4.1 – Light ray reflected by a plane mirror

Diffuse reflection

The term *diffuse reflection* is applied to reflection such that light incident upon a surface is reflected from every part of the surface in many directions. This is illustrated in Figure 4.2.

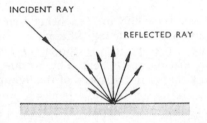

Fig. 4.2 – Light ray reflected by a matt surface

Diffuse reflection in which the spatial distribution of reflected flux is such that the luminance of the surface is the same in all directions – as from a dead matt surface – is termed *uniform diffuse reflection*. Diffuse reflection in which the spatial distribution of reflected flux is such that the luminance of the surface exhibits one or more maxima – as from a surface with considerable sheen – is termed *preferential diffuse reflection*. Reflection from many objects combines both direct and diffuse reflection, and is termed *mixed reflection*.

It is by diffusely reflected light that we see objects in the world around us, since it is this light which permits us to perceive detail and texture, these qualities being unobserved when the light from an object consists entirely of directly reflected light. (The surface of a mirror – provided it is clean – is practically invisible, because all the light falling on it is directly reflected. It requires the presence of dust or fingermarks – which provide diffuse reflection – to render the surface visible.)

Direct transmission

Some materials permit light to pass completely through them. Such light is said to be *transmitted*. Light transmitted without scatter – as by clear glass – is said to be *directly transmitted*.

Diffuse transmission

Transmission such that the light passing through a body is scattered in many directions, is termed *diffuse transmission*. Diffuse transmission in which the spatial distribution of transmitted flux is such that the luminance is the same in all forward directions, is termed *uniform diffuse transmission*. Diffuse transmission in which the spatial distribution of transmitted flux is such that the luminance exhibits one or more maxima, is termed *preferential diffuse transmission*. Transmission which combines both direct and diffuse transmission is termed *mixed transmission*.

Refraction

When a ray of light travelling in (i.e., being transmitted by) one medium passes into another having different optical properties its direction is changed (except in the special case where it enters normally). We say that the ray is bent. The bending, termed *refraction*, results from a change in the speed of the light on passing from

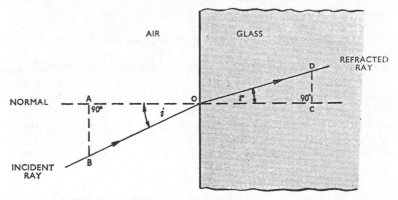

Fig. 4.3 – Light ray passing obliquely from air to glass

the one medium into the other. From the photographic point of view, the bending which occurs when light passes from air into glass and out again is of especial interest, since it is upon this bending that the formation of an image by a lens depends. Figure 4.3 illustrates what takes place when the ray *enters* the glass. It will be noted that when a ray passes into a "denser" optical medium, as in this case, it is bent towards the normal at the point of incidence.

The amount of bending which occurs when a light ray passing through air impinges obliquely upon a glass surface, is given by the equation:

$$\frac{\sin i}{\sin r} = n$$

where i and r are the angles of incidence and refraction respectively and n is the *refractive index* of the glass. This is illustrated in Figure 4.3 where BOD represents the path of the ray, and $\sin i$ is given by the ratio AB/BO and $\sin r$ by CD/DO.*

Refractive index varies from one type of glass to another. Values of refractive index for three common types of glass are given in the table below:

Glass	Refractive index
Crown	1·46–1·53
Flint	1·53–1·65
Dense flint	1·65–1·92

Refractive index also varies with wavelength, being greater for blue light than for red light. Thus, any quoted value of refractive index strictly applies only to one wavelength. From the physical point of view, the refractive index of a given medium is the ratio of the velocity of light in a vacuum (which is very close to its velocity in air) to its velocity in the medium. Variation of refractive index with wavelength results from the fact that the amount by which the speed of light changes when it enters a given medium, varies with wavelength.

Transmission of light through a glass block

In passing through a parallel-sided glass block, a ray is refracted at both surfaces of the block. This is illustrated in Figure 4.4 where it is seen that the ray is bent twice and that the emergent ray is displaced by its passage through the glass, but not deviated from its original direction. The magnitude of the displacement (d in the figure) depends on the angle of incidence, the thickness of the block, and the refractive index of the glass.

In passing through a block of glass whose sides are *not* parallel, i.e., a prism, as shown in Figure 4.5 the course of a ray of light is again altered twice, but, this time, on emerging from the block, it remains

---

* An explanation of the meaning of the term "sin" is given in the Appendix.

deviated from its original path. The amount of deviation, D, depends on the refracting angle, A, of the prism and on the refractive index of the glass. This means that, by placing in the path of light pieces of

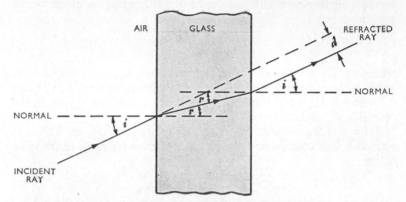

Fig. 4.4 – Light ray passing obliquely through a parallel-sided glass block

glass having suitably shaped surfaces, the direction of travel of light can be altered at will.

Dispersion

When *white* light passes through a prism it is not only deviated – it is also *dispersed*, i.e., split up into its component colours. This is because

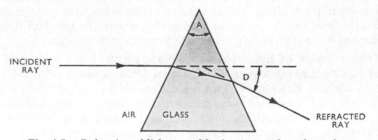

Fig. 4.5 – Refraction of light caused by its passage through a prism

the amount of deviation depends upon the refractive index, and, as already stated, the refractive index varies with the wavelength – and therefore the colour – of the light. Figure 4.5 applies only to a *monochromatic* beam of light, i.e., a beam of one wavelength only. When *white* light – which comprises a wide range of wavelengths –

passes through a prism it is split up into its component parts to form a band of coloured light, or spectrum, as shown in Figure 4.6.

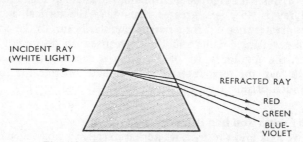

INCIDENT RAY
(WHITE LIGHT)

REFRACTED RAY

RED
GREEN
BLUE-
VIOLET

Fig. 4.6 - Dispersion of white light by a prism

We have seen that different kinds of glass differ in refractive index. They also differ in dispersive power, but dispersive power and refractive index do not necessarily vary together. Consequently, by placing two suitable prisms of different kinds of glass together, with their refracting angles turned in opposite directions, it is possible to neutralize the dispersion, i.e., the separation of the coloured rays, while retaining a considerable degree of deviation. This is an important fact, for upon it depends the production of lenses which can bring rays of different colours to a common focus.

Total internal reflection
In certain circumstances, light passing through a glass block may suffer *total internal reflection*, as shown in Figure 4.7.

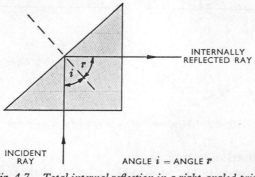

INTERNALLY
REFLECTED RAY

r
i

INCIDENT
RAY

ANGLE *i* = ANGLE *r*

Fig. 4.7 - Total internal reflection in a right-angled prism

This takes place when the angle of incidence *i* at the glass-air surface is greater than a certain value, termed the *critical angle*. A typical value for this angle, which depends on the refractive index of the glass, is about 42°. This property of light is made use of in certain right-angled prisms. In a right-angled prism, the angle of incidence for the central ray is 45°, i.e., greater than 42° – the critical angle – and remains greater than 42° for a narrow angular beam. In the case, however, of reversing prisms such as those used on document copying cameras, the angular width of the beam is comparatively large – too large, in fact, for total internal reflection to operate for the whole beam. Such prisms have, therefore, to be silvered.

Image formation in a mirror

When we look into a mirror, we appear to see in it objects which are in fact on the near side of the mirror. We say that we see an *image* of the objects in the mirror. This is illustrated in Figure 4.8. No light rays actually pass through the space occupied by the image and we cannot catch the image on a screen. The image is thus said to be *virtual*; no rays from the object actually pass through it. It appears erect, i.e., the right-way up, but objects in it are laterally reversed (reversed left-for-right).

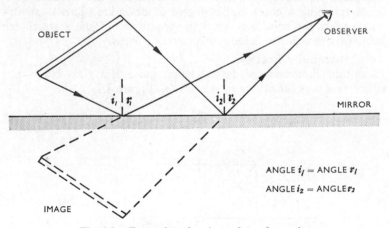

Fig. 4.8 – Formation of an image by a plane mirror

Image formation by a pinhole

When light passes through a small aperture an image is formed – but this is of quite a different kind from the image formed by a mirror. Image formation of this type can readily be illustrated by holding a piece of card pierced by a pin between a candle and a white screen.

Figure 4.9 shows the path of some of the image-forming rays when this is done.

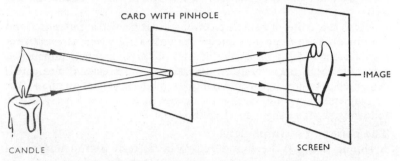

Fig. 4.9 – Formation of an image by a pinhole

The image of the candle is referred to as a *real* image, because it can be caught on a screen; rays from the object actually pass through it. It is apparent from the figure that because light travels in straight lines the image must be inverted.

Limitations of a pinhole as a producer of real images

There is an optimum size for a pinhole – in relation to the distance from the pinhole to the screen – for which the image will be sharpest. A larger hole will pass more light and give a brighter image, but the image will be less sharp. With a smaller hole, the brightness will be reduced, but strangely enough, the image will again be less sharp, this time because of diffraction (page 121). The optimum pinhole diameter is about 1/25th of the square root of the distance in millimetres from the pinhole to the screen. With a 150 mm camera this gives a pinhole diameter of 0·5 mm.

Cameras employing a pinhole to form the image – "pinhole cameras" – can be made without difficulty and will produce quite reasonable pictures. One of the advantages of the pinhole camera is that no focusing is needed – the camera has infinite depth of field. Other advantages include the complete absence of curvilinear distortion, the ease with which wide angles are obtained and, of course, cheapness. But, even with a pinhole of optimum size, the definition yielded by a pinhole camera is not good and exposures are too long for moving objects to be photographed. (A typical outdoor exposure time using a fast film in a pinhole camera is 5 seconds.) Obviously, therefore, there is a need for some other means of forming images, and this need is met in ordinary cameras by the lens.

The lens

A *lens* is a system of one or more pieces of glass bounded by spherical surfaces, all of whose centres are on a common axis – termed the *lens axis*.

A lens consisting of a single piece of glass is termed a *simple lens,* and one consisting of more than one piece of glass a *complex,* or *compound, lens.* Compound lenses usually consist of three or four components, some of which may comprise several pieces of glass ("elements") cemented together. In exceptional cases, a lens may contain up to 10 or 12 elements. Only the cheapest cameras have simple lenses. In the following pages we shall see why this is so.

The action of a simple lens

A simple lens may be considered to be formed from a number of prisms, as shown in section in Figure 4.10. Only five prisms are shown in the figure, but it will be apparent that if a greater number were used the outline of the section through the prisms would closely follow that of a lens.

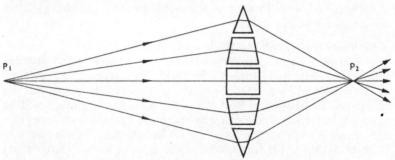

Fig. 4.10 – A simple positive lens considered as a series of prisms

Light spreading out from a point source P_1, and reaching the surface of the lens, is redirected according to the angle between the ray and the glass surface, and, provided that the angles of the prisms are suitable, the redirected rays will be brought together once more to form a real image at a point P_2. These rays are said to come to a *focus,* or to be *focused* at P_2.

The lens illustrated in Figure 4.10 has two convex surfaces, but lenses may be, and often are, constructed with two concave surfaces, or with one concave surface and one convex surface, as in the case of *meniscus* lenses – in which the centres of curvature of both surfaces are on the same side of the lens. In Figure 4.11, six different types of simple lens are shown in section.

A double convex (biconvex) or plano-convex lens will converge light to a point on the far side of the lens from the source. Such a lens is termed a *convergent*, or *positive*, lens. A double concave (biconcave)

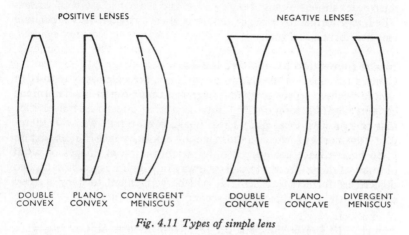

POSITIVE LENSES   NEGATIVE LENSES

DOUBLE   PLANO-   CONVERGENT   DOUBLE   PLANO-   DIVERGENT
CONVEX   CONVEX   MENISCUS   CONCAVE   CONCAVE   MENISCUS

Fig. 4.11 Types of simple lens

or plano-concave lens diverges light passing through it, and is described as a *divergent*, or *negative*, lens. A meniscus lens may be positive or negative according to its shape.

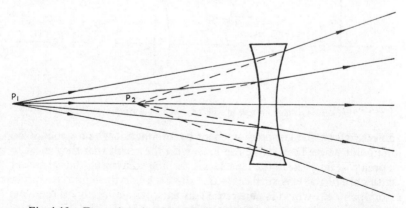

Fig. 4.12 – Formation of a virtual image of a point object by a negative lens

The formation of an image of a point object by a positive lens has already been illustrated in Figure 4.10. The formation of an image of a point object by a negative lens is shown in Figure 4.12. In this figure, P_1

is the object and P_2 the image. In contrast to the image formed by the positive lens shown in Figure 4.10, the image now is on the same side of the lens as the object. Like the reflected image obtained with a plane mirror, it cannot be caught on a screen and is termed a virtual image. The image formed by a negative lens is always virtual; only a positive lens can form a real image.

Image formation by positive lenses

Camera lenses, whether simple or complex, are essentially similar to simple positive lenses in their image-forming properties. They may contain negative components, but the overall effect must always be that of a positive lens, since a real image is required. We will, therefore, consider the formation of images by a positive lens in more detail.

So far, we have considered only the formation of images of point objects; of more interest to us is the way in which images of extended objects are formed by a lens. It will be convenient to consider two cases: firstly, near objects, and secondly distant objects.

Near objects

Figure 4.13 shows the path of light from a near object through a simple positive lens. Rays of light s, coming from point S_1 on the

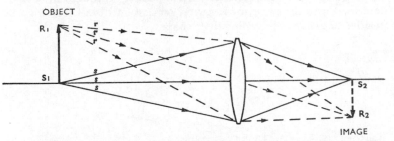

Fig. 4.13 – Image of a near object formed by a simple positive lens

object, fall on the lens and are bent by an amount which depends on the point where they strike the lens, with the result that they meet in a point S_2. As S_1 is on the lens axis – the line containing the centres of curvature of the lens surfaces – S_2 will also be on the lens axis. Rays r from point R_1, which is above the lens axis, fall obliquely on the lens, and come to a focus R_2 below the lens axis. Hence, the image is inverted – as in the case of the formation of an image by a pinhole.

Distant objects

All the rays of light reaching the lens from a point on a very distant object are very nearly parallel. An object so far from the lens that, for practical purposes, the light reaching the lens may be regarded *as parallel* is said to be at *infinity*, denoted by the symbol ∞. Figure 4.14 shows the path of light from such a distant object through a simple positive lens.

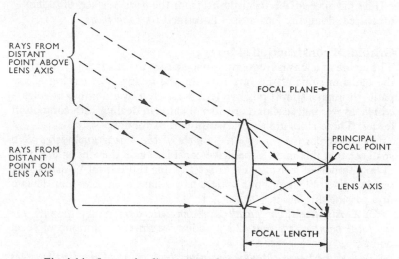

RAYS FROM DISTANT POINT ABOVE LENS AXIS

FOCAL PLANE→

PRINCIPAL FOCAL POINT

RAYS FROM DISTANT POINT ON LENS AXIS

LENS AXIS

FOCAL LENGTH

Fig. 4.14 – Image of a distant object formed by a simple positive lens

The action of the lens in forming an image of a distant object is exactly the same as in the case of a near object, but, because the pencil of rays from a distant point is parallel – and not diverging – the lens, bending the rays by the same amount as before, brings them to a focus nearer to the lens.

The plane in which the image of a distant object is formed by a lens is termed the *focal plane*. With a flat distant object and a perfect lens, every point of the image will lie in the focal plane. When we focus "on infinity" to obtain a sharp picture of distant objects, we are, in fact, adjusting the distance between the lens and the film so that the latter lies in the focal plane.

The point in the focal plane which lies on the lens axis is termed the *principal focal point*, or *focus*, of the lens, and the distance from this point to the lens is termed the *focal length* of the lens. If the lens be turned round, a second focal point is obtained, but the focal length is the same whichever way the lens faces. With thick lenses such as compound ones, we need to know to what points on the lens the focal lengths are to be measured, since the choice of these points will obviously affect the values obtained. The location of the appropriate points is considered in Chapter 9. Frequently, the term "focus" is used instead of focal length, as, for example, when we speak of a lens of "200 mm focus", meaning that the focal point, or focus, is 200 mm from the lens.

The distance of the focal point from the rear surface of a lens – measured along the lens axis – is termed its *back focus*.

Graphical construction of images

The action of a lens is frequently made easier to understand if we trace the paths of some of the rays forming the image. The tracing of ray paths through a simple positive lens is assisted by a number of rules – which, as we shall see later, are also of value in dealing with compound lenses. These rules are three in number, as follows:

(1) *A ray passing through the centre of the lens is undeviated.* We shall see that this must be so if we consider again the lens as made up of a number of prisms (Figure 4.10), for the central "prism" is a parallel-sided block of glass which, as we have seen, does not deviate rays passing through it.

(2) *A ray travelling parallel to the lens axis passes through the far focal point of the lens.* This follows from the definition of focal point.

(3) *A ray passing through the near focal point of the lens emerges from the lens parallel to the lens axis.* This also follows from the definition of focal point, if we remember that light follows the same path, in whichever direction it is travelling.

In Figure 4.15 we have used these rules to trace the path of light through a positive lens of known focal length, under a series of different conditions. As the figure shows, we can locate an image by using any two of the three rules, the image being located by the intersection of two rays.

Figures 4.15a, 4.15b and 4.15c represent conditions obtained in a camera or enlarger. In each of these examples, a real image is formed – as it must be if a photographic record of it is to be obtained – and the image is in each case inverted. The image varies in size, however, from being smaller than the object to being larger, depending upon the object distance. Figure 4.15d represents the condition obtained in, for example, a 35 mm transparency viewer.

Image formation by negative lenses

Although, in photography, our main concern is with lenses which can form real images, i.e., positive lenses, it is of interest to consider also the way in which we can trace rays through negative lenses, since

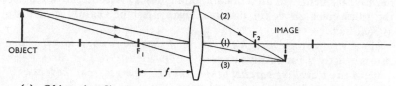

(a) *Object in distance or middle distance.* Image: real, inverted, smaller than object (i.e., diminished).

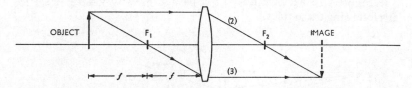

(b) *Object at twice focal length.* Image: real, inverted, same size as object.

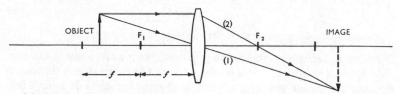

(c) *Object at between one and two focal lengths.* Image: real, inverted, larger than object (i.e., magnified).

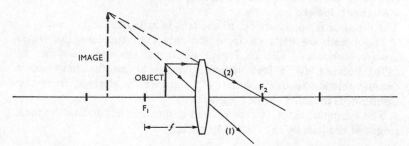

(d) *Object at less than one focal length.* Image: virtual, erect, larger than object (i.e., magnified).

Fig. 4.15 – Graphical construction of images formed by a positive lens

negative elements are used in compound lenses. With negative lenses, the rules given above for positive lenses must be slightly modified, as follows:

(1) *A ray passing through the centre of the lens is undeviated.* (This rule is exactly as for positive lenses.)

(2) *A ray travelling parallel to the lens axis emerges from the lens as if it had originated at the near focal point.*

(3) *A ray travelling towards the far focal point emerges from the lens parallel to the lens axis.*

In Figure 4.16 we have traced the path of light through a negative lens following these rules.

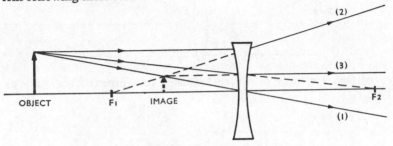

Fig. 4.16 – Graphical construction of image formed by a negative lens

As the figure shows, the image is virtual, erect and smaller than the object, i.e., diminished. This holds good whatever the object distance. Because the image that it produces is always diminished, a negative lens is sometimes termed a *reducing lens*.

Relation between object distance, image distance and focal length

The distance from the object to the lens is called the *object conjugate distance*, and the distance from the image to the lens the *image conjugate distance*. The conjugate distances, or *conjugates*, are so called because, for a lens of any given focal length, they bear a definite relation to one another. ("Conjugate" is derived from two Latin words meaning "yoked together".)

The conjugate distances are related to one another and to the focal length of the lens by the following equation:

$$\frac{1}{u} + \frac{1}{v} = \frac{1}{f}$$

where u is the object conjugate, v the image conjugate and f the focal length.

The derivation of this fundamental relationship, sometimes referred to as the *lens equation*, is given below.

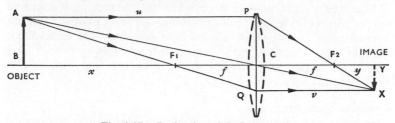

Fig. 4.17 – Derivation of the lens equation

In Figure 4.17, the object AB is at a distance u from the lens and the image XY at a distance v. AP is the ray from A entering the lens in a direction parallel to the lens axis. After refraction, it passes through the focal point F_2. AQ is the ray from A passing through the focal point F_1. After refraction, it proceeds parallel to the lens axis. ACX is an undeviated ray through the centre of the lens.

It can be shown that triangles ABC and XYC are similar.

Therefore:
$$\frac{AB}{XY} = \frac{BC}{YC} = \frac{u}{v} \quad \ldots \ldots \ldots \quad (1)$$

From the figure: $BF_1 = u - f \quad \ldots \ldots \ldots \quad (2)$

Also, because triangles ABF_1 and QCF_1 are similar:
$$\frac{BF_1}{CF_1} = \frac{AB}{QC} = \frac{AB}{XY} \quad \ldots \ldots \ldots \quad (3)$$

Substituting equations (1) and (2) in (3) we obtain:
$$\frac{u-f}{f} = \frac{u}{v}$$

Therefore: $u - f = \dfrac{uf}{v}$

Dividing by uf we have:
$$\frac{1}{f} - \frac{1}{u} = \frac{1}{v}$$

Or: $\dfrac{1}{u} + \dfrac{1}{v} = \dfrac{1}{f} \quad \ldots \ldots \ldots \quad (4)$

Although we have assumed a thin lens in deriving this equation, we can use it for thick lenses also, provided that we measure the distances from the appropriate points on the lens. The question as to where these points are is considered in Chapter 9.

From the point of view of image formation, the making of negatives in the camera, enlarging and projection are all essentially similar operations in which only the distances of the object and image from the lens vary. The same facts of image formation apply to each, and the fundamental relationship expressed in the lens equation is applicable to every type of work.

Practical lens formulae
The basic lens equation, given above, is ill-adapted to practical photography since it makes use of neither the object size, O, nor the image size, I, although both of these are usually known. Many other formulae have therefore been evolved to meet specific practical needs. The following three formulae are probably the most convenient for the problems that confront the ordinary photographer:

$$\text{(a)} \quad m = \frac{I}{O} = \frac{v}{u}$$

$$\text{(b)} \quad u = f\left(1 + \frac{1}{m}\right)$$

$$\text{(c)} \quad v = f\left(1 + m\right)$$

where m is the *magnification*, or *ratio of reproduction*.

Equation (a) is simply another form of equation (1) derived on page 59. Equations (b) and (c) are obtained by combining equation (a) with the "lens equation". It may be noted that when using equation (a) in practice, v will often approximate to f – which is generally known. (In many problems in practical photography concerned with exposure determination, v may be taken as equal to f if u equals or exceeds ten focal lengths. See page 71.)

In ordinary camera work, m will usually be less than 1. When using an enlarger, m will usually be greater than 1. (In enlarging, the distance from negative to lens should be taken as the object distance u, and the distance from lens to easel as the image distance v.)

CHAPTER 5

The Speed of a Lens

FOR reasons which will be apparent later, the beam of light passing through a photographic objective is limited by means of a *diaphragm*, or *stop*. The hole or aperture in this diaphragm may be fixed in size, or it may be capable of being varied to control the light admitted (page 178). A diaphragm with a continuously variable aperture is known – by analogy with the eye – as an *iris diaphragm*.

Aperture

The diameter of the beam of light incident upon a lens parallel to the lens axis, which completely fills the aperture of the diaphragm, is termed the *effective diameter* of the aperture, or the *effective aperture* of the lens. (It is also sometimes referred to as the "entrance pupil" of the lens).

When the diaphragm is in front of a lens, as in Figure 5.1, the diameter of the pencil of light incident upon the lens, and completely filling the aperture, is obviously equal to the diameter of the actual aperture of the diaphragm.

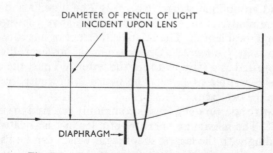

DIAMETER OF PENCIL OF LIGHT
INCIDENT UPON LENS

DIAPHRAGM→

Fig. 5.1 - Diaphragm in front of a simple lens

In the case, however, of a compound lens with the diaphragm between the components, the diameter of the pencil of light which passes through the lens, measured at the point of incidence, may be appreciably greater than the actual diameter of the aperture. This is because the front component acts as a condenser and converges the incident rays, so that a pencil larger in diameter than the actual aperture passes through (Figure 5.2). This also applies in the case of a simple lens with stop *behind* it.

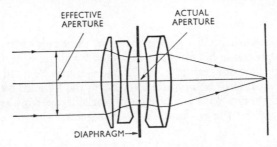

Fig. 5.2 – Diaphragm between components of a compound lens

Relative aperture

The number N obtained by dividing the focal length f of a lens by the diameter d of the effective aperture is referred to as the *relative aperture* of the diaphragm. Expressed mathematically: $N = f/d$. Thus, a lens with an effective aperture 25 mm in diameter and a focal length of 50 mm, has a relative aperture of 50/25, i.e., 2.

The numerical value of relative aperture is usually prefixed by the letter f and an oblique stroke, e.g., $f/2$. The letter f and the stroke serve as a reminder of the relation between relative aperture, effective aperture and focal length. The relative aperture of a lens is commonly referred to as its "*f-number*". On some lenses, however, the lens aperture is expressed as a ratio, without the letter f. Thus, the aperture of an $f/2$ lens is written as 1 : 2. The figure 2, however, has the same meaning in the two cases.

The relative aperture of a lens is commonly referred to simply as its "aperture". The maximum aperture of a lens is the relative aperture corresponding with the largest diaphragm which can be used with it, i.e., corresponding with the clear aperture. In passing, it may be noted that if an unsymmetrical lens is used in reverse, the relative aperture will usually be slightly different from its normal value. This is because, although the focal length is unchanged, the effective aperture alters slightly.

Relation between f-number and light-passing power of a lens

The speed of a lens, i.e., its ability to pass light from object to image, is determined by the geometry of the lens and by its *transmission* (page 73). We may – for want of a better term – refer to the speed of a lens as determined by its geometry alone as its *light-passing power*. The relation between the geometry of a lens and its light-passing power is illustrated in Figure 5.3.

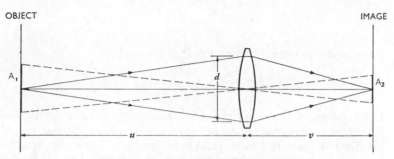

OBJECT   IMAGE

Fig. 5.3 – Passage of light through a lens

In this figure, A_1 is the area (in square metres) of a small portion of the object on the axis, and A_2 the area of the corresponding image. From each point on the object a cone of rays (one of which is shown by the solid lines) passes through the aperture of the diaphragm (not shown), being reunited by the lens in a corresponding point on the image. The object and image conjugates are u and v respectively (in metres).

Let the luminance of area A_1 of the object be L candelas per square metre. Then, the luminous intensity of area A_1 is the product of the area by its luminance, i.e.,

$$A_1 L \text{ candelas}$$

The resulting illumination in the plane of the lens is:

$$\frac{A_1 L}{u^2} \text{ lux (lumens per square metre)}$$

This follows from the inverse square law (page 39). The luminous flux entering the lens is the product of this illumination and the area of the effective aperture (diameter d), i.e.,

$$\frac{A_1 L}{u^2} \times \frac{\pi d^2}{4} \text{ lumens}$$

This light all travels to the image plane (assuming that the lens has a transmission of 100 per cent.), and is there distributed over area A_2. The illumination at the image is, therefore:

$$I = \frac{A_1 \, L}{u^2} \times \frac{\pi d^2}{4} \times \frac{1}{A_2} \text{ lux}$$

Now, it can be shown, by similar triangles, that:

$$\frac{A_1}{A_2} = \frac{u^2}{v^2}$$

Substituting in the expression for I above, we have:

$$I = \frac{\pi L}{4} \times \frac{d^2}{v^2} \text{ lux}$$

It will be noted that u has cancelled out, and that the image illumination depends only upon the luminance of the object and the ratio of the effective aperture d to the bellows extension v. This means that the image illumination is governed by the angle subtended by the lens at the film, and is independent of the angle subtended by the lens at the subject. We can therefore write:

$$I \propto \left(\frac{d}{v}\right)^2$$

Now, for all except close objects, v does not differ appreciably from the focal length f.* In these circumstances, we can write:

$$I \propto \left(\frac{d}{f}\right)^2$$

Therefore: $$S \propto \left(\frac{d}{f}\right)^2$$

where S is the light-passing power ("speed") of the lens.

This means that if we have two lenses of the same focal length, one of 25 mm effective aperture and the other of 50 mm effective aperture, the first lens will have a light-passing power of one-quarter, i.e., $(25/50)^2$, that of the second. If, in another instance, we have two lenses of the same effective aperture, one of 50 mm focal length and the other of 100 mm focal length, the first lens will have a light-passing power of four times, i.e., $(100/50)^2$, that of the second.

---

* We saw on page 60 that $v = f(1 + m)$. For all except close objects, m is very much smaller than 1 and can be ignored in this equation.

Now, we have already seen that $f/d = N$, where N is the numerical value of the relative aperture, i.e., the f-number. Therefore:

$$S \propto \frac{1}{N^2}$$

That is, *the light-passing power of a lens is inversely proportional to the square of its f-number.*

The light-passing powers S_1 and S_2 of two lenses of numerical apertures N_1 and N_2 are therefore related by the equation:

$$\frac{S_1}{S_2} = \frac{N_2{}^2}{N_1{}^2} \quad . \quad . \quad . \quad . \quad . \quad . \quad . \quad . \quad . \quad (1)$$

Referring again to the first example given above, let us suppose that the focal length of both lenses is 100 mm. Then, the relative apertures of the two lenses will be $f/4$ and $f/2$ respectively, and the ratio of the light-passing power S_1 of the first lens to the light-passing power S_2 of the second lens will be:

$$\frac{S_1}{S_2} = \frac{N_2{}^2}{N_1{}^2} = \frac{2^2}{4^2} = \frac{1}{4}$$

This agrees with our earlier finding.

Referring to the second example, let us suppose that the effective aperture of both lenses is 25 mm. Then, the relative apertures will be $f/2$ and $f/4$ respectively, and the ratio of the light-passing power S_1 of the first lens to the light-passing power S_2 of the second lens will be:

$$\frac{S_1}{S_2} = \frac{N_2{}^2}{N_1{}^2} = \frac{4^2}{2^2} = \frac{4}{1}$$

This, too, agrees with our previous finding.

These examples illustrate the rule that: *to find the ratio of the light-passing powers of a lens at two different relative apertures, we simply square the two f-numbers and divide the one square by the other, remembering always that the larger the f-number, the smaller the light-passing power of the lens.*

f-number and exposure

The *exposure* received by a film is governed by the strength of the light falling on it and by the time for which this light is allowed to fall (page 225). We have already seen that light falling on a surface is defined as illumination. The relation between exposure E, illumination I and exposure time t is expressed by the equation:

$$E = I.t \quad \ldots \ldots \ldots \ldots \quad (2)^\star$$

For a given subject brightness, I depends directly on the light-passing power S of the lens, and we see from equation (2) that, in these circumstances, assuming that t remains unaltered, E is proportional to S. For a fixed exposure time, then, the exposures E_1 and E_2 given by two apertures N_1 and N_2 respectively are related by the equation:

$$\frac{E_1}{E_2} = \frac{N_2{}^2}{N_1{}^2} \quad \ldots \ldots \ldots \ldots \quad (3)$$

which is obtained by writing E in place of S in equation (1) above.

Again, it follows from equation (2) that, for a given subject brightness, the exposure time t required must be varied inversely with the illumination on the film – and hence with the light-passing power S of the lens – in order to produce a given exposure E. Thus, the exposure times t_1 and t_2 required to produce equal exposures at apertures N_1 and N_2 respectively are related by the equation:

$$\frac{t_1}{t_2} = \frac{N_1{}^2}{N_2{}^2} \quad \ldots \ldots \ldots \ldots \quad (4)$$

which is obtained by writing $1/t$ in place of S in equation (1) above.

It should be noted that in the above paragraphs we have been using the word exposure in a special sense, namely to mean the actual amount of light falling on the film. In everyday use, when we ask, What exposure shall I give?, we are using the word in a different sense, to mean a combination of lens aperture and exposure time (sometimes distinguished as "camera exposure"), or simply exposure time alone.

Let us now see how we can apply the equations derived above.

Example 1. Suppose that we have been taking photographs with the aid of one lamp, and now wish to replace this by another lamp of four times the power. How must we alter the f-number, leaving exposure time unaltered, to obtain identical negatives, i.e., to keep the exposure, in the special sense explained above, unaltered?

The problem is to keep the amount of light reaching the film constant. Since the illumination on the subject is increased four-fold,

---

$\star$ The use of E for exposure and I for illumination is followed here because it is general practice in photographic literature. It should, however, be realized that the use of these symbols for this purpose differs from standard practice in illumination and photometry.

we must reduce the light-passing power of the lens to one-quarter. Let S_1 be the light-passing power of the lens at the original aperture N_1, and S_2 its light-passing power at the required aperture N_2. Then, from equation (1) above:

$$\frac{S_1}{S_2} = \frac{N_2{}^2}{N_1{}^2}$$

Therefore: $\dfrac{4}{1} = \dfrac{N_2{}^2}{N_1{}^2}$

Hence: $N_2 = 2N_1$

This means that we must double the f-number.

Example 2. We have determined a suitable exposure time and f-number to yield a correctly exposed negative with a certain subject. We now wish to reduce the exposure time to one-half, in order to be sure of "freezing" any movement of the subject. How must we alter the aperture in order still to obtain a correctly exposed negative?

Let t_1 be the original exposure time at aperture N_1, and t_2 the new exposure time for which we wish to find the aperture N_2. Then, from equation (4) above:

$$\frac{t_1}{t_2} = \frac{N_1{}^2}{N_2{}^2}$$

Therefore: $\dfrac{2}{1} = \dfrac{N_1{}^2}{N_2{}^2}$

Hence: $N_2 = \dfrac{N_1}{\sqrt{2}}$

This means that we must use the f-number obtained by dividing the original f-number by $\sqrt{2}$ (approx. 1·4).

Example 3. As in example 2, we have determined a suitable exposure time and f-number to yield a correctly exposed negative with a certain subject. We now wish to double the f-number in order to increase the depth of field (Chapter 6). How must we alter the exposure time in order still to obtain a correctly exposed negative?

Again, from equation (4):

$$\frac{t_1}{t_2} = \frac{N_1{}^2}{N_2{}^2}$$

$$\text{Therefore: } \frac{t_1}{t_2} = \frac{1}{4}$$

$$\text{Hence: } t_2 = 4t_1$$

i.e., we must increase the exposure time by a factor of 4.

Example 4. Again, let us suppose that we have determined a suitable exposure time and *f*-number to yield a correctly exposed negative with a certain subject. We now wish to change to a film which is only half as fast as the one originally used, and therefore requires twice the exposure (Chapter 19). How must we alter the aperture in order to obtain correctly exposed negatives, assuming that for some reason we wish to leave the exposure time unaltered?

Since, from equation (2) above:

$$E = I.t$$

to double E, keeping t constant, we must double I. To double I we must double S, the light-passing power of the lens. If N_1 is our original aperture and N_2 the new aperture, we can write, using equation (1) above:

$$\frac{S_1}{S_2} = \frac{N_2{}^2}{N_1{}^2}$$

$$\text{Therefore: } \frac{1}{2} = \frac{N_2{}^2}{N_1{}^2}$$

$$\text{Hence: } N_2 = \frac{N_1}{\sqrt{2}}$$

In other words, we must use the *f*-number obtained by dividing the original *f*-number by $\sqrt{2}$ (approx. 1·4).

Effect of subject distance on exposure

It might be thought that the distance of the subject from the camera would affect the illumination of the image – and therefore the exposure – since this distance does affect the illumination produced by each point of the subject at the lens, according to the inverse square law. In fact, however, the *size* of the image changes proportionately, so that the illumination of the image remains constant. (This agrees with our earlier statement that it is the angle subtended by the lens at the *film* – not at the subject – which governs exposure, for, although the angle subtended by the lens at the subject varies appreciably with distance, at normal subject distances the angle subtended at the film is practically constant. The angle subtended by the lens at the film does,

THE SPEED OF A LENS

however, alter when the subject distance is very small, i.e., when the bellows extension is appreciably increased. Then, allowance must be made for the reduced image illumination. This special case is discussed on page 70.)

Standard f-numbers

To simplify exposure calculations, the f-numbers engraved on a lens are usually selected from a standard series of numbers, each of which is related to the next number by a factor designed so that the amount of light passed by the lens when set to one number is half that passed by the lens when set to the previous number. Since the amount of light passed by a lens is inversely proportional to the square of the f-number, the numbers in the series are made to increase by a factor of $\sqrt{2} =$ approx. $1\cdot4$.

The series of f-numbers adopted as standard in most countries is:

$f/1$	$f/8$
$f/1\cdot4$	$f/11$
$f/2$	$f/16$
$f/2\cdot8$	$f/22$
$f/4$	$f/32$
$f/5\cdot6$	$f/45$ etc.

The maximum aperture of a lens may, and frequently does, lie between two of the standard numbers, and in this case will necessarily be marked with a number not in the standard series.

Some European lens manufacturers used a series of f-numbers which were similarly related among themselves, but had a different starting point. These numbers were:

$f/1\cdot1$	$f/9$
$f/1\cdot6$	$f/12\cdot5$
$f/2\cdot2$	$f/18$
$f/3\cdot2$	$f/25$
$f/4\cdot5$	$f/36$
$f/6\cdot3$	$f/50$ etc.

Both series of numbers serve equally well to simplify exposure calculations, provided the numbers are used consistently. Unfortunately, however, numbers from the two different series are sometimes engraved on the same lens, thus largely defeating the purpose of having standard f-numbers.

An alteration to the lens opening corresponding with a change in exposure by a factor of 2, is referred to as a change of "one stop" or as a "whole stop". Such a change is made when the f-number is altered from any one number to the next (in either direction), in the appropriate standard series. A change to the next larger f-number halves the exposure; a change to the next smaller f-number doubles the exposure. A change from one f-number to the next-but-one in the series is referred to as a change of "two stops"; exposure is then altered by a factor of 4. A change of aperture of "half a stop" alters exposure by a factor of $\sqrt{2}$, i.e., approx. 1·4. With an iris diaphragm, this change is made by setting the index midway between one standard f-number and the next. The smallest change of aperture usually considered in practice is "one-third of a stop", which corresponds with a change of exposure by a factor of $^3\sqrt{2}$, i.e., approx. 1·26. This change is made by moving the index of the diaphragm one-third of the way from one standard f-number to the next. When a lens opening is made smaller, i.e., the f-number made larger, the operation is described as "stopping down"; when the opening is made larger, and the f-number made smaller, the operation is described as "opening up".

Although lens diaphragms are usually marked only with standard f-numbers, i.e., with whole stops, exposure calculators and meters are frequently scaled to the nearest third of a stop. The series of f-numbers then employed includes numbers from both the "standard" and the old European series of numbers. The following list of f-numbers is taken from the lens aperture scale on the Weston exposure meter:

†$f/1·1$	†$f/3·2$	†$f/9$	†$f/25$
$f/1·2$	$f/3·5$	$f/10$	$f/28$
*$f/1·4$	*$f/4$	*$f/11$	*$f/32$
†$f/1·6$	†$f/4·5$	†$f/12·5$	
$f/1·8$	$f/5$	$f/14$	
*$f/2$	*$f/5·6$	*$f/16$	
†$f/2·2$	†$f/6·3$	†$f/18$	
$f/2·5$	$f/7$	$f/20$	
*$f/2·8$	*$f/8$	*$f/22$	

* These numbers are from the "standard" series.
† These numbers are from the old European series.

Effect of bellows extension on relation between f-number and exposure

It will be remembered that in deriving the relation between the light-passing power of a lens and its f-number, given on page 65, we assumed that the image distance (v) was equal to the focal length (f). With near objects this assumption is not valid; the image distance is appreciably greater than the focal length. We know that this is so in practice because, to obtain sharp focus with near objects, we have to rack out the lens by an appreciable amount beyond the position for focusing on distant objects, i.e., we have to increase the bellows extension. In these circumstances, we are not justified in substituting f for v, and the ratio governing the light-passing power of the lens is not f/d – the f-number – but v/d. We may call v/d the *effective f-number*. Since $v/d = f/d \times v/f$, we can obtain the effective f-number by multiplying the f-number marked on the lens by v/f – the ratio of the bellows extension to the focal length. Alternatively, since the exposure time required in any given circumstances is proportional to the square of the f-number (equation 4 on page 66), we can allow for the bellows extension by calculating the exposure time using the marked f-number and multiplying the indicated time by $(v/f)^2$.

Now, since: $$v = f(1 + m) \qquad \text{(page 60)}$$

$$\frac{v}{f} = 1 + m$$

$$\text{And } \left(\frac{v}{f}\right)^2 = (1 + m)^2$$

Using these relationships, we can determine the correction factor to the f-number (or exposure time) in terms of m, instead of in terms of v and f. This is sometimes found to be more convenient in practice.

The scale of reproduction at which it becomes necessary to allow for the extra bellows extension depends on the value of $(1 + m)^2$ in relation to the exposure latitude permissible in the work we are doing. In general, it is advisable to make the allowance at a scale of reproduction of $\frac{1}{8}$th and larger. At this scale of reproduction, the exposure factor is $(1 + \frac{1}{8})^2 =$ approx. $1\frac{1}{4}$; the object distance is then nine times the focal length and the bellows extension one and one-eighth times the focal length.

This exposure factor, which increases gradually from a value of 1 for distant objects, to $1\frac{1}{4}$ at an object distance of $9f$, increases very rapidly from this point as the magnification is increased. At same-size reproduction, where the object distance is $2f$, it has a value of 4.

In copying, where allowance for bellows extension must always be made, it is usually more convenient to base exposures on that required at same-size reproduction (which can easily be found by trial in the studio), rather than on that required for a distant object (which cannot readily be determined in the studio). Assuming that the exposure time for same-size reproduction, $m_1 = 1$, has been found by trial, the exposure time required at any other scale of reproduction m_2 can be found by multiplying the same-size exposure time by:

$$\frac{(1 + m_2)^2}{(1 + m_1)^2} = \frac{(1 + m_2)^2}{4}$$

Expressed in terms of bellows extension and focal length this factor becomes $(v/f)^2/4$.

Table of exposure factors for different scales of reproduction
For copying and other types of work involving bellows extensions considerably greater than f, a list of exposure factors such as is given in Table 5.1 can be of assistance in the determination of exposure times.

(1) Object distance	(2) Bellows extension	(3) Linear scale of reproduction	(4) Marked f-number must be multiplied by:	(5) or Exposure indicated for object at ∞ must be multiplied by:*	(6) or Exposure indicated for same-size reproduction must be multiplied by:*
(u)	(v)	$(m = v/f - 1)$	$(1 + m)$	$(1 + m)^2$	$((1 + m)^2/4)$
∞	f	0	× 1	× 1	× $\frac{1}{4}$
	$1\frac{1}{8}f$	$\frac{1}{8}$	× $1\frac{1}{8}$	× $1\frac{1}{4}$	× $\frac{5}{16}$
	$1\frac{1}{4}f$	$\frac{1}{4}$	× $1\frac{1}{4}$	× $1\frac{1}{2}$	× $\frac{3}{8}$
	$1\frac{1}{2}f$	$\frac{1}{2}$	× $1\frac{1}{2}$	× $2\frac{1}{4}$	× $\frac{1}{2}$
	$1\frac{3}{4}f$	$\frac{3}{4}$	× $1\frac{3}{4}$	× 3	×
$2f$	$2f$	1 (same-size)	× 2	× 4	× 1
	$2\frac{1}{2}f$	$1\frac{1}{2}$	× $2\frac{1}{2}$	× 6	× $1\frac{1}{2}$
	$3f$	2	× 3	× 9	× $2\frac{1}{4}$
	$4f$	3	× 4	× 16	× 4
	$5f$	4	× 5	× 25	× 6

* The exposure factors in columns 5 and 6 are practical approximations.

Table 5.1 – Exposure factors for different scales of reproduction

To use this table, first find either the bellows extension expressed in focal lengths (column 2), or the scale of reproduction (column 3). The latter can frequently be estimated with sufficient accuracy by visual comparison of the lengths of image and original. Exposure times can then be found by using the appropriate factor from columns 4, 5 or 6.

If we choose to derive the exposure factor from the bellows extension, for rapid working we require a focusing scale. If a scale is to be specially made, it will assist in exposure calculations if it is graduated in terms of the focal length of the lens, instead of in inches. The numerical value of bellows extension on this scale will then equal

$1 + m$, since $v/f = 1 + m$. Exposure times can then be found either by multiplying the exposure time for an object at infinity by the square of the bellows extension on this scale (column 5), or by multiplying the exposure time for same-size reproduction by one-quarter of the square of the bellows extension (column 6).

Losses of light by reflection and absorption within a lens

Because of losses due to absorption in the material of the lens, and, more serious, to reflection from the various air-glass surfaces, part of the light incident upon a lens is lost. The extent of the loss in a given lens depends primarily upon the number and composition of the glasses employed. An average figure for the loss due to reflection is 5 per cent. for each air-glass surface. If a lens has eight air-glass surfaces, the total loss due to reflection will be about 35 per cent. of the incident light.

The amount of light actually passed by a lens expressed as a percentage of the light that would be passed by a perfectly transmitting lens of similar construction is termed its *transmission*. If, in the case quoted above, we assume that losses by absorption are negligible, the transmission is 65 per cent. This value is typical of an uncoated four-element lens.

Flare, flare spot, ghost images

Some of the light reflected at the lens surfaces passes out of the front of the lens and causes no further trouble, but a proportion is re-reflected from other surfaces and may ultimately reach the film. Re-reflected "non-image-forming" light which is spread uniformly over the surface of the film is referred to as *lens flare*. The effect of flare is to compress the tones in the shadow areas of the image and to reduce the image luminance range. Not all the re-reflected light may be spread uniformly over the film; some of it may form a more-or-less out-of-focus image of the diaphragm ("flare spot") or of bright objects in the subject ("ghost image"). Lens flare can be minimised: (i) by coating (page 74); (ii) by using an efficient lens hood.

Light reflected from the inside of the camera body, e.g., from the bellows, will also produce flare. Flare from this cause is referred to as *camera flare*. It tends to be especially marked when the field covered by the lens is appreciably greater than the film size, so that considerable light falls on the bellows. Camera flare can be minimised: (i) by using an efficient lens hood; (ii) by using a camera with bellows well clear of the film, e.g., by exposing quarter-plate negatives in a half-plate camera. The latter remedy is recommended if camera flare is serious when copying.

The ratio of subject luminance range to image illumination range is termed *flare factor*. This is a somewhat indeterminate quantity, since it depends not only on the lens and camera but also on the distribution of light within the subject. The flare factor for an average lens and camera considered together, may vary from about 2 to 10 for ordinary scenes, with an average value in the region of 4. Serious flare – i.e., a high flare factor – is characteristic of subjects having high brightness range, such as back-lit subjects.

In the camera, flare affects shadow detail more than highlight detail; in the enlarger, flare affects highlight detail most. In practice, however, provided the negative is properly masked, flare rarely assumes serious proportions in the enlarger. This is partly because the luminance range of the average negative is lower than that of the average scene, and partly because the negative is not surrounded by bright objects, as may be the scene. In colour photography, flare is likely to lead to a desaturation of colours, since flare light consists of a mixture of light from all parts of the scene, which usually approximates to white light. It may also lead to colour casts, sometimes resulting from objects outside the scene photographed.

Coating

A process involving the coating of the air-glass surfaces of a lens with a thin film of a fluoride, is widely applied commercially as a means of reducing reflection at these surfaces. The process is known variously as "surface-treating", "blooming", and "coating".

Two principles are involved. The first depends on the fact that the proportion of light R reflected at a surface, for normal incidence is:

$$R = \frac{(n-1)^2}{(n+1)^2}$$

where n is the refractive index across the surface.

This means in practice that reflection increases rapidly with refractive index, and vice versa. It also means that if a lens is coated with a layer of refractive index equal to the square root of the refractive index of the glass, the total light reflected from the air-coating surface and the coating-glass surface will be less than the reflection at the untreated surface. Suppose, for example, that a glass with refractive index of 1·56 be coated with a layer of refractive index 1·25. The reflection at the uncoated surface will be 4·8 per cent., but at each of the coated surfaces it will be only 1·2 per cent., making a total in this case of only

2·4 per cent. Use of this first principle alone is sometimes referred to as "primitive" surface treatment.

"Controlled" surface treatment makes use of a second, additional, principle. This is, that if the optical thickness of the layer is one-quarter of the wavelength of the incident light, the two reflections will interfere, and, instead of being reflected – possibly out of the lens – will go to augment the light transmitted. In this way, the loss by reflection can be reduced still further. Figure 5.4 illustrates this second principle.

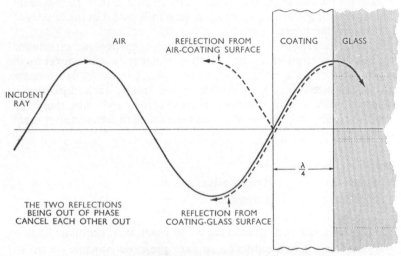

Fig. 5.4 – Principle of "controlled" surface treatment

As we have seen, application of the first principle alone can reduce the reflection at a single air-glass surface from about 5 per cent. of the incident light to 2½ per cent., and application of the second principle – in addition to the first – can reduce the reflection to about 1 per cent. With a lens having eight air-glass surfaces these figures correspond with transmissions of approximately 65 per cent. for the untreated lens, 80 per cent. with "primitive" surface treatment, and 95 per cent. with "controlled" treatment.

It is clear that complete satisfaction of the conditions required to apply these principles cannot be expected for all wavelengths of the spectrum, but, nevertheless, coating does in practice represent a worthwhile gain. As a compromise, the thickness of the coating is usually made to equal one-quarter of the wavelength of green light, i.e., approximately 130–140 nm.

The coating is applied by placing the newly polished lens in a chamber containing a tungsten wire coated with the coating medium. This substance must have suitable refractive index, must be capable of forming a uniform layer of the desired thickness, must be hard and must adhere well to glass. A number of fluorides, in particular, magnesium fluoride, meet these requirements. The chamber is then evacuated and a current is passed through the wire. The fluoride sublimates and some of it settles on the lens surface. Deposition is stopped by switching off the current when the lens has acquired a certain purple colour (minus green). This indicates that the lens is no longer reflecting green light, which in turn indicates that the layer is of the desired thickness.

Because the refractive index of magnesium fluoride is not exactly the required theoretical value the reflection is not reduced completely to neutral by such a coating, even at one wavelength. More complex antireflection coatings with two or three layers, each differing in refractive index, have therefore been evolved, and with these the reflection at an air-glass interface can be reduced to zero at one or more wavelengths.

Practical value of coating

A coated lens has the following advantages:

(1) Transmission is increased.

(2) Flare is reduced.

(3) Flare spots and ghost images are practically eliminated.

In the camera, the reduction in flare preserves shadow detail; in colour photography it also preserves the saturation of colours.

The coating of only the front surface of a lens increases transmission but does not reduce flare. To reduce flare, the internal surfaces must be coated. Coating of the front surface, may, therefore, be dispensed with if total transmission is considered unimportant. When the commercial application of coating was in its infancy, the coated layers obtained in practice were soft, and some manufacturers took advantage of the fact stated above to omit coating from the front surface – which, being exposed, necessitates a hard coating. Nowadays, coated layers able to withstand normal cleaning operations can be produced without difficulty, and it is usual practice for the manufacturer to coat all the surfaces of a lens.

Even with a coated lens, use of a lens-hood on the camera is still desirable to prevent flare which may arise as a result of reflection from the inside of the lens barrel or camera body.

Speed of a coated lens

If the speed of a lens is measured by the shadow detail produced in a negative, a coated lens is *slower* than a non-coated one, because the absence of flare reduces illumination in the shadows to a greater degree than the higher transmission increases it. A *longer* exposure is, therefore, necessary to obtain the same shadow density in the negative.

If, however, the speed of a lens is judged by highlight detail, e.g., by the density of the face, as in cine work, a coated lens is *faster*, since transmission is higher and the effect of flare on illumination in the highlights is negligible. Judged by this criterion, coating may yield a gain in speed of one-third to one-half a stop.

T-numbers

Because the transmission of a lens is never 100 per cent., its relative aperture, i.e., *f*-number, does not completely indicate its speed, although for many purposes we assume that it does. In practice, two lenses of the same *f*-number may differ widely in transmission and therefore have different speeds. The reason for this is found in losses of light due to absorption and reflection, which depend very much on the design of the lens, in particular on the number of components employed and on whether they are coated or not.

The introduction of the process of coating, to reduce surface reflection, has widened the gap between the best and the poorest lenses in respect of light transmission, and the need has arisen in some fields for a more precise unit than *f*-number for the measure of the speed of a lens. A new concept, the *T*-number, has therefore been introduced. Whereas an *f*-number represents a true geometrical measure of the relative aperture of a lens, it does not take into account transmission. A *T*-number is a photometrically determined measure taking into account both the geometry of the lens and its transmission. A *T*-number represents a measure of the amount of light passed by a lens in terms of the transmission of an ideal lens. Thus, a *T*-8 lens is one which passes as much light as a theoretically perfect *f*/8 lens. The relative aperture, or "geometrical aperture", of the *T*-8 lens will be about *f*/6·3.

The concept of *T*-numbers is of chief interest in cinematography and in colour work, i.e., in fields where exposure latitude is small and the speed of a lens must be known accurately. It is implicit in the *T*-number system that every lens should be individually calibrated.

If depth-of-field calculations are made using the *T*-number as if it were the relative aperture of the lens, the results obtained will, theoretically, be affected. The practical effect will, however, be small, and may usually be ignored, since depth-of-field calculations are in any case based on many assumptions which may or may not hold in a particular instance (page 107).

Variation of illumination across the field of a lens

The relationship derived earlier in this Chapter (page 65) between the light-passing power of a lens and relative aperture is strictly applicable only to the central parts of the field. (It will be noted that in Figure 5.3 we selected an object on the lens axis.) This is because the light-passing power of a lens – and hence the illumination on the film – falls off as we go from the centre of the field towards the edges. The fall-off in illumination arises from two causes: (1) vignetting, and (2) the "cos⁴ law".

Vignetting

Although the term vignetting is sometimes applied to the total fall-off in illumination at the edges of the field, it properly refers only to fall-off in illumination due to the cutting-off of oblique rays by the edges of the various components of the lens. It may help in visualizing how vignetting occurs to think of a lens barrel as an empty tube, as shown in Figure 5.5.

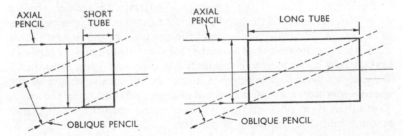

(a) With a short tube, the area of cross-section of the oblique beam is only a little less than the axial beam.

(b) With a long tube, the area of cross-section of the oblique beam is much smaller than the axial beam.

Fig. 5.5 – Cause of vignetting

No compound lens is entirely free from vignetting at full aperture. If *excessive* vignetting occurs, it is probably due to failure of the lens designer to provide sufficiently large glasses – especially at the front and back of the lens – in relation to the length of the lens barrel. A lens suffering seriously from vignetting will produce negatives which are less dense in the corners than in the centre, and colour transparencies which, if correctly exposed in the centre of the field, show dark corners. An enlarging lens suffering from excessive vignetting will produce prints with corners which are less dense than the centre. This may, however, serve to compensate to some extent for the "thinness" of the corners of negatives produced with a camera lens showing the same defect. Vignetting is reduced on stopping down. This is apparent from a consideration of the geometry of Figure 5.5b.

Cos⁴ law

Even with a lens which is completely free from vignetting, the illumination across the field still falls off as the fourth power of the cosine of the angle which the portion of the field considered makes with the axis. This falling off is due to the nature of light and the geometry of the system, and not to any defect in the lens. The reasons for it are as follows:

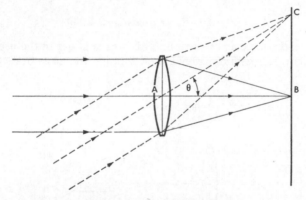

Fig. 5.6 – Lens-film distances

(1) As we progress from the centre of the field to the edges, the distance from lens to film increases. This is illustrated in Figure 5.6. As the illumination from the lens is inversely proportional to the square of the lens-to-film distance, the ratio of illumination at a point C to the illumination at the centre of the field B is $AB^2/AC^2 = \cos^2\theta$.

(2) When viewed from anywhere other than the centre of the field, the effective area of the aperture of the lens is an ellipse, not a circle. Its area – upon which the light-passing power of the lens depends – therefore appears smaller than the effective aperture as defined on page 61. From Figure 5.7, it will be seen that d_1, the minor axis of this ellipse, equals $d \cos\theta$, and it can be shown that the area of the ellipse therefore equals the area of the effective aperture multiplied by $\cos\theta$.

The light-passing power of the lens therefore falls off in proportion to $\cos\theta$.

(3) Light illuminating the edges of the field, falls on it obliquely. An oblique pencil therefore has to illuminate an area larger than an axial

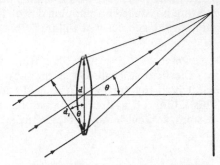

Fig. 5.7 – Light-transmission fall-off

pencil of the same cross-section. This area is larger in the proportion $1/\cos\theta$, so that the illumination falls off in proportion to $\cos\theta$ (Figure 5.8).

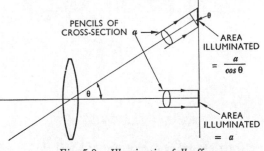

Fig. 5.8 – Illumination fall-off

The net result of these three effects is that the illumination at any point of the field other than the centre is reduced by a factor:
$$\cos^2\theta \times \cos\theta \times \cos\theta = \cos^4\theta.$$

With a lens of normal focal length, giving an angle of view of approx. 60°, the value of θ at the edges of the field is 30°, and $\cos^4\theta = (\sqrt{3}/2)^4 = 9/16 = $ approx. $\frac{1}{2}$. This means that a normal lens will show a fall-off in light at the extreme corners of the field of about 50 per cent., quite apart from any loss due to vignetting. The effect of this is normally masked by the latitude inherent in the photographic process.

On the other hand, with, for example, a wide-angle lens covering a total field of 90°, $\theta = 45°$ and $\cos^4\theta = \frac{1}{4}$, a figure which is much more serious. Consequently, manufacturers of wide-angle lenses have tried various means to reduce this difference between the illumination at the centre and at the edges of the field. For example, on the Hypergon lens, a wide-angle lens covering a field of 140°, there was fitted a star-shaped diaphragm which was rotated in front of the lens for a proportion of the exposure. With some other wide-angle lenses, e.g., certain types of lens used for aerial photography, a radially graded neutral filter is placed in the lens, in such a position that it restricts the light reaching the centre of the field. Uniformity of illumination in the image is particularly desirable in aerial photography, since in this work all parts of the field are of equal importance.

CHAPTER 6

Image Size, Angle of View, Perspective and Depth

THE size of the image produced in a camera depends upon a number of factors, as shown in Figure 6.1.

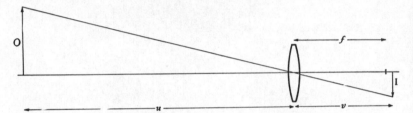

Fig. 6.1 – Factors governing image size

As the two triangles in this figure are similar we can write:

$$\frac{I}{O} = \frac{v}{u}$$

Whence: $I = O \times \dfrac{v}{u}$

Expressing this in words: the size of the image I produced in a camera depends upon the size of the object O and on the ratio of the image conjugate v to the object conjugate u. Now, we have seen that, except for near objects, the image conjugate does not differ greatly from the focal length. In these circumstances we can write:

$$I = O \times \frac{f}{u}$$

Therefore: $\dfrac{I}{O} = \dfrac{f}{u}$

$$\text{That is: } m = \frac{f}{u}$$

where m is the ratio of reproduction.

Ratio of reproduction is thus seen to depend upon the focal length of the camera lens and the distance of the object. With a given object distance, the ratio of reproduction achieved is determined by the focal length of the lens. With a given lens, the ratio of reproduction is determined by the distance of the object.

Focal length and angle of view

We have just seen that the focal length of a lens is one of the factors determining the scale of reproduction of the image. For any given film size the focal length of the lens also determines the *angle of view*, and therefore the amount of the subject included in the negative. Angle of view is generally taken as the angle at A included between the lines AB and AC, where AF is the focal length of the lens and BC the diagonal of the negative (Figure 6.2).

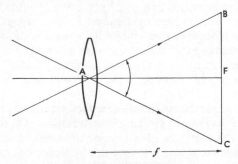

Fig. 6.2 – Angle of view

The angle of view corresponding to a given focal length and size of negative may be calculated from Table 6.1. To use this table, the diagonal of the negative should be divided by the focal length of the lens, when the angle of view can be read against the quotient obtained.

For extreme close-ups, the distance from the lens to the film appreciably exceeds the focal length, and the angle of view is then smaller than usual. For example, a lens which normally – i.e., for distant objects – gives an angle of view of 53°, gives an angle of only 28° for same-size reproduction. Obviously, the ordinary type of viewfinder does not provide a reliable guide to the field covered in such circumstances, but, since most extreme close-up work is done with

Diagonal focal length	Angle of view	Diagonal focal length	Angle of view
0·35	20°	1·27	65°
0·44	25°	1·40	70°
0·54	30°	1·53	75°
0·63	35°	1·68	80°
0·73	40°	1·83	85°
0·83	45°	2·00	90°
0·93	50°	2·38	100°
1·04	55°	2·86	110°
1·15	60°	3·46	120°

Table 6.1 – Table for deriving angle of view

cameras which permit the field covered to be examined on a ground-glass screen, difficulty due to the reduced angle of view seldom arises in practice.

However we vary our distance from an object, we can if we wish obtain an image of it of constant size – i.e., we can keep the scale of reproduction constant – simply by altering the focal length of the lens used. This is illustrated by Figure 6.3. Two things will, however alter. The first is angle of view: this will decrease as the object distance, increases – assuming that film size is kept constant. The second factor to alter is the perspective: this will become "flatter" as the object distance is increased. Perspective is discussed later in this Chapter, on page 89.

A reasonably narrow angle of view facilitates the task of the lens designer and is capable of yielding best definition. On the other hand, the narrower the angle, the greater must the object distance be – for a given image size – and, not only may this be inconvenient, but perspective may become unacceptably flat. In practical photography, therefore, a compromise has to be struck between narrow and wide angles.

Covering power of a lens

Every lens projects a circular field of light, the illumination of which falls off towards the edges – at first gradually and then very rapidly. The limit to this *circle of illumination* is set by the very rapid fall-off – which results from vignetting (page 78).

As we proceed outwards from the centre of the field, the distinctness, or *definition*, of the image produced by the lens also falls off – at first gradually and then more rapidly. If we set a standard of the definition which we are prepared to accept, we can locate a *circle of good definition* within which our standard is everywhere reached or surpassed.

This will lie appreciably inside the circle of illumination. Since it is definition which limits the field of a lens from a practical point of view, it is customary to state the field in terms of this circle of good

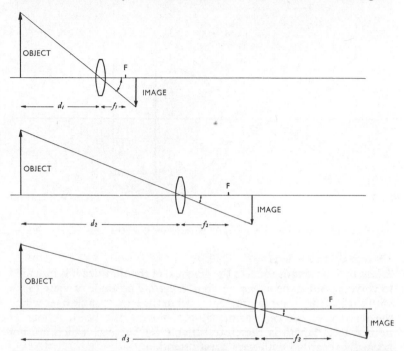

Fig. 6.3 – Image size kept constant irrespective of object distance, by suitable choice of lens

definition. Field is usually expressed in terms of the angle – or, sometimes, half the angle – subtended by the lens at this circle. The circles of illumination and good definition are illustrated in Figure 6.4.

Sometimes, the field of a lens may be defined in terms of a film or plate size, e.g., "to cover a half-plate". This means that the circle of good definition of the lens is large enough to contain a rectangle measuring, in the example quoted, 120×165 mm. The circle must, therefore, have a diameter of at least 205 mm – preferably more, to allow for the use of camera movements (Chapter 12).

Effect of stopping down on covering power
Both the illumination and definition at the edges of the field of a lens are normally improved on stopping down. Illumination is improved

because vignetting is reduced on stopping down (page 79). Definition is improved because most of the lens aberrations present at the edges of the field are reduced on stopping down. (See Chapter 7.)

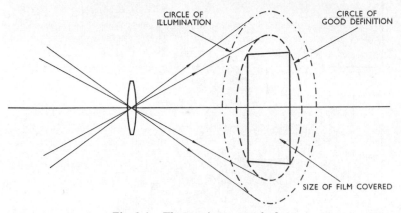

Fig. 6.4 – The covering power of a lens

"Normal" focus lens

A lens of focal length equal to the diagonal of the film size it is intended to cover is said to be of *normal focal length*. The angle of view (53°), with such a lens, is approximately equal to the largest angle over which the inattentive eye can roam, without moving the head. A lens of normal focal length is therefore suitable for subjects which are not normally regarded with very great attention.

Wide-angle lens

A lens capable of covering a film whose diagonal is appreciably longer than the focal length of the lens is termed a *wide-angle lens*. A wide-angle lens has a shorter focal length than the normal focus lens – for the same film size. The angle of view with a wide-angle lens is commonly of the order of 75°, although lenses of special construction are available embracing fields much wider than this.

The use of wide-angle lenses includes work under cramped conditions where the camera-to-subject distance is limited, work in which it is desired to emphasize certain aspects of the subject and subordinate others, and occasions when a false impression of size is required, e.g., to make a room look lofty, majestic and spacious, to make a short garden appear long, or to make a small car look more roomy than it is – for advertising purposes. (In the latter case, a low viewpoint helps to add to the illusion!) These effects are achieved by making use of the steep perspective associated with a wide camera angle (page 90).

When a wide-angle lens is used, spheres and cylinders at the edge of the field appear elliptical, for the reason shown in Figure 6.5. When group photographs are taken in a confined space, e.g., at social functions, a wide-angle lens is frequently used to enable the whole group to be covered on one film. The heads of people at the edges of the film are, then, likely to appear broadened as a result of the phenomenon illustrated.

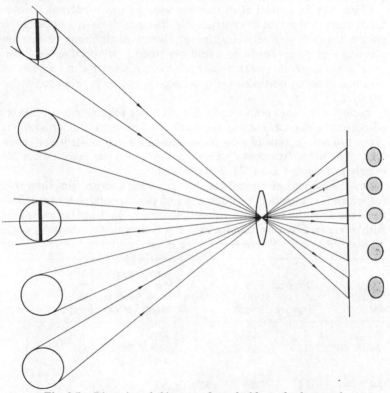

Fig. 6.5 – Distortion of objects at edges of wide-angle photograph

Wide-angle lenses for large-format cameras are often of relatively small working aperture, e.g., $f/8$ or smaller. To assist in focusing on a ground-glass screen, it is possible with some wide-angle lenses to open the stop to a wider aperture, e.g., $f/5\cdot6$, where the definition, although not good enough for photography, is adequate for focusing.

Long-focus lens

A lens designed to cover a film whose diagonal is appreciably shorter than the focal length of the lens is termed a *long-focus lens*. Such a lens gives a narrow angle of view – commonly about 30° – and should be used for subjects which are generally regarded with good attention, since, when concentrating, the angle over which the eye can wander with comfort is much narrower than usual – probably no more than 20°. Long-focus lenses are therefore recommended for work such as portraiture and catalogue illustration.

(This may be looked at in another way. Just as a portrait painter takes care to work at a considerable distance from his subject, to ensure that the size relationships of objects in different planes are pleasing – in other words, to avoid too steep a perspective – so, too, must a photographer work well back from his sitter if he wishes to produce pleasing portraits, using a long-focus lens in order to fill the negative.)

Long-focus lenses are valuable for any work requiring large images of objects which cannot be approached. The name "telephoto" is given to a certain type of long-focus lens of special construction (page 136). The word "telephoto" should not, however, be used indiscriminately as a name for *any* long-focus lens.

On using a lens of normal focal length with a *larger* film than that for which it is intended, a wider angle of view is obtained, but definition falls off at the edges and vignetting occurs. On using the same lens with a *smaller* film than that for which it is intended, a narrower angle

Negative size	Diagonal of negative	Normal lens Focal length	Angle of view	Wide-angle lens Focal length	Angle of view	Long-focus lens Focal length	Angle of view
mm	mm	mm		mm		mm	
24 × 36	43	50	48°	28	75°	85	28°
				35	66°	135	19°
						200	12°
60 × 60	85	80	56°	50	81°	120	39°
						250	20°
						500	10°
102 × 127	165	150	58°	100	79°	250	36°
						300	30°

Table 6.2 – Typical values of focal length and angle of view for normal-focus, wide-angle and long-focus lenses for three widely used film sizes

of view is obtained, but definition suffers over the whole field compared with a lens of the same focal length designed to cover the smaller negative size only. True wide-angle lenses and true long-focus lenses are specially computed to cover unusually large and unusually small fields respectively. Like other lenses, they function properly only when used with films of the size that they are designed to cover.

Typical values of focal length and angle of view for normal-focus, wide-angle and long-focus lenses for three widely used film sizes are given in Table 6.2.

Perspective

The apparent relation between the shape, size and position of visible objects is termed *perspective*, *linear perspective* or, sometimes, *drawing*. If two objects of the same size, standing one behind the other, are viewed by an observer, the sizes of the objects will appear to be in inverse ratio to their distances from the observer.

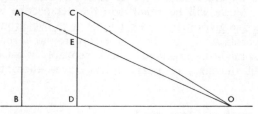

Fig. 6.6 – Dependence of perspective upon viewpoint

Referring to Figure 6.6, if *AB* and *CD* are two objects of equal size viewed by an observer at *O*, then the apparent height of *AB* in relation to *CD* will be *ED*. Since triangles *ABO* and *EDO* are similar:

$$\frac{ED}{AB} = \frac{DO}{BO}$$

Therefore: $\dfrac{ED}{CD} = \dfrac{DO}{BO}$

i.e., the apparent heights of the two objects are in inverse ratio to their distances from the observer.

Let us suppose that the distance between the two objects is 10 metres, and that the nearest object is 20 metres from the observer. Then, the relative sizes of the two objects will be 20 : 30 × 2 : 3. That is, the more distant object will appear to be only two-thirds the size of the nearer object. If we move back until we are, say, 90 metres from the nearer object, the ratio will become 90 : 100 = 9 : 10. That is, the more distant object will appear almost as large as the nearer one.

From these examples, it will be apparent that if the depth of the subject is large in relation to its distance from the observer, there will be considerable difference between the apparent sizes of foreground and background objects, but if the depth is small relative to the subject distance there will be little difference in size. This illustrates the fact that the perspective achieved when viewing a scene depends on the ratio that the depth of the subject bears to its distance from the observer. The perspective obtained with a given scene therefore depends solely on the viewpoint – whether we are looking at the scene or photographing it. If the scene be viewed from a short distance, there will be a great disparity between the apparent sizes of foreground and background objects. Foreground objects will have increased prominence and background objects reduced prominence. The perspective in this case is described as *steep*. If the scene be viewed from a great distance, the apparent difference in size between foreground and background objects will be small, and the perspective will be *flat*. Such perspective gives increased prominence to background objects, but the importance of objects in the foreground is not seriously diminished as might be expected. This is probably because the mind, knowing well the sizes of near objects, gives them their usual importance.

Perspective on taking a photograph

As we have already seen, the perspective obtained on *taking* a photograph – sometimes termed the *true perspective* – is governed solely by the viewpoint. If the viewpoint is fixed, there can be no change in perspective, even if we change to a lens of different focal length – although, as we have seen earlier, the image size will alter. If, however, the viewpoint is altered, so will be the perspective, and no change of lens will re-create the perspective obtained at the first viewpoint. *Altering the distance of the viewpoint from the object, without changing the lens, alters both perspective and image size. Altering the focal length of the lens, without changing the viewpoint, alters image size only – leaving perspective unaltered.*

We saw on page 84 that if we wish, we can, by changing viewpoint *and* focal length, keep the image size of a selected object constant and vary the perspective from flat to steep. This is illustrated again in Figure 6.7, where the size of the front of the house has been kept constant in all three views. We shall consider a little later (page 93) the factors determining the *best* perspective for a given subject.

Perspective on viewing a photograph

The perspective obtained on viewing a print – sometimes termed the *apparent perspective* – depends, firstly, on the relative sizes of objects in the print – and hence on the perspective obtained in the negative on taking the photograph – and, secondly, on the distance at which the print is viewed.

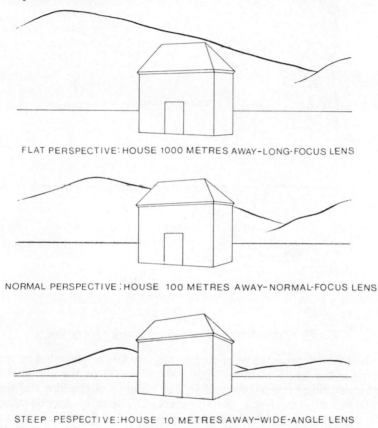

FLAT PERSPECTIVE: HOUSE 1000 METRES AWAY-LONG-FOCUS LENS

NORMAL PERSPECTIVE : HOUSE 100 METRES AWAY- NORMAL-FOCUS LENS

STEEP PESPECTIVE: HOUSE 10 METRES AWAY-WIDE-ANGLE LENS

Fig. 6.7 - Perspective

Correct perspective is said to be obtained when a print is viewed in such a way that the apparent relation between objects as to their size, position etc., is the same as in the original scene. This is achieved when the print is viewed at such a distance that it subtends at the eye the same angle as was subtended by the original scene at the lens. The eye will then be at the *centre of perspective* of the print, just as, at the moment of taking, the lens was at the centre of perspective of the scene.

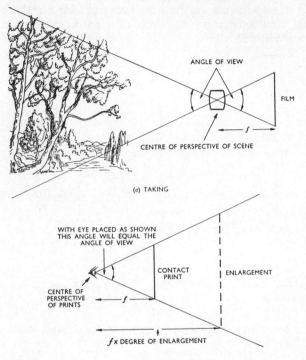

Fig. 6.8 - Perspective on taking and on viewing a photograph

Now, as we may see from Figure 6.8, the angle subtended by the scene at the lens is identical with that subtended by the film at the lens, and this angle is governed by the diagonal of the film and the bellows extension, which – for all except close objects – may be taken as equal to the focal length. *For correct perspective, therefore, a contact print should be viewed at a distance equal to the focal length of the taking lens. An enlargement should be viewed at a distance equal to the focal length multiplied by the degree of enlargement.* (This is a simple sum in proportion.) If we view a print at a distance other than the correct one, the perspective achieved will be distorted.

If the perspective achieved on taking a photograph is steep, the perspective achieved on viewing the print "correctly" will also be steep, and vice versa. "Correctness" of perspective on viewing a print does not necessarily imply that the perspective achieved will be pleasing.

How important is perspective in a photograph?

We have considered the factors governing the perspective achieved on taking and on viewing a photograph. We need now to consider how important it is to achieve a particular kind of perspective at each of these two stages.

We have seen that, *on taking a photograph*, we have a choice of perspectives – ranging from flat to steep. Although *unusual* perspective, i.e., too flat or too steep, is normally to be avoided, perspective achieved by standing well back from the subject generally yields a better proportioned view than does steep perspective. In order to fill the frame with the image, while standing well back from the subject to achieve flattish perspective, we require a lens of relatively long focal length. Thus, we associate the use of a lens of long focal length with good "drawing". This must, however, not be pushed to extremes, for, if the focal length is too long, we obtain the excessive flattening of perspective which, when a telephoto lens is used, makes a cricket pitch look only a few metres long.

A long-focus lens is, however, by no means suitable for all types of photography. It gives a narrow angle of view, and, when working in cramped conditions, it is often essential to use a lens of very much shorter focal length – either a "normal" focus or a wide-angle lens – in order to include all the subject in the picture. In this case, the perspective will necessarily be steeper. Frequently, steep perspective cannot be avoided when photographing interiors of buildings, etc., but, provided that the prints are viewed under correct viewing conditions, steep perspective is not usually objectionable with such subjects. Since, however, steep perspective gives disproportionate importance to objects in the foreground, particular care should be taken in the choice and arrangement of objects in the front of the picture.

For most ordinary photography, we require a lens of focal length sufficiently long to give reasonably flat perspective, but not so long that it gives a very small angle of view. For general work, therefore, a compromise is struck at a lens of focal length approximately equal to the diagonal of the film. (We have arrived at this conclusion from considerations of perspective; on page 86 we arrived at the same conclusion from a consideration of angle of view. Obviously, perspective and angle of view are two aspects of the one story.)

On viewing a photograph, the impression of realism is generally enhanced if it is examined under "correct" viewing conditions, as defined on page 91. Correct viewing conditions are, however, by no means always essential, since with many subjects the eye will tolerate considerable distortion of perspective. For example, en-prints in the popular 90 × 90 mm size are invariably viewed at a distance much greater than the "correct" viewing distance; yet this causes no difficulty. Although the perspective is distorted, this is not noticed (see page 95). On the other hand, the perspective of photographs taken with a wide-angle lens and showing steep perspective, does usually appear distorted if these are examined at other than the correct viewing distance. Objects at the *edges* of wide-angle photographs may appear distorted even when the photographs are viewed at the correct distance (page 87).

In general, it would appear that so long as the perspective on taking is average, i.e., neither very steep nor very flat, considerable departure from "correct" viewing can be tolerated. On the other hand, if the perspective on taking is very steep or very flat, the resulting photograph is likely to appear distorted unless viewed at the "correct" distance.

Here, we may note that the perspective of a print viewed from too great a distance tends to appear steep, while that of a print viewed from too short a distance tends to appear flat. This is the reverse of the perspective effects achieved on taking the picture.

Viewing prints in practice

In practice, an observer generally chooses the distance at which he views a print from considerations of personal comfort – i.e., to be such that the eye can comfortably scan the print – rather than with a view to obtaining correct perspective. It is, therefore, usually the *size* of the print and not the focal length of the camera lens – which is more often than not unknown to the viewer – which governs the viewing distance. (The case referred to above, of a photograph taken with a wide-angle lens, reinforces this contention. As was stated there, if a picture of this type is viewed at the "correct" viewing distance its perspective appears correct. Instead, in practice, we normally view it from a comfortable distance and complain that the perspective is distorted!)

Now, the nearest distance from which we can view a print and take it all in without turning the head, is the diagonal of the print. A viewing distance of about equal to or a little longer than the diagonal of the print is, therefore, normally adopted for comfortable viewing. A whole-plate print, with a diagonal of approximately 250 mm, will thus be viewed at a distance of about 250 mm and larger prints at correspondingly longer distances.

Comfortable viewing conditions and *correct* viewing conditions are achieved simultaneously if the diagonal of the print equals the focal length of the camera lens in the case of a contact print, or the focal length of the lens multiplied by the degree of enlargement in the case of an enlargement. *A close approximation to this is achieved in practice when printing from the whole of a negative taken with a lens of normal focal length* (assuming that the print is not smaller than a whole plate).

The nearest comfortable distance for viewing prints with the unaided eye is about 250 mm. This distance is considerably greater than the distance at which en-prints commonly require to be viewed for correct perspective, i.e., about 125 mm. For correct perspective, such prints must therefore be viewed with the aid of an eye-lens of 125 mm focal length, or they should be enlarged by a further two diameters and viewed at 250 mm. When they are viewed with the unaided eye, the perspective of such small prints is too steep from a technical point of view. It is interesting to note, however, that this rarely causes difficulty – the distortion is accepted – although there is probably an unnoticed loss of realism.

Definition in photographs

Any scene can be considered as made up of a large number of points. A perfect lens would form a point image of each of these; a cone of light corresponding to each point on the object converges from the lens to a point, termed a focus, and then diverges again, a point image being formed when the cone is at its narrowest. If we place a film in the image space at right angles to the lens axis, we can, by suitably adjusting the distance from lens to film, bring the sensitive surface of the film to the intersection of the cone and catch the point image (Figure 6.9). We make such an adjustment each time that we *focus* a lens.

The distance of the point image from the lens will depend upon the distance of the object point from the lens, the image and object distances (conjugates) being related by the lens equation (page 58). If all points on the object lie in one plane, so also – in a perfect lens – will the image points. But, if two object points lie in planes at *different* distances from the lens, so will the image points. It will, then, be impossible for the film to be placed so that it is at the intersection of the cones of light corresponding with *both* object points at the same time. Each can be brought into focus in turn, by the operation of focusing, but the two cannot be made to form sharp images simultaneously; when the image of one point is sharp, the other will be represented by a disc or *circle of confusion,* and vice versa (Figure 6.10). These circles are cross-sections of pencils of light coming to a focus behind or in

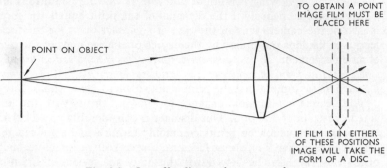

TO OBTAIN A POINT
IMAGE FILM MUST BE
PLACED HERE

POINT ON OBJECT

IF FILM IS IN EITHER
OF THESE POSITIONS
IMAGE WILL TAKE THE
FORM OF A DISC

Fig. 6.9 – Lens-film distance for accurate focus

front of the surface of the film. (Alternatively, of course, the film may be placed so that the images of both points take the form of circles of confusion.)

From this, it would appear that when photographing an object with

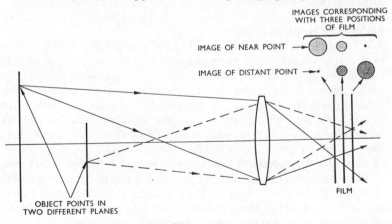

IMAGES CORRESPONDING
WITH THREE POSITIONS
OF FILM

IMAGE OF NEAR POINT →

IMAGE OF DISTANT POINT →

FILM

OBJECT POINTS IN
TWO DIFFERENT PLANES

Fig. 6.10 – Object and image points

depth, only one plane can be in sharp focus, all other planes, whether nearer or further from the camera, being *out-of-focus.* Yet, we know that in practice we do obtain pictures of objects with considerable depth that appear sharp all over. It would seem, therefore, that the eye is satisfied with something less than pin-point sharpness.

This, in fact, is true. There is a limit to the smallness of detail which the eye can perceive, or *resolve*, so that an image appears sharp as soon as the eye cannot distinguish between it and a sharper image. In order to be able to decide when an image in a print will appear out-of-focus we must therefore consider the resolving power of the eye.

Resolving power of the eye

Let us suppose that we have an object consisting of two parallel black lines of equal width separated by a white space of the same width. If we view this from an increasing distance, there will come a point where we can no longer distinguish between the two lines; they will appear instead as a single line. We have then reached the limit of resolution of the eye. Eyes vary in their ability to resolve detail, but it has been shown that the limit of resolution with the average eye is reached when the distance of such a test object from the observer is 2500 times the distance between the centres of the lines. The angle subtended by the lines at the eye is then about 1 minute of arc. This figure applies to an object of high contrast – black and white. With a less contrasty object, the lines would appear merged at a shorter distance, say, 1000 times the distance between the lines. For very many purposes in photography we can take the resolving power of the eye as being at the lower figure, i.e., about 1 in 1000, or about 3 minutes of arc. For work that will stand the closest scrutiny, however, the more stringent standard of 1 in 2500 must be used.

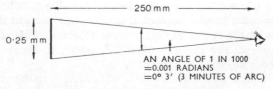

Fig. 6.11 – Circle of confusion

Now, just as at the limit of resolution the eye cannot distinguish between two lines, so, in a print, the eye cannot see any difference between a circle of confusion and a true point if the diameter of the circle is less than one-thousandth of its distance from the eye. To put it in another way, a print will appear perfectly sharp if the circle of confusion corresponding to each and every point on the object sub-tends at the eye an angle not greater than 1 in 1000, i.e., 3 minutes of arc. This is equivalent to a circle 0·25 mm in diamter at 250 mm, the nearest distance of distinct vision (Figure 6.11).

The principle of expressing resolving power as an angle agrees with our practical experience that the eye sees things more clearly the nearer they are. Thus, any test of eyesight that involves the reading of figures or letters, must specify both the size of the figures and the distance at which they are to be read.

Depth
The property of the eye of accepting a disc for a point gives us a certain degree of freedom in photography as regards:
(1) The plane in which the film is located, and
(2) The plane in which the object is located,
without sacrificing the degree of sharpness of the picture.
(1) corresponds with *depth of focus* and (2) with *depth of field*,* both of which are thus seen to depend upon the degree of sharpness required in the given circumstances.

Permissible diameter of the circle of confusion in prints and negatives
In calculations of depth of field and depth of focus it is necessary, first of all, to decide on a numerical value for the largest diameter of the circle of confusion that we can permit without detectable loss of definition. In such calculations, it is customary to specify the permissible diameter of the circle of confusion in terms of the negative. We must, however, consider first the print, since it is in terms of this that we decide whether or not a photograph is sharp. When we have decided on what can be permitted in the print, we can then simply divide this by the degree of enlargement to obtain a figure applicable to the negative. For contact prints, of course, the same figure will apply to both negatives and prints.

Now, we have seen that the circle of confusion in the print may be such that it subtends, at the observer's eye, an angle not exceeding 1 in 1000. The question then arises, at what distance the print will be examined–for this will profoundly affect the permissible diameter of the circle of confusion. We considered this problem earlier when dealing with perspective (page 94), and there we distinguished between "correct" viewing conditions and "comfortable" viewing conditions,

---

* The term "depth of focus" is sometimes applied indiscriminately to the two quantities distinguished in this book by the terms "depth of focus" and "depth of field". To avoid confusion, however, it is desirable that the two should be referred to by different names. This can be achieved without difficulty by confining the use of the term "depth of focus" to its proper meaning.

and defined the viewing distance applicable to each. The permissible diameters of the circles of confusion corresponding to these two types of viewing conditions are as follows:

"Correct" viewing conditions
Viewing distance:
Focal length of lens (f) × degree of enlargement (e).
Permissible diameter of circle of confusion in print:
$f × e/1000$.
Permissible diameter of circle of confusion in negative:
$f/1000$.

"Comfortable" viewing conditions
Minimum viewing distance:
Diagonal of print.
Permissible diameter of circle of confusion in print:
1/1000th of diagonal of print.
Permissible diameter of circle of confusion in negative:
1/1000th of diagonal of that part of negative used to make print.

The circle of confusion based on "comfortable" viewing conditions will equal that based on "correct" viewing conditions when "comfortable" and "correct" viewing conditions are achieved simultaneously, as described on page 95.

With reference to the above figures it may be noted that, since the minimum viewing distance of the unaided eye is 250 mm, in no case *need* the permitted diameter of the circle of confusion in the print be less than 250/1000 mm, i.e., 0·25 mm, or, in the negative, 0·25 mm divided by the degree of enlargement. This consideration principally concerns small prints.

It should, perhaps, be made plain that it is impossible to provide satisfactorily for all viewing conditions. Both of the sets of formulae given above are open to abuse, although it is believed that the second set gives, on the average, results nearer to practical experience than the first. An interesting example of conditions under which formulae based on "correct" viewing fall down is given on page 106. Both sets of formulae break down, however, in face of the visitor to an exhibition who goes right up to a photo mural to detect signs of retouching. But then, his viewing conditions are neither correct nor comfortable!

Depth of focus
Depth of focus is the distance through which the film may be moved

before the image of a flat object becomes noticeably unsharp (Figure 6.12).

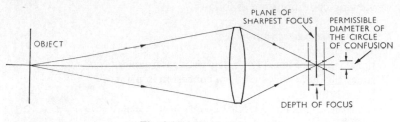

Fig. 6.12 – Depth of focus

Depth of focus varies with:

(1) The permissible diameter of the circle of confusion in the negative – the larger the permissible diameter, the greater the depth.

(2) The angle subtended by the lens at the film, i.e., for most purposes, the *f*-number – the larger the *f*-number, the greater the depth.

A mathematical expression for depth of focus can be obtained from a consideration of Figure 6.13.

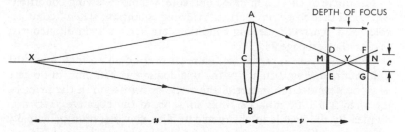

Fig. 6.13 – Derivation of formula for depth of focus

Lens AB is focused on a point object X at a distance u, and a point image is formed at Y at a distance v. If we assume that the depth of focus is such that its limits lie in the planes through M and N, then the diameter of the image DE ($= FG$) formed in the plane of the film through M is the diameter c of the permissible circle of confusion in the negative. In the figure, since triangles DEY and ABY are similar:

$$\frac{MY}{CY} = \frac{DE}{AB}$$

Whence: $MY = \dfrac{DE \times CY}{AB} = \dfrac{cv}{d}$

where $d = AB$, the effective diameter of the lens aperture. Then

$$\text{Depth of focus} = MY + YN = 2MY = \frac{2cv}{d}$$

Since f/d equals N, the f-number of the lens, this equation can be written:

$$\text{Depth of focus} = 2cN\frac{v}{f}$$

$$\text{But } \frac{v}{f} = 1 + m \text{ (page 60)}$$

Hence: Depth of focus $= 2cN (1 + m)$ . . . . . . (1)

For all except extreme close-ups, m is very small compared with 1 and can be neglected, so that the last equation can be simplified to:

Depth of focus $= 2cN$ . . . . (2)

This is the basic formula for depth of focus. It contains N, an expression of the lens aperture at which we are working, and c, the permissible diameter of the circle of confusion in the negative, which we can derive using whichever of the formulae given on page 99 that we choose.

If, for example, we adopt a value for c of $f/1000$, we can write:

$$\text{Depth of focus} = \frac{2fN}{1000} \quad \text{. . . . . (3)}$$

From this expression, it is immediately apparent that the smaller the aperture, i.e., the larger the f-number, the greater the depth of focus, and vice versa. The equation also shows that, in normal circumstances, the longer the focal length the greater the depth of focus. (The last statement is qualified because it holds true only in circumstances when use of a lens of greater focal length permits a larger circle of confusion to be adopted, as, for example, when changing to a larger camera. It does not hold good when the film size is unchanged.)

A further way in which we can express the depth of focus formula, is in terms of the effective diameter of the lens aperture, for, since $N = f/d$, we obtain, on substitution in equation (3):

$$\text{Depth of focus} = \frac{2f^2}{1000d}$$

We shall see later (page 104) that $1000d$ is a measure of the hyperfocal distance h, so that we can write:

$$\text{Depth of focus} = \frac{2f^2}{h} \quad \text{. . . . . (4)}$$

It should be noted that equations (2), (3) and (4) above, all assume that the object distance is fairly large. Equations (3) and (4) also assume that the print is viewed under correct perspective conditions; only equation (2) is applicable to all viewing conditions.

Practical value of depth of focus
Depth of focus tells the camera manufacturer how flat the film must be, and how much tolerance there can be on film positioning and lens measurements. Miniature cameras must obviously be made with precision, since the small *f*-numbers and short focal lengths of the lenses with which they are normally equipped both make for small depth of focus.

Depth of focus is employed by the photographer when using film that is not quite flat, or dark-slides which do not exactly register, and also when using the focusing adjustment on the camera to obtain an image of an exact size – focus being allowed to go slightly out – and hoping that on stopping down it will come into sharp focus.

Depth of field
Depth of field is the distance through which the subject may extend, when the camera is focused as sharply as possible on one part of it, without the image becoming noticeably unsharp (Figure 6.14).

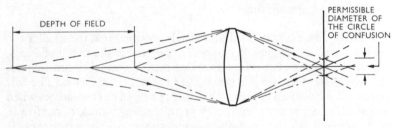

Fig. 6.14 – Depth of field

The part of the subject over which the depth of field extends is sometimes termed the *region of sharp focus*. Outside this region, definition falls off, becoming progressively poorer as the distance from the object to the nearest point in focus increases.

Depth of field varies with:

(1) The permissible diameter of the circle of confusion in the negative – the larger the permissible diameter the greater the depth.

(2) The angle subtended by the lens at the film, i.e., for most purposes, the *f*-number – the larger the *f*-number the greater the depth.

(3) The square of the ratio of reproduction – the smaller the ratio of reproduction the greater the depth.

Expressing depth of field mathematically
Whereas depth of *focus* is disposed equally about the plane of sharpest focus, depth of *field* is not usually so disposed. For most subjects, it is greater beyond the distance focused on than in front. As a result, the formula for total depth of field is complicated and will not be given here. A simplified form of this formula, applicable to near objects only, is, however, given later in this Chapter (page 106).

The fact is that we are not usually primarily interested in the *total* depth, but rather in the *limits* of the region of sharp focus – i.e., the distances from the camera of the nearest and furthest points which are just in acceptable focus – and we can calculate these distances quite easily by introducing a quantity termed *hyperfocal distance*. This we may define as the distance from the lens to the nearest object which is just acceptably sharp when the camera is focused on infinity. A mathematical expression for hyperfocal distance can be obtained from a consideration of Figure 6.15.

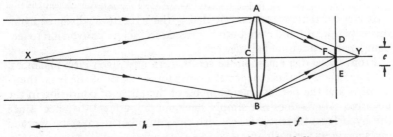

Fig. 6.15 – Derivation of formula for hyperfocal distance

Lens *AB* is focused on a point object at infinity, and a point image is formed at *F*, where *CF* equals the focal length *f* of the lens.

If we assume that the depth of field is such that *X* is the nearest point which is rendered in acceptably sharp focus, then the diameter of the image *DE* formed in the plane of the film through *F* is the diameter *c* of the permissible circle of confusion in the negative. A point image of *X* would be formed at *Y*. *XC* is the hyperfocal distance *h*.

Now, the lens equation: $\dfrac{1}{u} + \dfrac{1}{v} = \dfrac{1}{f}$

can be rearranged to read: $u = \dfrac{vf}{v - f}$

In the case of the conjugate points X and Y, this becomes:

$$XC = \frac{CY.f}{FY}$$

Now, since triangles ABY and DEY are similar:

$$\frac{CY}{FY} = \frac{AB}{DE}$$

Therefore: $XC = \frac{AB}{DE} f$

That is: $h = \frac{d}{c} f$

where $d = AB$, the effective diameter of the lens aperture.

Since f/d equals N, the f-number of the lens, this equation can be written:

$$h = \frac{f^2}{cN} \quad \cdots \cdots \cdots \cdots \quad (5)$$

It is a convenience when calculating the hyperfocal distance using this equation, if f and c are both expressed in inches, conversion to feet being made from the final answer.

From the above equation we see that, in any given circumstances, the hyperfocal distance depends on the focal length of the lens, the f-number and the permissible diameter of the circle of confusion in the negative. A lens does not simply have one hyperfocal distance; since the hyperfocal distance varies with the f-number it must be worked out separately for each aperture.

The basic formula for hyperfocal distance given above can be written in other forms. If, for example, we take a value of $f/1000$ for the permissible diameter of the circle of confusion in the negative, we can write:

$$h = \frac{1000f}{N} \quad \cdots \cdots \cdots \cdots \quad (6)$$

Or, again, still taking c as $f/1000$, we can write, since $N = f/d$:

$$h = 1000d \quad \cdots \cdots \cdots \cdots \quad (7)$$

where d is the effective diameter of the lens aperture.

Relation between hyperfocal distance and depth of field
It follows from the definition of hyperfocal distance given earlier, that

the shorter the hyperfocal distance the greater the depth of field available when the camera is focused on infinity. This principle holds good at other object distances, and hyperfocal distance thus serves as a useful guide to the order of the depth of field available in any given circumstances; the shorter the hyperfocal distance the greater the available depth of field, and vice versa.

It can be shown that the relation between hyperfocal distance and the limits of the region of sharp focus for any given focusing distance u is given approximately by the following two equations:

Distance from lens to nearest point in acceptably sharp focus $= \dfrac{h \times u}{h + u}$ . . . . . (8)

Distance from lens to farthest point in acceptably sharp focus $= \dfrac{h \times u}{h - u}$ . . . . . (9)

Depth of field is represented by the difference between these two distances. Although these equations are only approximate, they are sufficiently accurate to be useful for most practical purposes.

From equation 9, it will be seen that when the camera is focused on the hyperfocal distance, i.e., when $u = h$, the region of sharp focus extends to infinity. Thus, an alternative definition of hyperfocal distance is: the distance on which a lens has to be focused for the depth of field to extend just to infinity. The region of sharp focus then extends on the near side to half the hyperfocal distance, and the depth of field is at its greatest value. This property of hyperfocal distance is made use of in simple fixed-focus cameras, which are normally focused on the hyperfocal distance, rather than on infinity.

Focusing to cover two objects at different distances

From equations (8) and (9) above, it can be shown that u, the distance focused on, equals: $\dfrac{2xy}{x + y}$

where x is the distance of the nearest point and y the distance of the farthest point just in focus. This equation is useful when it is required to know at what distance to focus the camera to obtain the best definition on two objects at known distances x and y.

Depth of field for close-ups

For near objects, depth of field is small and extends by about the same amount on either side of the distance focused on. In such circumstances, a formula for total depth – from the nearest point just in focus to the farthest point just in focus – is sometimes useful.

This formula is as follows:

$$\text{Total depth} = \frac{2\,cN\,(m\,+\,1)}{m^2}$$

Control of depth of field

The normal way of increasing depth of field with a given subject, is to reduce the angle subtended by the lens at the film – by stopping down. This increases the f-number N, and, as we have already seen from the basic formula for hyperfocal distance given as equation 5 on page 104, this decreases the hyperfocal distance and thus increases the depth of field. If the depth available at the smallest practical aperture is insufficient, the camera movements of swing front and/or swing back can be brought into play to make better use of the depth available. (See Chapter 12.)

When the limit given by these controls is reached, the ratio of reproduction, i.e., the image size, must be reduced. We stated on page 103 that depth of field depends on the ratio of reproduction – the smaller the ratio of reproduction the greater the depth available – and this is illustrated by the formula for close-ups given immediately above. Change of image size can be effected in two ways:

(1) If the perspective is required to be unaltered, the viewpoint must remain unchanged, and a lens of shorter focal length must be used. This is often most readily done by changing to a smaller camera.

(2) If perspective may be altered, we can use the original lens but move further from the subject.

For a given reduction in image size, the gain in depth is the same whichever of the two methods is used, and, in both cases, this gain still holds good when the image is enlarged.

Depth of field at constant image size in negative

If we try to obtain increased depth by using a lens of shorter focal length, *and, at the same time, try to maintain image size by bringing the camera closer to the object*, we shall achieve nothing except ruin of the perspective.

In the circumstances described, the permissible diameter of the circle of confusion is constant for all the prints, since being of the same size they will, in practice, all be viewed side by side; i.e., "comfortable" viewing conditions will be employed. Now, for a given circle of confusion, depth of field is dependent only upon the f-number of the lens and the ratio of reproduction, both of which are constant in the example quoted. Hence, the depth of field obtained will be constant.

(If we assume "correct" viewing conditions in this example, and take c as $f/1000$, we reach the conclusion that a shorter focal length lens gives *less* depth of field! Here then is a case where basing the value for the circle of confusion on "correct" viewing conditions is definitely misleading.)

Depth obtained in practice

So far, we have treated depth on the lines of geometrical optics, which assumes that a lens is perfect and that light travels in straight lines. We have also assumed that the film is capable of resolving any image, however fine. In fact, no lens is perfect, light travels in waves – not in straight lines, and the resolving power of an emulsion is limited by its structure. Consequently, the foregoing remarks concerning depth need to be qualified.

Effect on depth of lens imperfections and the wave nature of light

Because of lens imperfections and the fact that light travels in waves, no lens forms a point image of a point source even in the plane of sharpest focus. (See Chapter 7.) Lens errors may combine to form a disc larger than the permissible circle of confusion, so that the image is nowhere sharp; but, because the eye then has no standard of definition, there may *appear* to be greater depth than would normally be obtained under the given conditions. (What is in fact a poorly corrected lens may therefore appear to give great depth of field! Conversely, an extremely well corrected lens may appear to give little depth of field.) Further, the region of sharp focus may not be distributed about the distance focused on in accordance with the laws of geometrical optics. For example, one type of lens correction results in a lens having most of its depth in *front* of the plane of sharpest focus and not behind – as would be expected from calculation. Again, the distribution of depth about the plane of sharpest focus may vary with the *f*-number. Curvature of field, too, may obviously affect depth of field.

In practice, this all means that the user must get to know his own lens, using depth of field tables only as a guide, and then trust his eyes. Whenever possible, final focusing adjustments (assuming that focusing is done visually) should be made with the lens stopped down to the aperture at which the exposure is to be made. This is especially important for close-ups, where depth is very limited. Experience with a magnifier to which one is accustomed will enable one to determine what is required in the way of definition. If a low level of illumination makes focusing difficult, a torch may be placed at the extremes of the scene in turn while the camera is being focused.

Effect on depth of resolving power of the emulsion

The resolving power of an emulsion (page 221) has limits, and, even if a lens is capable of resolving a given circle of confusion, the film may not be. In practice, although the resolving power of an emulsion is usually lower than that of a good lens, it is normally high enough to resolve the permissible circle of confusion.

When, however, very small films are used, as for example in narrow-gauge cinematography, the permissible diameter of the circle of confusion may be smaller than the film can resolve. Theoretically, pictures taken in such circumstances will nowhere be sharp, but, in practice, the sharpest areas will normally be accepted as sharp. In such circumstances, the permissible diameter of the circle of confusion is imposed by the resolving power of the emulsion, rather than by the resolving power of the eye. To obtain values of depth of focus and depth of field, we may then take as the permissible diameter of the circle of confusion the reciprocal of half the number of lines per millimetre resolved by the film (page 122).

Example: Resolving power of film = 40 lines per millimetre
Permissible diameter of circle of confusion
= 1/20 mm

Depth of field scales

Depth of field *tables* for a given lens are usually obtainable from the lens manufacturer. For convenience, however, depth of field *scales* are now normally marked on the lens or camera itself. Such scales enable the depth at any aperture to be read, whatever the distance focused on. Two typical scales are illustrated in Figure 6.16. On such scales, the two index marks corresponding with each *f*-number indicate the nearest and furthest distances in acceptably sharp focus when the camera is focused on the distance indicated by the central arrow.

Scales of this type depend on the fact that depth of *focus* – the counterpart in the image space of depth of field – is constant at any given aperture for all distances. With a scale as shown in Figure 6.16a, the separation of the *f*-number marks on the scale is actually equal to the depth of focus. (This correspondence between depth of field and depth of focus is a reminder that we cannot make use of depth of field *and* depth of focus at one and the same time. To make full use of depth of field, for example, the film must be truly flat and accurately located in the focal plane.)

Depth of field tables and scales are usually based on a circle of confusion derived from the focal length of the lens, a value of $f/1000$ being commonly used. This is the permissible diameter for the circle of confusion in the negative when a print is to be examined under "correct" viewing conditions (page 99), and automatically makes allowance for any degree of enlargement. A criterion based on "correct" viewing is adopted in tables, etc., because the focal length of a lens is something about which the lens or camera manufacturer can be quite certain, whereas the criterión for "comfortable" viewing is not a fixed quantity for any given lens.

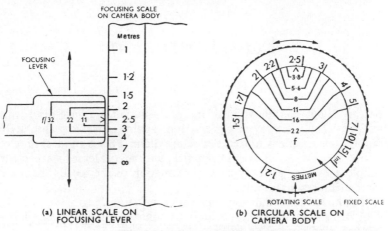

(a) LINEAR SCALE ON FOCUSING LEVER

(b) CIRCULAR SCALE ON CAMERA BODY

Fig. 6.16 – Depth of field scales

Depth of field tables and scales can be used with confidence whenever "comfortable" viewing conditions correspond with "correct" viewing conditions. As the two sets of viewing conditions frequently do coincide in practice (page 94), such tables and scales are found to be of value by many photographers.

Focusing "one-third in"

In the absence of definite figures for depth of field, a popular rule is to focus "one-third in"; e.g., if the part of the subject in which we are interested extends from 3 metres to 12 metres from the camera, the lens is focused on 6 metres, i.e., 3 metres plus one-third of 9 metres – the depth of the subject. This rule is based on the fact that, at middle distances, the depth of field beyond the distance focused on is roughly double the depth in front. Application of the rule usually ensures sharp focus of foreground objects, and is therefore helpful, because an out-of-focus foreground is usually more objectionable than an out-of-focus background. Although this rule is approximately correct for groups, interiors, etc., it is misleading with close-ups, since depth is then almost equally disposed in front of and behind the distance focused on. For scenes extending from relatively near objects to the horizon, it is usually best to focus on the hyperfocal distance, since depth is then at its maximum and just includes objects at infinity (page 105).

CHAPTER 7

Lens Aberrations

So far, in our consideration of image formation, we have dealt with lenses as though they were perfect, and capable of forming absolutely faithful images of any objects set before them. This is an ideal state of affairs which does not exist in practice; with actual lenses – especially simple ones – we get only an approximation to the ideal. There are three main reasons for this:

(1) The refractive index of glass varies with wavelength.

(2) Lens surfaces can only readily be polished if they are spherical – and spherical surfaces do not bring light to a focus.

(3) Light behaves as if it consists of waves.

The ways in which the image departs from the ideal, as a result of the above, are referred to as *lens errors*, or *aberrations*. Errors due to (1) are called *chromatic* errors, errors due to (2) *spherical* errors and errors due to (3) *diffraction* errors.

The chromatic and spherical errors from which an image may suffer are seven in number. Two of them are formed in all parts of the field – including the centre – but the other five affect only rays passing through the lens obliquely, and so do not appear in the centre of the field but only towards the edges, increasing in severity with the distance from the lens axis. The names of the errors are:

Direct errors – affecting all parts of the field

(1) Chromatic aberration.

(2) Spherical aberration.

Oblique errors – not present in centre of field

(3) Lateral colour.

(4) Coma.

(5) Distortion.

(6) Astigmatism.

(7) Curvature of field.

Chromatic aberration and lateral colour are chromatic errors; spherical aberration, coma, distortion, astigmatism and curvature of field are spherical errors. Each of these is described in detail below. Although, in practice, lens errors are largely interrelated, it will be assumed in considering each error that the lens is free from other aberrations.

Chromatic aberration

The refractive index of all transparent media varies with the wavelength of the light passing through, shorter wavelengths being refracted most. The focus of a lens therefore varies with the wavelength – and hence, the colour – of the light employed. Figure 7.1 shows, in

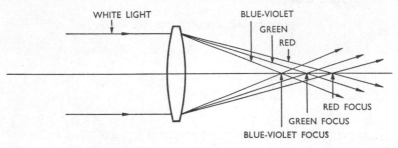

Fig. 7.1 – Chromatic aberration in a simple lens

exaggerated form, the separation into the various spectrum colours which takes place when white light from a distant point source is brought to a focus by a simple lens. The focus for blue-violet light is nearer to the lens than the focus for red light, with the focus for green light between the two. The image formed by such a lens is said to suffer from *chromatic aberration*.

The practical effect of this is that when a simple lens is employed, the visual focus – which is in the middle of the green region of the spectrum – does not coincide with the chemical focus,* which is in the blue-violet region. Hence, if the camera is focused visually, the negative will be unsharp.

The following steps may be taken to overcome chromatic aberration:

(1) An allowance may be made in focusing for the difference between the chemical and visual foci. For example, with a stand camera, after visual focusing, the camera may be racked in by a small amount. With a fixed-focus camera, the lens may be positioned so that the chemical – and not the visual – focus coincides with the film plane.

---

* By chemical focus, we mean the focus of the light to which non-colour-sensitive materials respond. Even orthochromatic and panchromatic materials derive their main sensitivity from this region.

(2) The lens may be stopped down. This increases the depth of focus and thus minimizes the practical effect of chromatic aberration.

The simultaneous application of these two principles has permitted

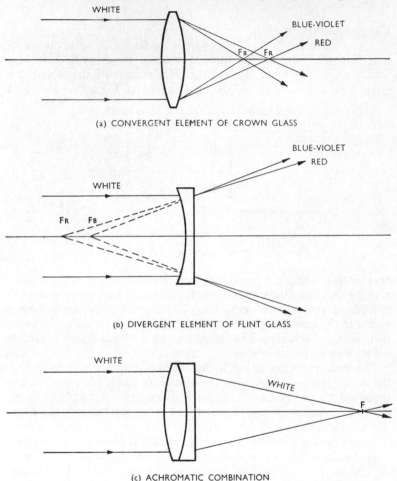

(a) CONVERGENT ELEMENT OF CROWN GLASS

(b) DIVERGENT ELEMENT OF FLINT GLASS

(c) ACHROMATIC COMBINATION

Fig. 7.2 – The principle of an achromatic lens

simple lenses of small aperture to be used with a fair degree of success in millions of inexpensive cameras. However, a simple lens has serious limitations, and early in photography attention was directed to obtaining lenses which were free from chromatic aberration, and the experience of workers in other fields – in particular, astronomy – was drawn upon.

It had been shown by Dollond as early as 1757, that, if a lens be made of two elements instead of one, it is possible for chromatic aberration to be considerably reduced by making the aberration in one element cancel out the aberration in the other. To do this, the two elements must be made of two types of glass which differ in chemical composition. A single lens corrected in this way may consist of:

(1) A convergent element of crown glass – a glass of fairly low refractive index and low dispersive power, and

(2) A divergent element of flint glass, which has a higher refractive index and very much higher dispersive power.

The crown glass component is selected to give more bending than the flint component, and the two components are normally cemented together. A lens corrected in this way is termed an *achromatic lens* or, simply, an *achromat* (Figure 7.2).

An achromat is usually corrected so that the green ("visual") and blue-violet ("chemical") foci coincide. Sometimes, e.g., for three-colour work, a higher degree of correction is required, and for this purpose lenses are made in which the foci of blue-violet, green and red coincide. Lenses of this type are known as *apochromats*.

Spherical aberration

When we first studied the formation of an image by a simple lens, we said that a lens could be considered as made up of a number of prisms which, provided they were of suitable angle, would focus rays passing through them (page 52). Now, the angle at which each ray strikes and leaves a lens is governed by the shape of its surfaces, and these in practice are almost invariably spherical. Spherical surfaces are employed because they are the only type of surface which can be produced economically with the desired precision, but they are not the best surfaces for forming point images. (*Aspheric* surfaces are employed occasionally, but their production presents considerable manufacturing problems.) When a beam of light parallel to the axis passes through a lens with spherical surfaces, rays passing through the outer zones of the lens come to a focus nearer to the lens than the rays through the central zone.* Consequently, the image is unsharp, wherever the film is placed. This failure of the lens to form a point image of a point source is termed *spherical aberration*, and is illustrated in Figure 7.3.

---

* A "zone" is a ring-like area, the various parts of which are equidistant from the lens axis.

Spherical aberration is reduced on stopping down, but the image then shifts axially; in effect, the focal length changes with aperture. Spherical aberration in a simple positive lens can be minimized by

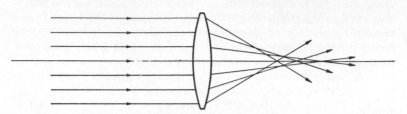

Fig. 7.3 – Spherical aberration in a simple lens

designing the lens so that the bending of light that it has to perform is shared equally by the two surfaces. Applying this principle, it is found that in a simple double-convex lens, spherical aberration is at a minimum when the radius of curvature of the back surface is about six times that of the front surface (Figure 7.4).

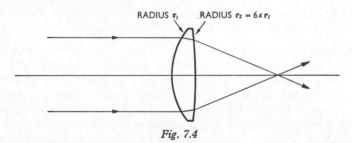

Fig. 7.4

Correction of spherical aberration in a compound lens is achieved by combining a positive lens with a suitably shaped negative lens in which the spherical aberration is of equal magnitude but of opposite sign. Sometimes, it is possible to combine the correction for spherical aberration with the correction for chromatic aberration in one pair of elements. Although spherical aberration is considerably reduced in a corrected lens, all lenses show residual amounts of this as of other aberrations. For critical work, therefore, visual focusing of a camera should always be checked with the lens stopped down to the aperture at which the exposure is to be made.

Lateral colour
Lateral colour, sometimes termed *lateral chromatic aberration,* or

chromatic difference of magnification, is a peculiarly distressing error which appears in the form of colour fringes at the edges of the image. Whereas chromatic aberration concerns the *distance* from the lens at which the image is formed, lateral colour concerns the *size* of the image. The presence of lateral colour usually proves serious only for colour separation work of high precision with long-focus lenses, as, for example, in photomechanical work. Lateral colour is *not* reduced on stopping down. It can be controlled in manufacture by use of a symmetrical construction (page 129).

Coma

In considering spherical aberration, we saw that in an uncorrected lens different zones of the lens have, in effect, different focal lengths. The effect of this, in the case of oblique rays, is that rays passing through different zones of the lens fall on the film at different distances from the axis, instead of being superimposed. The result is that the image of a point off the axis appears as a comet-shaped fuzz, and is said to suffer from *coma* (Figure 7.5). Coma may thus be regarded as spherical aberration of the oblique rays.

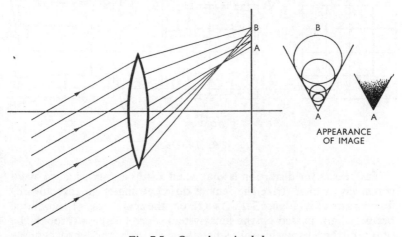

Fig. 7.5 – Coma in a simple lens

Coma may take the form of "outward coma" – with the tail of the comet pointing away from the lens axis (as shown), or "inward coma" – with the tail of the comet pointing towards the lens axis. Coma, like spherical aberration, is reduced on stopping down. Stopping down may, however, cause the image to shift laterally (just as the image shifts axially if spherical aberration is present). Coma can be reduced in a single lens by employing a stop in such a position that it restricts the area of the lens at which oblique rays strike it. This method is adopted to minimize coma in simple box cameras. In compound lenses, coma is reduced by balancing the error in one element by an equal and opposite error in another; in particular, by use of a symmetrical construction.

Distortion

The term *distortion,* or *curvilinear distortion,* is applied to lateral distortion of the image resulting from variation of magnification over the field of the lens. The image of a square object produced by a lens suffering from distortion appears with its sides bowed outwards or inwards, as in Figure 7.6. The two types of distortion shown in this figure are referred to as *barrel distortion* and *pincushion distortion* respectively. Unlike other aberrations, distortion does not affect the sharpness of the image but only its shape.

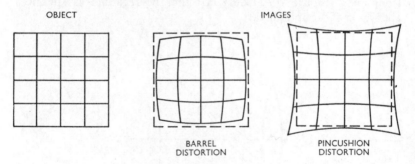

OBJECT   IMAGES

BARREL
DISTORTION

PINCUSHION
DISTORTION

Fig. 7.6 – Distortion

The reason for distortion is that when a stop is used, e.g., to avoid coma, rays which strike the lens at different angles go through different parts of it (Figure 7.7). As a result, the central ray of an oblique beam of light passed by the lens system, does not pass through the centre of the lens itself. And, since the surfaces of the lens where the oblique central ray does meet it are not parallel, this ray does not go straight on, as is assumed in theory based on thin lenses. This leads to images in which the edges are too small in scale (barrel distortion), or too large in scale (pincushion distortion).

It is apparent that the type of distortion obtained with a partic-ular lens depends upon the *position* of the stop. Distortion shares with lateral colour the property of not being reduced on stopping down, i.e., it is not influenced by the *size* of the stop. Distortion can be corrected

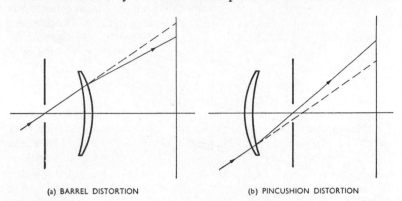

(a) BARREL DISTORTION   (b) PINCUSHION DISTORTION

Fig. 7.7 – Cause of distortion

in manufacture by making the lens symmetrical, or nearly symmetrical (Figure 7.8). The first symmetrical lens, the *Rapid Rectilinear* (page 130), took its name from the fact that it gave distortion-free images.

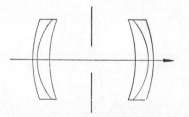

Fig. 7.8 – Symmetrical lens (Rapid Rectilinear)

The first component of this lens – used alone – gives "pincushion" distortion, and the second "barrel" distortion, but when the two components are used together the two defects cancel one another. Use of a symmetrical construction eliminates not only distortion but also coma and lateral colour.

Astigmatism
Astigmatism is a defect whereby the image of a point object off the lens axis consists nowhere of a point but varies from a radial to a tangential line according to the position of the focusing screen

(Figure 7.9). Astigmatism is one of the oblique aberrations – which affect only the margins of the field.

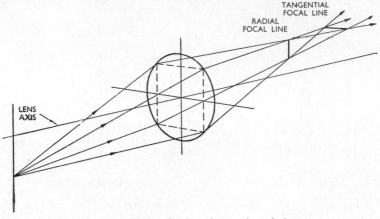

Fig. 7.9 – The production of an astigmatic image

The distribution of astigmatism over the field of a lens is generally shown by a diagram of the type given in Figure 7.10.

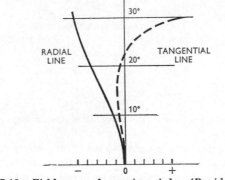

Fig. 7.10 – Field curves of an astigmatic lens (Rapid Rectilinear)

The effect produced on lines in an image by an astigmatic lens will depend on the relation of these lines to the lens axis, as shown in Figure 7.11.

It is misleading to say that a lens showing astigmatism renders horizontal lines as sharp and vertical lines as unsharp, and vice versa. As will be seen from Figure 7.11, this will be true only if the horizontal lines happen to be radial and the vertical lines tangential to the lens axis, and vice versa.

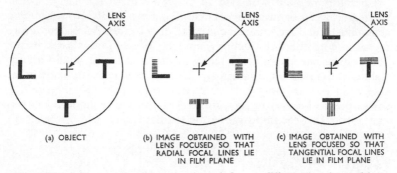

(a) OBJECT

(b) IMAGE OBTAINED WITH LENS FOCUSED SO THAT RADIAL FOCAL LINES LIE IN FILM PLANE

(c) IMAGE OBTAINED WITH LENS FOCUSED SO THAT TANGENTIAL FOCAL LINES LIE IN FILM PLANE

Fig. 7.11 – Images produced by an astigmatic lens at different focusing positions

Astigmatism is reduced to some extent on stopping down. Its complete correction involves the use of a compound lens employing glasses having a particular relationship between refractive index and dispersive power. See page 130.

Curvature of field

Curvature of field is a defect of a lens whereby its plane of sharpest focus is not flat, but saucer-shaped. With a lens suffering from this

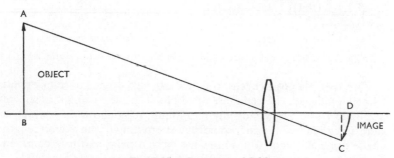

Fig. 7.12 – Curvature of field

error it is impossible to obtain a sharp image all over the field; when the centre is sharp the edges are blurred, and vice versa.

If we consider the simple lens shown in Figure 7.12, we see that curvature of field is to be expected. Because the off-axis object point A is further from the lens than the axial object point B, the image of A, at *C*, will necessarily be nearer to the lens than the image of *B*, at *D*, thus leading automatically to a curved field.

Curvature of field is related to astigmatism. In the early days of photography, curvature of field could be corrected only by introducing astigmatism, and astigmatism corrected only by introducing curvature of field. With the introduction, however, of the Jena glasses in the 1880s it became possible to correct astigmatism and obtain a substantially flat field simultaneously. Lenses in which astigmatism has been reduced in this way are termed *anastigmats* (page 130). Figure 7.13 shows the field curves of (a) a simple lens, and (b) a modern anastigmat, illustrating the improvement in the flatness of field of the latter.

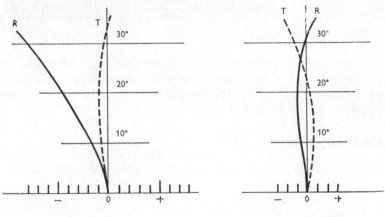

Fig. 7.13 – Field curves of (a) a simple lens and (b) an anastigmatic lens

With a simple positive lens, the field can be flattened to some extent by making the lens of a suitable meniscus shape and using it as shown in Figure 7.14a. The arrangement in Figure 7.14b, however – which is sometimes adopted in order to effect a shortening of the overall length of the camera – leads to a somewhat curved field, and it is common practice to give the film a cylindrical form to compensate for this.

In some scientific instruments, where curvature of field cannot be avoided, the film or plate is bent to follow the field. Plates intended for use in such instruments are coated on specially thin glass, to facilitate this bending.

Stopping down helps to reduce the practical effect of curvature of field by increasing the depth of focus.

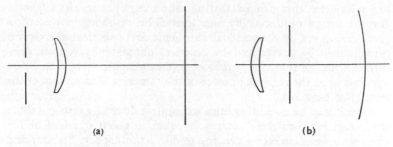

(a)   (b)

Fig. 7.14 – Use of meniscus lenses in simple cameras

Diffraction

Even when all the chromatic and spherical errors in a lens have been reduced to a minimum, errors still remain due to *diffraction*. Diffraction is the name given to the phenomena which occur when light passes through a very narrow aperture or close to the edge of an opaque obstacle, and which arise from light deviating from the rectilinear path. Diffraction is explained by the wave theory of light.

Because of this phenomenon, the image of a point source formed by even a theoretically perfect lens is not a point, but a circle of light of finite diameter. The diameter of this circle, or *Airy disc*, can be shown to be:

$$2 \cdot 44 \lambda \frac{v}{d}$$

where λ is the wavelength of the light, v the distance of the image from the lens, and d the effective diameter of the lens aperture. For all except close-ups, this can be written:

$$2 \cdot 44 \lambda N$$

where N is the f-number of the lens.

With blue-violet light of wavelength 400 nm, the diameter of the Airy disc becomes $N/1000$ mm, e.g., $0 \cdot 008$ mm for an $f/8$ lens.

The formula for the Airy disc illustrates two things. The first is that the shorter the wavelength of the light the less serious is the diffraction, and, therefore, the higher the resolving power theoretically possible (see below). This is the basis of ultra-violet photomicrography. The second is that diffraction *increases* on stopping down. The practical effects of this are considered below.

Resolving power of a lens

The ability of a lens to resolve fine detail is termed its *resolving power*. This is normally expressed in terms of the number of black lines per millimetre that can be distinguished as separated in a photographic image produced by the lens. The resolving power of a given lens is set by the residual chromatic and spherical aberrations present, and by diffraction. In practical photography, we are concerned with the resolving power of a photographic system, and this depends upon the resolving power of the film as well as on that of the lens. (See page 221.)

Here, it may be noted that lines will appear distinctly resolved if the separation between their centres is equal to about one-half of the effective image diameter according to diffraction theory. An Airy disc of 0·008 mm diameter thus corresponds with a resolving power of about 250 lines per millimetre.

Effect of stopping down on definition

If the aperture of a lens be stopped down gradually, starting from maximum aperture, the chromatic and spherical aberrations (lateral colour and distortion excepted) are reduced, but the effect of diffraction becomes greater. At large apertures, the resolution of a lens is limited by the residual chromatic and spherical aberrations, the effect of diffraction being quite small. On stopping down, therefore, the definition of the image at first improves progressively, as the chromatic and spherical aberrations are reduced. Meanwhile, however, the effect of diffraction is increasing, until a point is reached where this sets the limit to the resolving power of the lens. On stopping down beyond this point, definition actually falls off. For a given lens there is, therefore, an optimum aperture, or range of apertures, yielding highest definition. Since definition is generally poorer at the edges of the field than in the centre, stopping down a little beyond the optimum position for central definition, to reduce still further the oblique spherical errors, may give better overall definition (i.e., average of central and edge definition) with only a slight loss of central definition.

Many general-purpose lenses, in particular those intended for use with large negative sizes, give their best definition when stopped down. The aperture at which the best definition is obtained will depend on the maximum aperture of the lens and its construction, but with lenses of fairly long focal length (excluding process lenses) this is generally between $f/16$ and $f/22$. With more highly corrected lenses, however, in which chromatic and spherical errors are extremely small even at wide apertures, loss of definition due to diffraction may become apparent at a much smaller f-number.

In close-up work – in particular photomacrography – and in enlarging, v/d is considerably greater than the f-number of the lens, and the diffraction disc is therefore considerably greater than when the same lens is used for ordinary photography. Undue stopping down of the lens in these instances should therefore be avoided. In general, the effective aperture should not be less than about one-hundredth of the image conjugate v. At same size, this corresponds with a relative aperture of $f/50$. In enlarging, v is the distance from the lens to the easel, so that it is with big enlargements that care should be taken.

The considerations that apply in photomacrography apply to an even greater extent in photomicrography, and diffraction is then the principal factor limiting resolution.

CHAPTER 8

The Camera Lens

A LENS consisting of a single piece of glass exhibits all the defects described in the foregoing Chapter, to a greater or a lesser extent. In such a lens, chromatic aberration, spherical aberration, lateral colour, coma, astigmatism and curvature of field all combine to give poor definition, while distortion leads to distorted images. We may sum up this state of affairs by saying that the *image quality* of a simple lens is poor.

We have stated that all lens aberrations are present "to a greater or lesser extent", because, in the design of even a simple lens, aberrations can be controlled to a certain degree, in particular by choice of suitable curves for the two surfaces and by careful positioning of a stop of suitable size. Reference was made to this possibility in the previous Chapter. If, in addition, the field covered be restricted, it is possible, even with a simple lens, to obtain image quality that is acceptable for some purposes, even if it is still very poor by the highest standards.

The best simple lens that we can produce is, however, limited, not only as regards image quality but also as regards relative aperture, i.e., speed, and field covered. It was early realised that for the photographic process to be exploited to the full, improved performance of the lens in all three of these properties was required, the first need, in view of the slowness of the sensitised materials then available, being of increased speed, to enable portraits to be taken without inconveniently long exposures.

Compound lenses

The reason that the performance of a lens consisting of a single piece of glass cannot be improved beyond a certain point, is the limited number of variables, or "degrees of freedom", which the designer has at his command. It is, however, apparent that by using two pieces of glass – two *elements* – instead of one, the number of degrees of freedom available to the lens designer is immediately increased. Not only has he now four surfaces instead of two over which to spread the desired bending of light, but he can employ different types of glass for the two elements and can also vary their spacing. His freedom increases further as he employs more and more elements in the lens, although the introduction of other considerations prevents this being extended too far. Summarizing the most important of the factors with which the designer of a compound lens can conjure, we have:

(1) Radii of curvature of lens surfaces.

(2) Maximum aperture – set by stop.

(3) Position of stop.

(4) Number of separate elements.

(5) Spacing of elements.

(6) Use of types of glass differing in: (a) refractive index, and/or (b) dispersive power.

Compound lenses were introduced as a means of controlling lens errors in order to provide better image quality, wider apertures and greater covering power than are given by simple lenses. The way in which each of the chromatic and spherical errors can be corrected in a compound lens by careful design has already been indicated in Chapter 7. The general principle followed is to balance an error in one element by an equal but opposite error in another. It is not, however, usually possible to eliminate any error entirely; it is simply reduced to an acceptable level.

Frequently, the correction of one error affects another and a compromise has to be made. With a lens intended for general use the designer has to steer a middle course. If, however, maximum correction is desired in a lens designed with one particular use in mind – and which will therefore be employed only under a narrow range of conditions, e.g., always at full aperture, or always at one scale of reproduction – the designer can frequently obtain improved performance under these conditions at the expense of the performance under other conditions, e.g., at other apertures or different scales of reproduction. Lenses of the highest correction are, therefore, usually designed to give their best performance at or about one scale of reproduction, at one aperture and with light of a given quality. One apochromatic lens, for example, is advertised as being suitable for ratios of reproduction of from $\frac{1}{5}$ to 5. In general, the requirements of high definition, large aperture, and wide covering power are mutually opposed. When the very highest performance in any one of these respects is therefore required, the two other factors must be sacrificed to some degree.

Development of the photographic lens

In the continuing struggle to obtain improved performance in photographic lenses, many thousands of different designs have been produced. These represent different ways of approaching the problem with the knowledge available at the time they were introduced. Some are relatively simple; others very complex. Although, as we have stated, the use of many elements gives the designer greater freedom of action, it does not necessarily follow that the most complicated lens is the best.

In the following pages, we shall outline the development of photographic lenses from the beginnings of photography to the present day. We shall not be concerned so much with individual lenses as with indicating the means of correction available to the designer at any given time, and will refer only briefly to the chief types of lenses which were produced using the available means.

Lenses in general are employed either to form images of original objects, or to receive images formed by other lenses in order to modify them in some way. Lenses receiving light from original objects are termed *objectives*. Camera lenses – which, of course, come in this category – are therefore commonly referred to as objectives.

We can consider five main stages in the development of the ordinary photographic objective, viz.:

(1) Simple lenses.

(2) Petzval lenses.

(3) Doublets.

(4) Anastigmats.

(5) Triplets.

This classification is necessarily somewhat arbitrary and lenses will be found which do not exactly fall into any one of these groupings. The outstanding steps in the development of the photographic lens are shown in Table 8.1 (page 134).

Simple lenses

We may take the year 1839, in which details of the processes of both Daguerre and Fox Talbot were first made public, as marking the beginning of practical photography. The first use of lenses goes back well beyond this date, however, for such purposes as astronomy, microscopy and the camera obscura, although the requirements of none of these fields, in the way of lenses, were exactly the same as in photography.

The lenses employed by the first photographers were generally camera obscura lenses – termed "landscape" lenses. The simplest type of lens capable of forming an image on a photographic plate is a double-convex lens. As we have seen (page 114), spherical aberration can be reduced in such a lens by making the radii of curvature in the ratio of about 1 to 6, but the lens still suffers severely from curvature of field and only the centre of the field is at all sharp. In 1812, however, Wollaston showed that a much better image could be obtained by making the lens of meniscus form and placing a stop as shown in Figure 8.1. The meniscus shape helps to flatten the field and the stop minimizes cóma. (See also page 120.)

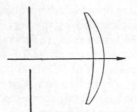

Fig. 8.1 – Landscape lens of Wollaston

This type of lens was widely used in the very early days of photography, and gave an image of satisfactory sharpness up to a maximum aperture of about $f/14$.

Single achromats

An improvement on the lens consisting of a single piece of glass can be obtained by combining two elements. An achromatic lens – comprising two elements – had been produced by Dollond in 1757 for use as a telescope objective (page 113). At the time when the demand for photographic lenses first arose, the experience of telescope practice

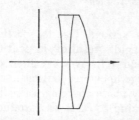

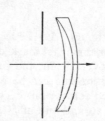

Fig. 8.2 – Achromatic landscape lens of Chevalier

Fig. 8.3 – Grubb's landscape lens

was applied and single achromatic lenses were used. Two early lenses of this type are shown in Figures 8.2 and 8.3.

The combination of two elements enabled chromatic aberration and, to some extent, spherical aberration to be corrected, but the oblique errors (astigmatism, distortion, etc.) remained, and simple achromats could therefore only be used at small apertures over relatively small fields.

Petzval portrait lens

As the simple lens was found too slow for portraiture, many attempts were made to produce a lens which could be worked at a larger aperture. Opticians in the first half of the last century had a good understanding of the lines on which the problem could be tackled, but they were seriously handicapped by the very limited range of optical glasses available. In 1840, however, J. Petzval computed a lens with the then extremely wide aperture of $f/3\cdot7$ – fifteen times faster than the lenses used by Daguerre. The "Petzval portrait lens", as this was called, consisted of two dissimilar and widely separated achromatic combinations, the front pair being cemented together and the back pair separated by an air space (Figure 8.4). This was the first lens mathematically computed specifically for photography. It was made by Voigtländer.

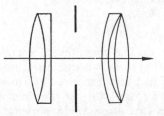

Fig. 8.4 – Petzval portrait lens

Although the Petzval lens shows serious defects, particularly astigmatism and marked curvature of field – resulting in poor definition over all but the centre of the field – it gives excellent central definition and can be worked at a large aperture. Petzval lenses intended for portraiture were commonly made covering a small angle with an aperture of $f/4$, and one working at $f/2\cdot2$ was produced by Dallmeyer as early as 1860. The poor edge definition gives a characteristic softness which is not unpleasing in portraiture.

Figure 8.5 shows a type of unsymmetrical doublet introduced by R. Steinheil in 1881 as an improvement on the Petzval lens. Working at $f/4$, it is practically free from astigmatism over a small angle. It is of

interest mainly on account of its similarity to some modern anastigmats. Known as the Portrait Antiplanat, this lens could almost be

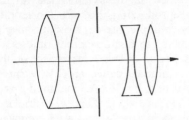

Fig. 8.5 – R. Steinheil's Portrait Antiplanat lens

classed as a triplet (page 132). In later lenses of this type, Steinheil
employed a cemented lens in place of the two separate glasses of the
back combination.

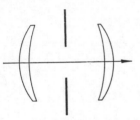

Fig. 8.6 – Steinheil's Periskop lens

Symmetrical doublets

Petzval's lens, which proved invaluable to the portrait photographer,
followed hard on the introduction of photography, but the landscape
photographer had to wait many years before a lens of similar speed was
produced capable of giving good definition over a wide field. This
was achieved in the *symmetrical doublet*.

The earliest symmetrical doublet was the Periskop lens (Figure 8.6),
introduced by C. A. and H. A. Steinheil in 1865, and based on an
arrangement used by Wollaston for microscope objectives. It consisted of two plain meniscus lenses separated by a central diaphragm,
and was at one time used in fixed-focus cameras. It is free from
distortion and gives a flat field, but is not achromatic and therefore
must be adjusted to its "chemical" focus, i.e., focus for blue-violet
light. The Periskop lens is important as marking the introduction
of the use of the "symmetrical" construction – a construction which
enables the oblique errors of lateral colour, coma and distortion to be

almost entirely eliminated. The term "symmetrical" applied to a lens today does not necessarily imply *exact* symmetry, but is used to describe any lens based on the symmetrical form. Exact symmetry favours same-size reproduction, but, for lenses intended mainly for landscape work, for example, the construction may be made to depart slightly from symmetry to favour distant objects.

The most familiar form of the symmetrical doublet was the Rapid Rectilinear lens – commonly called an R.R. – introduced independently by Dallmeyer and by H. A. Steinheil (by the latter as the Aplanat) in 1866 (Figure 8.7). This was similar to the Periskop, except that single meniscus lenses were replaced by achromatic combinations. Rapid Rectilinear (Aplanat) lenses were usually made to work up to a nominal aperture of $f/8$, and gave excellent results. Astigmatism was, however, always present, and at full aperture the marginal definition was not perfect, so that for critical work stopping down was necessary.

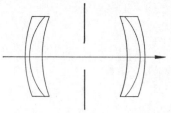

Fig. 8.7 – Rapid Rectilinear lens

Anastigmats

The lenses described so far, permit the control of all errors except astigmatism and the associated error of curvature of field. With the glasses available in the early days of photography, astigmatism and curvature of field could not satisfactorily be corrected simultaneously with other errors. The limitation on the glasses then existing was that refraction and dispersion both increased with the optical density of the glass. In the 1880s, however, Abbe and Schott produced glasses in which a high dispersion was associated with a relatively low refractive index, and others in which the reverse was the case. This was a development of the first importance, and led to the introduction of *anastigmatic lenses*, i.e., lenses in which, for the first time, astigmatism was reduced to acceptable proportions. One of the first lenses incorporating the new glasses was the Ross Concentric lens (Figure 8.8) introduced in 1888. This is sometimes termed a "new achromat", and the Rapid Rectilinear lens an "old achromat".

The peculiarity of the Concentric was the use of plano-convex crowns, and the fact that the exposed surfaces were concentric. The field of this lens was limited to about 53°. The Zeiss Protar (1890), which combined in effect the front half of a Rapid Rectilinear lens

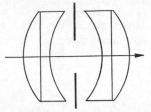

Fig. 8.8 – Ross Concentric lens

(old achromat) with the rear half of the Concentric (new achromat), and yielded a wider field, was the first lens to bear the name "anastig-

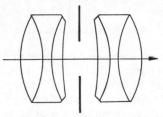

Fig. 8.9 – Goerz Dagor lens

mat". Another lens introduced (in 1892) shortly after the Protar was the Goerz Dagor (Figure 8.9).

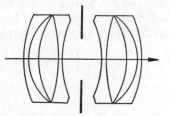

Fig. 8.10 – Zeiss Double Protar lens

This employed a combination of triple cemented glasses, and gave a flat field with freedom from astigmatism up to an aperture of $f/7\cdot7$, later increased to $f/6\cdot8$.

The Zeiss Double Protar (1894), is an extension of the same principle, a pair of quadruple components being used (Figure 8.10). Each component consists essentially of an achromat of the old type cemented to an achromat made from the newer glasses. Lenses similar to the Double Protar have been produced with five cemented glasses to each lens, but the cost of manufacture is high.

Triplets

All the anastigmatic lenses so far described are of "symmetrical" construction. The Cooke lens, designed by H. Dennis Taylor and introduced by Taylor, Taylor and Hobson in 1893, marks a distinct departure (Figure 8.11).

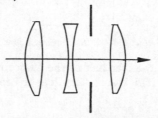

Fig. 8.11 – Cooke triplet lens

This lens consists of three single separated lenses, two of which are convex lenses of crown glass of high refractive index and low dispersion. These are separated by a biconcave lens of light flint glass, which serves the purpose of flattening the field. The outstanding feature of the Cooke lens is its simplicity of construction; its three elements give just sufficient degrees of freedom to do all that was possible in earlier lenses consisting of 6, 8 or even 10 elements. In its first form, the *Cooke triplet*, as it has become known, was intended for portraiture, and was designed to work at an aperture of $f/4\cdot5$ (later $f/3\cdot5$), but modified lenses on the same plan have been produced for other purposes, including highly corrected process lenses.

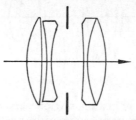

Fig. 8.12 – Zeiss Tessar lens

The Zeiss Tessar lens (Figure 8.12), first introduced in 1902, is not unlike the Cooke lens, although a cemented meniscus is used for the back component in place of the single glass of the Cooke.

Modern camera lenses

High-class camera lenses made today are usually based on either the symmetrical or triplet construction, although in many cases more glasses have been added to permit a still greater degree of correction. Many medium-priced cameras have lenses of the triplet type, although for lenses of very wide aperture and for lenses intended for process work, copying, and any work in which the scale of reproduction approaches same-size, the symmetrical construction is generally favoured. Most modern high-speed lenses are derivatives of a symmetrical lens based on the use of a pair of telescope objectives suggested originally by Gauss. These are generally described as *Double Gauss* type. Lenses for cine-cameras are frequently of the triplet type. Single meniscus lenses – and sometimes single achromats – continue to be employed in simple cameras, in transparency viewers and in magnifiers. The introduction of rare-earth glasses – of very high refractive index – has extended the possibilities of lens design.

The introduction of "coating" also has influenced modern lens design, permitting the use of constructions which would formerly have been impossible on account of the flare or light losses which would have been associated with the design.

The construction of some modern camera lenses is illustrated in Figure 8.13.

Lenses for special purposes

We have so far confined our study of the development of the photographic lens to ordinary camera lenses. Most of the types that have been described are available in a range of focal lengths – to cover negatives of various sizes – and with varying maximum apertures. While these lenses meet most requirements, other types of lens have been produced for special purposes. Some are of only limited interest, but the following types are in general use:

Soft-focus lenses.
Telephoto lenses.
"Reversed" telephoto lenses.

Soft-focus lenses

For pictorial purposes, especially in portraiture, it is sometimes desired to produce an image in which detail appears veiled or diffused. Putting an ordinary lens out-of-focus does not achieve the desired effect, but suitable quality can be obtained by using an uncorrected lens such as a meniscus lens, or a compound lens specially designed to leave a large residual amount of spherical aberration. With a true

Type of lens	Degree of correction of aberrations							Maximum aperture on introduction	Approx. field covered at maximum aperture
	Chromatic aberration	Spherical aberration	Lateral colour	Coma	Distortion	Curvature of field	Astigmatism		
Simple lenses									
Wollaston landscape (stop in front) 1812	Poor	Satisfactory	Very poor	Satisfactory	Poor	Satisfactory	Poor	*f*/14	53°
Landscape with stop behind	Poor	Satisfactory	Very poor	Satisfactory	Poor	Satisfactory (if film is curved)	Poor	*f*/14	53°
Chevalier landscape (achromatized) 1828	Good	Good	Poor	Satisfactory	Poor	Satisfactory	Poor	*f*/12	28°
Petzval lens (1840)	Good	Good	Poor	Satisfactory	Poor	Satisfactory	Poor	*f*/3·7	20°
Doublets									
Steinheil Periskop (not achromatized) 1865	Poor	Good	Very much reduced	Very much reduced	Very much reduced	Satisfactory	Poor	*f*/10	90°
Rapid Rectilinear ("old" achromat) 1866	Good	Good	Good	Good	Good	Satisfactory	Poor	*f*/8	44°
Anastigmats (Jena glasses)									
Ross Concentric ("new" achromat) 1888	Good	Satisfactory	Good	Good	Good	Good	Good	*f*/16	53°
Zeiss Anastigmat (Protar) (= half "old" achromat, half "new" achromat) 1890	Good	Good	Good	Good	Good	Good	Good	*f*/8	60°
Triplets									
Cooke 1893	Good	Good	Good	Good	Good	Good	Good	*f*/4·5	53°
Tessar 1902	Good	Good	Good	Good	Good	Good	Good	*f*/5·5	53°

Table 8.1 – Some outstanding steps in the development of the photographic objective

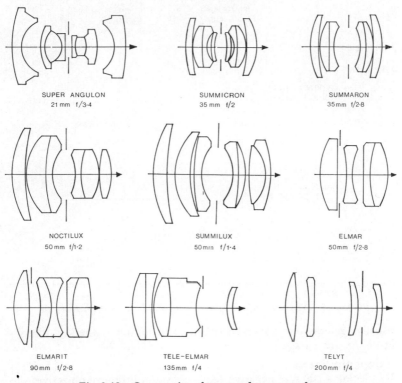

SUPER ANGULON
21mm f/3·4

SUMMICRON
35mm f/2

SUMMARON
35mm f/2·8

NOCTILUX
50mm f/1·2

SUMMILUX
50mm f/1·4

ELMAR
50mm f/2·8

ELMARIT
90mm f/2·8

TELE-ELMAR
135mm f/4

TELYT
200mm f/4

Fig. 8.13 – Construction of some modern camera lenses

soft-focus lens the image of a point is not a point alone, but a point surrounded by a halo of decreasing intensity (Figure 8.14). Whereas ordinary Petzval lenses give soft focus at the edges of the field, and sharp central definition, in a true soft-focus lens the softening of definition is uniform over the entire field.

In some soft-focus lenses, a selected amount of spherical aberration can be left in by varying the position of one of the components. In others, the degree of soft focus is controlled by the stop.

The effect of using a soft-focus lens on the *camera* is to spread the highlights into the shadows; i.e., in the final print the highlight areas appear larger, and the print as a whole "sunnier". If a soft-focus lens – or any other method of achieving diffusion – is used on the *enlarger*, the effect is to spread the shadows into the highlights (page 386). The shadow areas then are enlarged and the print as a whole appears "gloomier". From the point of view of the final effect, therefore, it is

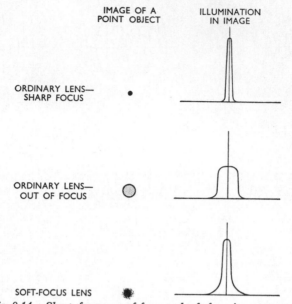

Fig. 8.14 – Sharp-focus, out-of-focus and soft-focus images compared

usually preferable to obtain softening of definition – when required – at the negative stage.

Telephoto lenses

By placing a suitable negative lens behind an ordinary objective, the pencil of rays is rendered less convergent and comes to a focus as though it had been formed by an objective of much greater focal length; i.e., the principal planes (Chapter 9) are well in front of the lens. The required camera extension, however, is very much less than would normally be needed for a lens of such long focus (Figure 8.15).

On this principle, *telephoto attachments* were formerly used in conjunction with ordinary lenses for obtaining a variety of focal lengths with relatively short camera extension. This system, however, yielded focal lengths much too great for general utility and resulted in greatly reduced apertures. Telephoto attachments have, therefore, now been very largely replaced by complete *telephoto lenses*, all the components of which are fully corrected, and which yield more useful values of focal length.

The ratio of the focal length of a telephoto lens to its back focus is termed its *power*. The effect of using a telephoto lens of, say, 2 × power is approximately to produce an image twice the size (linear) of

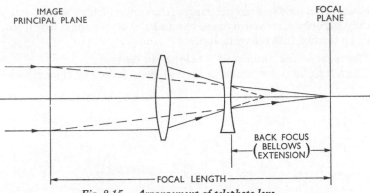

Fig. 8.15 – Arrangement of telephoto lens

that given by a normal lens with the same back focus. A telephoto lens power of less than 2 is not worthwhile from the design point of view, and, conversely, a power much greater than 3 results in too small an aperture. Maximum apertures of modern telephoto lenses approach those of lenses of normal design.

Except that it projects a considerable distance in front of its flange, a telephoto lens can be used like any other, and allows pictures twice or three times the normal size (linear) to be obtained with single-extension cameras. Telephoto lenses are, therefore, very useful with reflex cameras. As a class, telephoto lenses have not the highest definition, but they usually have adequate definition for most purposes. They tend to suffer to some extent from distortion, but provided the angle of view is small this is not usually very serious. Telephoto lenses are very useful for obtaining pictures on a larger scale in the case of distant subjects, and also for semi-close-up work – such as child and animal photography. Assuming that a long-focus lens is needed, the telephoto construction reduces the risk of camera shake, because the camera is better balanced than with an ordinary long-focus lens. Telephoto lenses are less likely to be damaged than ordinary long-focus lenses because they project less; they also have the advantage of being lighter in weight.

So far as their use is concerned, telephoto lenses differ in only one respect from ordinary anastigmats. This difference, which is due to the type of construction, relates to the manipulation of the camera when photographing a subject containing vertical lines with the camera in a tilted position. In such circumstances, with an ordinary lens, the camera back needs to be swung so as to bring the film into a vertical plane, otherwise parallel lines in the subject will appear in the photograph to converge upwards (page 202). With a telephoto lens, however, in the same circumstances, the camera back should be swung through only part (approximately one-half) of the angle which would bring the film into the vertical plane.

"Reversed" (or "inverted") telephoto lenses
The telephoto construction in reverse gives a *short* focal length with a

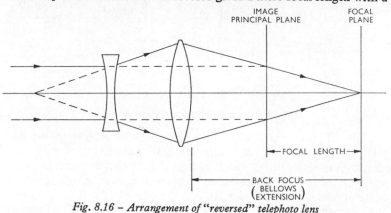

Fig. 8.16 – Arrangement of "reversed" telephoto lens

long back focus (Figure 8.16). This construction is useful when a lens of short focal length is being used and it is desired to insert some device such as a shutter, a beam-splitter or a mirror (as in a reflex camera) between the lens and the film.

Zoom lenses
If the separation of the positive and negative components of a tele-photo lens is varied, the focal length varies. At one time – in the days before enlarging was common – variable separation telephoto lenses were popular, but modern telephoto lenses are almost invariably of fixed separation. The variable separation telephoto lens is, however, perpetuated in the *varifocal*, or *zoom*, *lenses* introduced initially for use in cinematography and television. In a zoom lens the various lens controls are coupled mechanically, or optical compensation is employed, so that when the focal length is altered the image is kept sharp and the *f*-number kept constant. (With an ordinary variable separation telephoto the aperture varies with the separation.) The variation of focal length in some zoom lenses is such that the effect produced can be varied from "wide-angle" to "telephoto".

Zoom lenses for use with still cameras have been available for some years but initially attracted little interest. Their use with 35 mm still cameras is, however, now growing.

CHAPTER 9

Formation of Images
by Thick and Compound Lenses

WHEN we are dealing with thin lenses, the thickness of the lens is usually small in relation to the conjugate distances and the lens focal length, so that we can carry out lens calculations without being unduly concerned as to the exact points on or in the lens to which we should measure these distances. When, however, we are dealing with a thick lens or a photographic objective consisting of several components, different values of object and image distances will be obtained according to whether we measure from the front or the back surface of the lens, or from some point in between. The question therefore arises, are there any points from which these distances can be measured to give consistent results, or must the several elements of the lens be treated separately?

Before we consider the subject in detail, let it be said that almost all the problems which the photographer using ordinary photographic lenses is likely to encounter *in practice*, can be solved by treating the lens as a thin one and measuring the object and image distances from a point midway between the front and back surfaces of the lens. When, however, special types of lens are employed, or a high degree of accuracy is required, this simplification cannot be applied, and a more fundamental approach must be made, using Gaussian optics – the study of image formation by thick lenses.

Definitions of some of the concepts employed in Gaussian optics are given in the following pages for those who may be interested, but the study of these pages can safely be omitted by most readers. The reader who requires a complete treatment of Gaussian optics should refer to a standard textbook on light or optics.

Outline of Gaussian optics
It was proved by Gauss that it is not necessary in lens calculations to

consider the several elements of a compound lens separately. The lens can be treated as a whole and the ordinary formulae for the thin lens applied, provided that the object and image distances are measured from two theoretical planes, fixed with reference to the lens. The rays from the object are then considered to diverge to the one plane and converge from the other to the image.

Gaussian optics defines six *cardinal*, or *Gauss, points* for any lens or system of lenses. These are: two principal focal points, two principal points and two nodal points. The focal length of a lens is defined in Gaussian optics as the distance from a principal point to the corresponding principal focal point. Thus, a lens has two focal lengths – an object focal length and an image focal length (Figure 9.1).

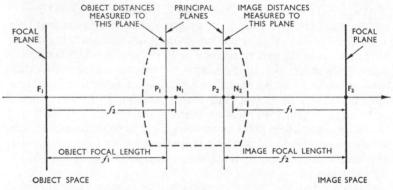

Fig. 9.1 – The cardinal points of a lens

Definitions and properties of the cardinal points of a lens are as follows:

Object principal focal point (F_1). This is the point whose image is on the axis at infinity (to the right in the figure).

Image principal focal point (F_2). This is the point occupied by the image of an object on the axis at infinity (to the left in the figure).

The two principal focal points are usually referred to simply as the focal points, or foci. The planes through the focal points at right angles to the lens axis are called the focal planes. We have already referred to the properties of the focal points of a thin lens on page 55; the focal points of a thick or compound lens have similar properties.

Object principal point (P_1). This is the point from which all object distances are measured. It is distant the object focal length from the object principal focal point.

Image principal point (P_2). This is the point from which all image distances are measured. It is distant the image focal length from the image principal focal point.

The planes through the two principal points at right angles to the lens axis are termed the *principal planes*. These are the planes in which, as shown by Gauss, we may assume that the bending of light by the lens takes place. An important property of the principal planes is that conjugate rays meet the two planes at the same distance from the axis. (See Figure 9.3.)

Object nodal point (N_1). *Image nodal point* (N_2). These are a pair of points such that rays reaching the lens in the direction of the object nodal point, leave the lens going parallel to their original direction and as if they came from the image nodal point. The ray passing through the nodal points of a thick lens is undeviated but displaced. It may be compared with the ray which passes through the centre of a thin lens and is undeviated (Figure 9.2).

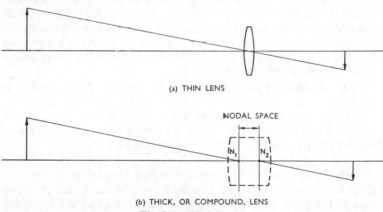

(a) THIN LENS

NODAL SPACE

N_1 N_2

(b) THICK, OR COMPOUND, LENS

Fig. 9.2 – Nodal points

If we take a lens with its optical axis horizontal, and rotate the lens about a vertical axis through the image nodal point, the image of a distant object will remain stationary. This principle is used in lens-testing to locate the nodal points. It is also made use of in panoramic cameras.

If the refractive index of the medium in the object space equals the refractive index of the medium in the image space – as it does in ordinary photography, the medium being air in both cases – then the object and image focal lengths are equal, and their common value is referred to as the *equivalent focal length* of the system. Hence, if we specify the focal length of an ordinary camera lens, we do not need to state which particular focal length is meant.

Now, as can be seen from Figure 9.1, the distance from the object nodal point to the object focal point is equal to the *image* focal length, and the distance from the image nodal point to the image focal point is equal to the *object* focal length. Therefore, when the two focal lengths are equal, the nodal points coincide with the principal points which then combine the properties of the nodal points with their own properties.

As stated, in all ordinary photography the same medium is to be found on both sides of the lens. This is not so, however, with an oil-immersion microscope objective or with the lens in the human eye, and the simplification made above does not then apply.

Value of the cardinal (Gauss) points

No matter how many components a lens system contains or how many media of different refractive indices the rays may travel through, if the position of the object be given and the cardinal points of the system are known, the position and magnification of the image can at once be deduced. It is not necessary to know anything about the position or curvature of the refracting surfaces, or the nature of the intermediate media through which the rays travel.

Strictly speaking, the properties of the cardinal points hold true only when images are formed by rays inclined at a small angle to the axis, i.e., paraxial rays, because all practical lenses show aberrations. The points are, however, important as giving a first approximation to the theory of the majority of optical instruments.

Graphical construction of images using Gaussian optics

Figure 9.3 illustrates the way in which use is made of the principal planes in the graphical construction of images. It is assumed that the nodal points lie in the principal planes.

In this particular example, the object principal plane PP_1 is shown in its normal position, i.e., before the image principal plane PP_2. Sometimes, the two planes may be "crossed", as in the case of the Rapid Rectilinear lens. The image principal plane then comes before the object principal plane.

The principal planes are sometimes referred to as *planes of unit magnification*. This description draws attention to the fact that the image of an object placed in one plane is the same size and the same way up as the object and lies in the other plane. The "object", in practice, is usually an image formed by another lens system.

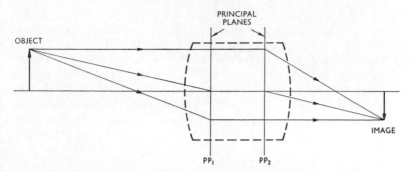

Fig. 9.3 – Use of principal planes in the graphical construction of images

Nodal space

The distance measured along the lens axis between the nodal points – or principal points in an ordinary camera lens – is referred to as the *nodal*, or *internodal*, space (Figure 9.2). With the usual types of camera lens, the nodal points can be regarded *very roughly* as being separated by one-third of the length of the lens, and located one-third of the length of the lens in from its surface.

If we set up a copying camera to give a same-size image, i.e., a magnification of unity, we have:

$$u = f (1 + \frac{1}{m}) = 2f$$

$$v = f (1 + m) = 2f$$

$$\text{Whence: } u + v = 4f$$

If, however, we measure the distance from original to image we will find that it differs from $4f$ by a small amount; this is a measure of the nodal space.

CHAPTER 10

The Camera

Introduction

A CAMERA is essentially a light-tight box with a lens at one end and a fixture to hold light-sensitive material at the other. In all but the simplest cameras there is provision for variation of the lens to film distance in order to focus upon objects at various distances from the lens. Light is normally prevented from reaching the sensitive material by a shutter, the function of which is to give an exposure time of a required duration. During this exposure time the amount of light reaching the film is controlled by an iris diaphragm, the aperture of which may also be varied as required. The settings of the shutter and iris diaphragm may be determined by an exposure measuring system as part of the camera, possibly measuring through the lens. Finally, the camera must have a viewfinder system by which the amount of subject area included on the film may be determined.

Survey of development

The outstanding feature in the development of the camera since the primitive forms used in the early 19th century is the continuous fluctuation in weight, size and shape with the innovations and improvements in design. Such changes are due to parallel developments in emulsion technology, optical design and manufacturing techniques as well being directly related to the camera format, materials of construction and versatility of function.

Camera format

For the last decades of the 19th century and continuing well into the 20th, the majority of photographs were taken on glass plates. Contact printing was the normal practice and to obtain large prints plate sizes up to 305 × 381 mm were not uncommon. Indeed, quarter-plate (82 × 108 mm) was regarded as the minimum useful size. Apart from the commonly adopted plate sizes there were some unusual ones for specific cameras. Steady improvements in lenses, emulsions and illuminants soon made projection printing a feasibility and started the steady decrease in format size. The advent of roll film hastened this process and brought the 60 × 90 mm format on 120 size material to great popularity just before the start of World War II. By this time the 24 × 36 mm format on 35 mm film was beginning to be less of a novelty.

This latter format has stabilised in spite of sporadic efforts to introduce variations such as 24 × 32 mm and 28 × 40 mm. In more recent years the "half-frame" format of 18 × 24 mm has also proved popular and given rise to a wide range of very compact camera designs.

Roll films have been manufactured in very many sizes but most are now obsolete or obsolescent. At the time of writing, the available sizes are 126, 127, 120, 220, and 70 mm. The 126 size is in the form of plastic easy-load cartridges with a format size of 28 × 28 mm. The 127 size is obsolescent, no new cameras for this size having been introduced for some years. Formats of 30 × 40 mm, 40 × 40 mm and 40 × 65 mm were commonly used, giving 16, 12 and 8 exposures respectively per roll. The most commonly used roll film at present is the 120 size and this gives a choice of format sizes: 45 × 60 mm, 60 × 60 mm, 56 × 72 mm and 60 × 90 mm, giving 16, 12, 10 or 8 exposures respectively per roll. These numbers are doubled for the newer 220 size, of the same width as 120 but twice as long and minus the backing paper. The same formats are used on 70 mm perforated film, but the choice of emulsions is limited. A variety of folding roll film cameras, twin-lens and single-lens reflex cameras as well as technical cameras use the 120, 220 and 70 mm film sizes.

Flat films were once considered an inferior alternative to plates. The introduction of new plastic base materials such as polyester, with improved dimensional stability, has contributed to the decline in the use of plates for many purposes in recent years. Professional work has tended to become standardized on 102 × 127 mm and 203 × 254 mm sizes, while 60 × 90 mm, quarter-plate, half-plate and whole-plate formats are becoming obsolete.

A large format size does not always mean bulk as well because ingenious construction methods have been used to reduce the size of the camera for carrying purposes. Technical cameras, even of the monorail type, may be collapsed to moderate dimensions. Cameras using 35 mm film began as very compact pieces of apparatus but have steadily increased in bulk as their versatility has been extended.

Cameras using 120 size film began as bulky box cameras which were superseded by compact folding models. These in their turn were replaced by the bulk of the modern twin-lens and single-lens reflex cameras. Many cameras have an adaptation feature to take a smaller format, e.g., roll film backs for technical cameras and 35 mm adapters for 120 size cameras.

The true pocket-size camera has existed in various forms for many years and generally uses 16 mm film with a format size of about 11 × 17 mm.

Materials of construction

The materials used are an important feature in determining the weight of a camera. Early plate cameras were constructed of mahogany and brass with leather bellows. These gave low weight and reasonable precision. Ingenious methods of construction were used to reduce the size of the camera for carrying purposes.

Modern technical cameras of die-cast alloys and brass have increased greatly in weight but the bulk remains much the same. Bellows of square, taper or bag construction are still used except for aerial and press cameras.

Small format cameras demanded a precision of construction given only by metal construction and small manufacturing tolerances. The all-metal construction meant a heavy camera, even if of only moderate size. Bellows were used to reduce size but are now obsolete.

Modern requirements of versatility have progressively increased the weight and bulk of these cameras.

Simple cameras have progressed from bulky, cloth-covered plywood boxes to constructions of modern plastics and light alloys. This has led to increased precision with a reduction in bulk but no increase in weight.

Versatility of function

On early cameras, features such as triple-extension bellows, extensive range of movements, interchangeable lenses and interchangeable backs were taken for granted. As types of cameras developed many of these features were lost. For example, restricted focusing movements often allowed lenses to be focused no closer than one metre; for closer work special attachments were needed. This trend has now reversed and the standard lens on most cameras will focus continuously down to about 500 mm without attachments.

Large-aperture lenses require precision-built camera bodies, which entails the loss of camera movements, but the limited circle of sharp definition of such lenses would not permit their use anyway.

Interchangeable lenses became a rarity until the advent of modern small format cameras, especially those of the single-lens reflex type. The facility of interchangeable backs is still limited to a few cameras.

The above comments, of course, do not apply to technical cameras, which have retained all these features and have been much improved by modern innovations such as modular construction, optical bench construction, "international" backs and electronic shutters.

The continuing trend with small-format cameras is to incorporate features to increase versatility, but unfortunately bulk and weight also increase. In accordance with such requirements, 24 × 36 mm and 60 × 60 mm format cameras are now produced as the basic unit in a "system" of interchangeable lenses, viewfinders and backs, remote control, motor drive, attachments for photo-micrography and photo-macrography etc. Such a system increases versatility enormously in comparison to haphazardly produced accessories.

Another welcome trend is the consideration of ergonomics in camera design. Cameras are increasingly being designed to be more easily operated when held in the hand. Such improvements include the increased legibility of scales and calibrations, the direction and amount of movement in focusing rings, larger and better sited controls, large eyepieces in viewfinders, ease of loading and rapid-loading systems.

Another aspect introduced by the versatility of a camera is the increased possibility of faults in the complicated mechanism. Repairs may be more frequent and call for increased skill on the part of the repairer. Simple maintenance such as changing batteries that operate electronic shutters and CdS type exposure meters is the responsibility of the user.

Camera types

There have been many different types of camera manufactured both for general work and for specialised purposes in conjunction with a range of accessories.

It is usually possible to place a particular camera into one of these fairly well-defined types although some designs, of course, are unique and not easily categorised. The following are the main types marketed today (see Figure 10.1):

Simple cameras
Rangefinder cameras
Twin-lens reflex cameras
Single-lens reflex cameras

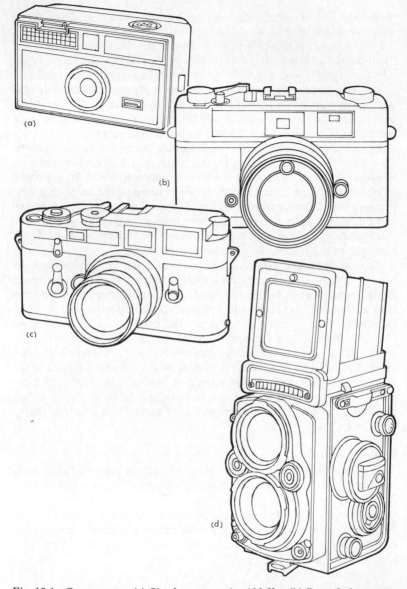

Fig. 10.1 – Camera types: (a) *Simple camera using 126 film;* (b) *Rangefinder camera with fixed lens;* (c) *Rangefinder camera with interchangeable lens;* (d) *Twin lens reflex with fixed lenses*

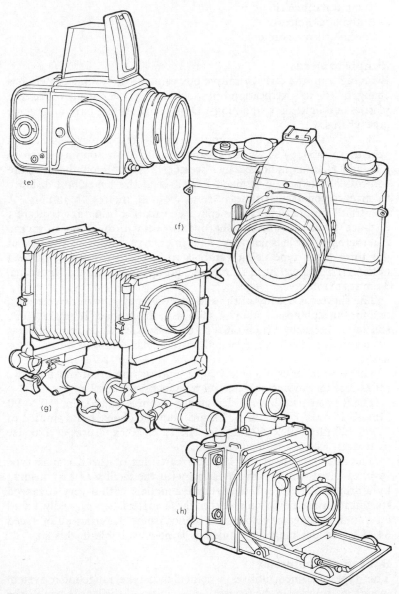

Fig. 10.1 continued: (e) *Single lens reflex for 120 film;* (f) *Single lens reflex for 35 mm film;* (g) *Technical camera, monorail;* (h) *Technical camera, folding baseboard*

Technical cameras
Automatic cameras
Special-purpose cameras

Simple cameras

Evolving from the early primitive box camera, the simple camera has changed little in specification but much use has been made of modern plastics and light alloy stampings. Design and styling have undergone great changes.

Basically the camera has a simple meniscus or doublet lens with an aperture of about $f/11$ with perhaps a facility for stopping down to $f/16$ and $f/22$, as indicated by "weather" symbols on the aperture control. The lens may be fixed-focus, set at the hyperfocal distance to give reasonable sharpness from about 2 metres to infinity. A "portrait" supplementary lens may be available, bringing the nearest distance giving reasonably sharp focus down to about 1 metre. Alternatively, the lens may have an elementary focusing mechanism of the three-point type using symbols to indicate the depth of field obtained; e.g. portrait, 1–2 metres; group, 2–8 metres; landscape, 3 metres to infinity.

The shutter is usually of the simple everset type with two settings, one for 'instantaneous', about 1/40th sec., the other a 'B' setting. The shutter is normally synchronized for flash work and many cameras have a built-in flash gun for small, capless flashbulbs or a fixture for flashcubes.

The viewfinder is either a bright, optical one or of the brilliant, reflex type for viewing only and with no focusing function.

The formats used have varied greatly, from 8 on 120 film (60 × 90 mm) to 16 on 127 film (30 × 40 mm), but the choice has dwindled to 12 on 120 film (60 × 60 mm), or the 12 or 20 exposures of 126 size cartridges, with 28 × 28 mm format.

The introduction of the 126 size cartridge of the Kodapak type revolutionised simple camera design with the facility of easy loading by a drop-in cartridge. Indeed, camera models with a very advanced specification are now available for these materials. Originally based on a limited range of colour and monochrome materials all of speed 64ASA, a wider range of emulsions is now available in this size.

Rangefinder cameras

This type of camera utilises a coincidence-type rangefinder system (page 185), coupled to the focusing mechanism of the lens to enable the lens to be accurately focused at the subject distance. Some cameras do not have the rangefinder coupled and the indicated distance must be transferred to the lens.

This method of focusing appeared with the introduction of the early 35 mm cameras, such as the Leica and Contax, being essential for the accurate focusing of large aperture lenses, especially at close range. The method was soon adopted in cameras using other formats, up to and including half-plate technical cameras. Both swinging mirror and rotating optical wedge systems were in common use. Design advanced rapidly in conjunction with improvements in viewfinders and soon combined range-viewfinders with bright line frames were common. Small format roll-film cameras evolved similarly but many ingenious solutions were required to give an accurate rangefinder system when a folding bellows design was used. Press cameras favoured a robust coupled rangefinder, but as a separate item and not as part of the view-finder. Interchangeable lenses presented a problem as the fixed base-length of the rangefinder meant that focusing accuracy decreased with increase in focal length. Also the limited mirror movement meant that the closest focusing distance was progressively further away from the camera with increase in focal length. In technical cameras, changing lenses also meant changing the focusing cam for the feeler arm coupled to the rangefinder mirror. Each lens had to have an individually calibrated cam. In 35 mm cameras the feeler arm operated on a cam on the lens barrel. Close-focusing devices for rangefinder cameras were clumsy arrangements, in general.

The use of a rangefinder does, however, permit a compact camera design. Rangefinder cameras now fall into distinct categories. Mainly they are 35 mm cameras of moderate specification with a non-interchangeable lens, but there are one or two types of the highest quality, e.g., the Leica M4. A number of medium-format press type cameras use coupled range-viewfinders as do some large-format technical cameras of the folding baseboard type. The latter also have normal ground-glass screen focusing facilities.

Twin-lens reflex cameras

This type of camera has enjoyed great popularity for many years since the introduction of the earliest version in the form of the first Rolleiflex. Much of this popularity is due to simplicity in use and versatility. Such a camera really consists of two cameras mounted one on top of the other, the upper for viewing and focusing and the lower for exposing the film (Figure 10.2). The two lenses must have the same focal length but the one used for viewing may be of simpler construction

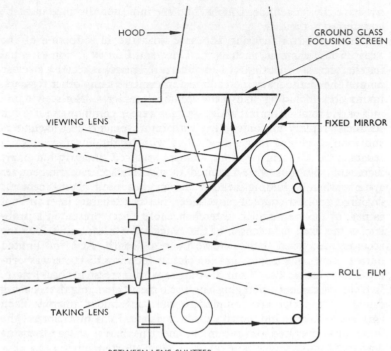

HOOD ————►

GROUND GLASS
FOCUSING SCREEN

VIEWING LENS

FIXED MIRROR

ROLL FILM

TAKING LENS

BETWEEN-LENS SHUTTER

Fig. 10.2 – Principle of the twin-lens reflex camera

and have a larger aperture to facilitate focusing in dim light. The two lenses are mounted on the same panel which is moved bodily to provide continuous viewing and focusing. The reflex mirror gives an upright, laterally reversed image on a ground-glass screen. The screen is shielded for focusing by a collapsible hood with a flip-up magnifier. This hood may be interchangeable with a pentaprism system for eye-level viewing and focusing. The focusing screen may incorporate a fresnel lens, split-image rangefinder or a microprism to assist focusing. The viewing lens is always used at full aperture. The operations of film transport and shutter setting are normally done by means of a folding crank device.

This type of camera has been designed for many formats and film sizes, including short-lived 35 mm and 102 × 127 mm types. The most common sizes were 60 × 60 mm and 40 × 40 mm given by 12 exposures on 120 and 127 film respectively. But even the 40 × 40 mm format is obsolete and the use of 120 or 220 film is predominant. The square format was originally chosen so that the camera could always be held vertically for viewing and focusing, the negative being "cropped" during enlargement to give the final composition. Alternative formats on 120 film were obtained by means of adapters and 35 mm film could also be used in some models. Specialised accessories taking plates, 70 mm film and Polaroid film are also available.

Two disadvantages of the twin-lens reflex camera are its bulk and its non-interchangeable lens. To overcome the latter disadvantage some cameras were supplied with lenses of longer or shorter focal lengths than the standard 75 mm or 80 mm usually fitted, but these were short-lived. However, a new lease of life was given to the camera type with the introduction of interchangeable lenses on the early Mamiyaflex model in the late 1950's. This camera has since evolved into a "system" with a range of bodies, viewfinders, focusing screens, backs and lenses. The outstanding feature of the system is the provision of a series of pairs of interchangeable lenses, complete with shutter, mounted on a common lens panel and the ability to focus very close due to the bellows arrangement used.

One of the problems associated with all twin-lens reflex cameras is the field-of-view error in the viewfinder screen due to the separation between viewing and taking lens. Attempts at solving this problem have included the use of a viewing screen of reduced area, a swivelling viewing lens, moving masks and moving pointers to delineate the top of the field of view. The problem becomes more acute with close focusing; use of a wedge-shaped prism over the viewing lens when supplementary lenses are used is a partial answer, but a lifting device to raise the camera bodily on a tripod by the distance between optical axes is needed for accurate work.

The twin-lens reflex camera is usually fairly rapid in its action when provided with crank-lever operation and convenient placement of controls. The disadvantage of earlier models in providing only 12 exposures on 120 film has now been offset by the facility of using 220 film to obtain double that number.

Single-lens reflex cameras

This type of camera has been popular since its introduction in the late 19th century, apart from a temporary slump when the twin-lens reflex design was introduced. Now, after a period of intensive development in the 35 mm and 120 roll film sizes, it is perhaps the leading design. Most of the recent innovations in camera design have first appeared in a single-lens reflex camera.

The principle of the camera is illustrated in Figure 10.3. A plane, surface-silvered mirror at 45° to the optical axis is used to form the

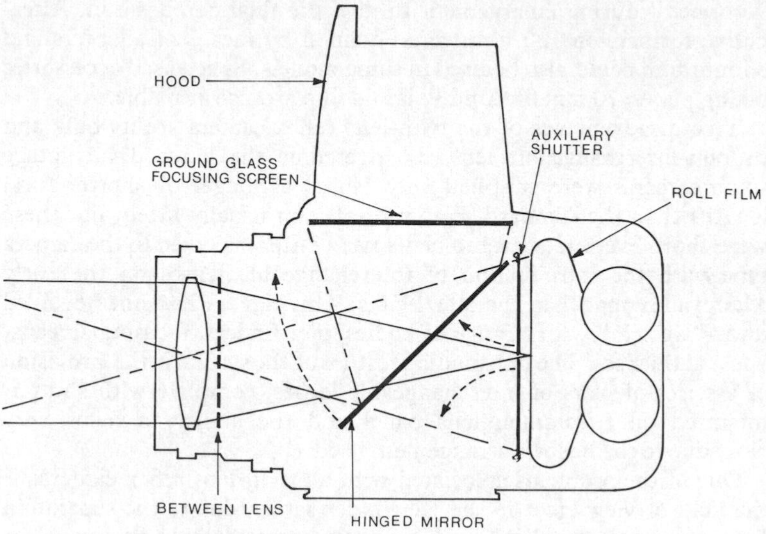

HOOD

GROUND GLASS
FOCUSING SCREEN

AUXILIARY
SHUTTER

ROLL FILM

BETWEEN LENS

HINGED MIRROR

Fig. 10.3 – Principle of the single-lens reflex camera (Hasselblad)

image from the camera lens on a screen where it may be focused and composed. For exposure the mirror is swung out of the way before the camera shutter opens. The mirror is then returned to the viewing position. These simple operations have evolved to ones of great complexity, involving many sophisticated mechanical operations, details of which are given in Chapter 11.

The great advantages of this design are the ease of viewing and focusing, and the freedom from field-of-view error, especially important for close-up work. The effect of the depth of field at the selected aperture may also be judged.

The earliest designs were for quarter-plate and 102×127 mm formats. A rotating back was an essential part of the design so that upright or horizontal pictures could be composed on the rectangular format. The interchangeable lenses had only an iris diaphragm and were focused using a bellows arrangement on a rack-and-pinion drive. The counterweighted, pivoted mirror was raised by pressure on the release lever which first lifted the mirror out of the way and then released a focal-plane shutter.

After the decline in the use of this type of large-format camera, due to the advent of the twin-lens reflex, the design appeared again for 35 mm, 127 and 120 size films, an important early model being the Kine-Exakta. Such cameras were popular due to their small size. Innovations included a focal-plane shutter with an extended range of speeds and the mirror was spring-operated, returning to the viewing position upon winding-on the film.

The use of the rectangular formats of 24×36 mm and 45×60 mm was inconvenient when a vertical framing was required for a picture. Usually a direct-vision viewfinder had to be used. The square format of 60×60 mm allowed the camera to be held in one position for all photographs and the picture shape determined at the composing or printing stages.

Shortly after World War II, the pentaprism viewfinder was introduced and this boosted the popularity of the single-lens reflex camera enormously. Now eye-level viewing and focusing was possible and the image remained erect and un-reversed for both horizontal and vertical formats.

The principle of the pentaprism viewfinder is illustrated in Figure 10.4.

Design innovations and improvements initially were all for the 24×36 mm format cameras, but the 60×60 mm type was also developing, albeit in much fewer numbers, and is now on a par with the smaller format. Among the improvements were reliable focal-plane shutters with a wide range of shutter speeds. Flash synchronization of these shutters had always been a problem, but now some for the smaller format are capable of synchronization with electronic flash at speeds up to 1/125th sec. Following the introduction of the instant-return mirror the operation of the iris diaphragm, once always manually stopped down just before exposure, evolved into the *fully-automatic diaphragm mechanism (FAD)*.

Improved viewfinder focusing screens with microprisms and optical rangefinders became standard fittings, often with a choice of alternative screens for specialised purposes.

A vast range of lenses, many from independent manufacturers, became available to fit the cameras, ranging from fish-eye to extreme long-focus types. A feature generally confined to the 60×60 mm format was the facility of interchangeable magazine backs.

A further great advance in the design of the single-lens reflex camera first became available in mid-1960's. This was *through-the-lens* (TTL) *metering*. The availability of reliable cadmium sulphide (CdS) cells of the required sensitivity and spectral response, coupled with the ease of showing the measurement area in the viewfinder of this type of camera, ensured rapid development of the system. (See page 191.)

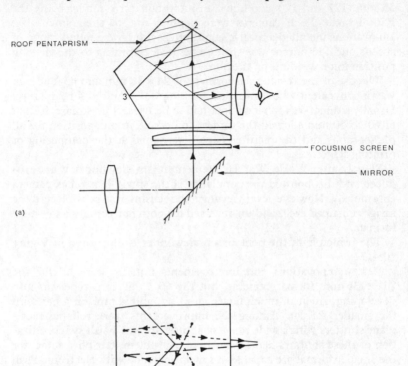

ROOF PENTAPRISM

FOCUSING SCREEN

MIRROR

(a)

(b)

Fig. 10.4 – Action of a pentaprism viewfinder

The great advantages of the single-lens reflex design have meant that it has become probably the most highly developed system camera and the basic unit for a wide range of accessories. Especially in the case of the medium format roll-film type, it is increasingly replacing the technical camera for many of those functions which do not specifically call for a large format or use of camera movements. Improvements in optics and emulsions for the smaller camera have ensured high quality results.

Technical cameras
The term technical camera is used to cover two types of camera. The

first is the monorail type, as illustrated in Figure 10.1. This is based on the optical bench principle giving the widest possible range of camera movements. All focusing and composition is done on the ground-glass screen and the camera must therefore be used on a rigid support. The second is the folding baseboard type, as illustrated in Figure 10.1. This camera is of precision manufacture, normally equipped with a coupled rangefinder and optical viewfinder as well as a ground-glass screen, and may therefore be used in the hand as well as on a tripod.

The rationalisation of the technical camera to these two types is another example of continuing improvements in design, manufacture, functional capabilities and automation of operation.

The early wood and brass studio and field cameras were adequate for large format work but very slow in operation. Improvements in lenses and the preference for smaller formats called for greater precision in manufacture. Metal was substituted for wood in the camera body to achieve this, but of course weight was substantially increased. A measure of standardisation was achieved in the sizes of items such as lens panels and backs for darkslides.

Technical cameras have been made in a large number of formats but the number have gradually been reduced. The term "medium format" covers cameras using 56 × 72 mm and 60 × 90 mm negative sizes, but there are few cameras in this category, monorail models being especially rare. The term "large format" covers film sizes of 102 × 127 mm to 203 × 254 mm, but the intermediate sizes of half-plate and whole-plate are rapidly becoming obsolescent. Most cameras in this range feature *reducing backs* as an accessory permitting the use of smaller formats when required for reasons of convenience or economy.

As with other camera types, the modern technical camera is now usually a "system" camera. The basic camera body may be fitted to or adapted with a host of accessories, covering alternatives to almost every component. This is especially true for the monorail camera which is usually designed on modular principles so that rails, front and rear standards, bellows, focusing screens, lenses and shutters are interchangeable to adapt for a range of formats or types of work.

The folding baseboard camera uses a high precision rangefinder normally coupled to three alternative lenses. Viewing is by means of a multiple-frame, bright-line viewfinder. Flat films, roll films, plates and Polaroid materials may all be used. Offsetting its capability of being used in the hand it has a much more limited range of movements than the monorail type. The ground glass screen must be used for close-up work or camera movements because the rangefinder is then no longer operative. The bellows is usually of the triple-extension type. Recent developments for technical cameras have included forms of through-the-lens exposure measurement, pre-set mechanisms for shutter speed and aperture settings, electronic shutters, extreme wide-angle lenses of large, usable aperture and binocular viewing and focusing devices.

Automatic cameras

Many of the operations of a camera once determined and set by the user are now operated by mechanisms of electrical, mechanical and optical nature, thus qualifying for the generic title of automatic. Actually the function should be classed as semi-automatic or fully-automatic, because many rely on some manual assistance. The amount of automation in a camera varies enormously from model to model; some of the most advanced cameras require only a film speed to be set and the shutter release pressed after selecting the subject.

Automatic film advance after exposure was one of the earliest functions to be adapted as it was comparatively easy to incorporate in a camera. Early cameras with this feature were clockwork motor driven but modern versions tend to use small electric motors powered by a battery. The film is wound on to the next frame, the shutter set and the frame-counter operated when the release button is returned to its normal position. A number of cameras offer a motor-drive as an accessory. The picture taking rate is usually variable, up to about 5 frames per second. Such an accessory has a number of well-defined uses. The bulk and weight of the camera are considerably increased.

The iris diaphragm has been automated in a number of ways. It may incorporate a fully-automatic diaphragm mechanism (page 158) for use in single-lens reflex cameras. It may be set by a built-in exposure metering system according to the subject luminance. For flashwork some iris diaphragms are coupled to the focusing mechanism so that once a flash factor has been set, alteration of focus for subjects of varying distance automatically adjusts the aperture to the correct value for constant exposure.

The meaning of automatic as applied to most cameras, however, refers to the built-in exposure determination system. Frequently, this operation is not *fully* automatic, however, because the shutter speed or aperture ring must be turned to bring into coincidence two needles, one being operated by the meter mechanism. The true automatic camera sets the aperture or shutter speed according to a programme when the release is pressed to fire the shutter, the meter cell being actuated and operating the mechanism prior to the moment of exposure. Electronic shutters are now widely used for this purpose because they are continuously variable over their exposure time range. Pressing the release opens the shutter, the CdS meter cell circuit then closes it when sufficient light for exposure has been recorded. This works even when flashbulbs are used. A signal usually indicates if an exposure of longer than 1/30th second will be needed, so that a tripod may be used.

The automatic camera is generally a smaller format type such as 24 × 36 mm or 28 × 28 mm.

Special-purpose cameras

Many cameras do not easily fit into any of the above classifications because they are specially designed in terms of format, materials available and specification to perform limited but specialised functions. Some of these cameras are as follows:

Press cameras

Cameras for press work were once almost exclusively of large format, typically 102 × 127 mm using plates to facilitate rapid processing. Often they were a simplified version of the folding baseboard type of technical camera, usually only retaining camera movements on the front standard carrying the lens. Other simplifications included limited bellows extension or a rigid box construction. The coupled rangefinder was retained and a focal-plane shutter was used in order to obtain high shutter speeds. Flash synchronization, using Class FP bulbs, was essential. The design emphasis was on speed of operation and sturdiness. Cameras using smaller formats have almost replaced these early press cameras, but several medium-format roll film cameras retain the basic features with some improvements. Ruggedness and swift operation is combined with lens changing by bayonet fittings, coupled range-viewfinders and rapid film advance by lever wind.

Aerial cameras

Most aerial cameras are rigid, remote-controlled fixtures in an aircraft, but for hand-held oblique aerial photography a few special cameras may be obtained. These are much simplified versions of technical cameras without any movements, rigid bodies and lenses set permanently on infinity focus. A fixture for filters is an important feature and a simple direct-vision metal viewfinder completes the requirements. Ample handgrips with incorporated shutter release are also supplied. If roll-film is used, normally 70 mm material, film advance may be by lever wind or electrically driven.

Polaroid Land Cameras

The Polaroid Corporation of America produces many cameras to take its range of sensitised materials. These materials are available in roll film, flat film and film pack forms and the formats used range from 60 × 90 mm to 102 × 127 mm. Both colour and black and white material are supplied. The cameras used range from simple plastic types with minimal controls to sophisticated, complex models with such refinements as electronic shutters and exposure measurement systems. Many accessories are available. Other film types cannot be used in these cameras.

Sub-miniature cameras

Cameras of this type have been popular since the earliest days of photography, appearing in many novel forms, but their common feature is the use of a very small and often unusual format. In general, the term sub-miniature camera is nowadays applied to cameras using film of a smaller width than 35 mm perforated material. Usually this is 16 mm film, perforated or unperforated, and loaded in special cassettes to give a moderate number of exposures. In spite of their small dimensions many have a comprehensive specification including automatic exposure determination and electronic shutters. Many accessories are also available to extend their usefulness and applications.

Underwater cameras

Many cameras can be housed in a pressure container with an optically flat window to enable them to be used underwater. This is usually part of the range of accessories for the camera. Unfortunately these casings are cumbersome. However, a few cameras have been designed as watertight casings usable to specific depths for underwater work. They are also useful in adverse conditions on land where water, mud or sand would ruin the mechanism of most cameras. The cameras have a simple direct-vision viewfinder and focusing control. The lenses are interchangeable. A short-focus lens is fitted as standard to compensate for the optical magnification due to change in apparent distance caused by the refractive index of water. An equivalent field of view to a standard lens on a normal camera is then obtained.

Stereo cameras

Stereo cameras have been produced for many formats on plates, flat film and roll film but the majority now use 35 mm film, giving stereo pairs with formats of about 23 × 24 mm. Pairs of matched lenses and shutters, on an otherwise normal camera body, have their optical axes separated by the human interocular distance.

Ultra wide-angle cameras

When a large enough angle of view cannot be obtained by the normal range of lenses available for a camera, and when perspective and distortion considerations rule out the use of fish-eye lenses, then one of two types of camera embracing a large angle of view may be used.

Firstly, a camera body of shallow depth with a non-interchangeable lens of a large angle of view; e.g., an angle of view of 110° on the diagonal may be obtained on 24 × 36 mm and 102 × 127 mm format by the use of lenses of 15 mm and 65 mm focal length respectively. Focusing of such a lens is usually by scale and the viewfinder may be a simple direct-vision or optical type. A spirit level on the camera body is essential. Other features of the camera are as normal.

Secondly, a panoramic camera may be used. Typically, 140° horizontally and 50° vertically may be covered by rotating a normal design lens about its rear nodal point and imaging the scene on a slit which exposes the film sequentially during the exposure time. A high aspect ratio format is employed in such cameras.

CHAPTER 11

The Elements of the Camera

As indicated in Chapter 10, many of the advances in camera design and the emergence of the confirmed popularity of certain types, have been due to developments in design of one or more of the elements of the camera. Owing to the complexity and variations of each of these elements, together with their interdependence, it is worth examining each major design element in detail. The following will be considered in this Chapter:

The lens

Lens accessories:
    lens hood
    filters
    supplementary lenses
    stereo attachments
    diffusion discs
    teleconverters
    afocal converters
    extension tubes and bellows

The shutter:
    between-lens shutters
    focal-plane shutters
    some other types of shutter

The diaphragm:
    conventional diaphragms
    automatic diaphragms

The viewfinder:
    simple viewfinders
    direct-vision optical viewfinders
    ground glass screen viewfinders

The focusing mechanism:
    front cell focusing
    movement of entire lens
    coincidence-type rangefinders
    split-image rangefinders
    ground glass screen focusing
    focusing scales

The exposure meter: types of meter cell
    accessory exposure meters
    built-in exposure meters with external
        cell
    through-the-lens exposure measurement
    automatic exposure control
Flash synchronization: synchronization of between-lens
        shutters
    synchronization of focal-plane shutters

The lens

In previous Chapters we have already considered the principles of image formation, the properties and aberrations of lenses and the most common types of construction. Progressing from these fundamental concepts, there have been great improvements in design and performance of lenses in the years since World War II. These may be ascribed to four interrelated innovations:

(1) *Lens coating* (page 74)

The widespread use of lens elements with antireflection layers of various properties, has enabled lens designers to incorporate many more elements than before. The contrast, performance at extremes of aperture and field angle as well as colour balance have all been improved.

(2) *Optical glass*

New types of optical glass have become available, with higher refractive indices and lower dispersions, as glass manufacturers have extended their ranges of products. Chemical elements such as lanthanum are commonly used in newer glasses, and materials such as fluorite are used for some applications.

(3) *Use of computers*

The tedious task of calculating ray paths through optical systems, an essential design step, has been greatly speeded by use of digital computers. Often a computer is programmed to optimise a design as far as possible, human judgement then determining further progress.

(4) *Evaluation of results*

The emergence of complex electronic methods for the objective evaluation of lens performance has contributed to improvements in design and to the quality control essential during manufacture.

The direct results of the above have been a considerable increase in the range of focal lengths available for the various formats, larger usable apertures, unusual lens designs for specific functions and an overall improved performance. The range of lenses offered by a manufacturer, for given formats, may nowadays be as follows:

6·5 mm to 1000 mm focal length for 24 × 36 mm format
38 mm to 1000 mm focal length for 60 × 60 mm format
65 mm to 1000 mm focal length for 102 × 127 mm format.

An example of improvements in a class of lens is well illustrated by the case of the wide-angle lens. The old problems of poor covering power, low marginal resolution, small usable apertures and flare have been largely overcome by newer designs. Typically, for the 24 × 36 mm format; 28 mm $f/2\cdot8$, 35 mm $f/1\cdot4$ and 35 mm $f/2$ lenses are commonly available in symmetrical and retrofocus designs. The 60 × 60 mm format has available lenses of 40 to 50 mm focal length and aperture $f/4$. Large formats also have wide-angle lenses with usable apertures of about $f/5\cdot6$ and sufficient covering power to permit limited use of camera movements.

At the extreme ends of the available range of focal lengths, the "fish-eye" lens and mirror lens designs are now common. The fish-eye design is a wide-angle lens with no correction for linear distortion and commonly has an angle of view of 140° to 180° or more. The mirror lens, on the other hand, uses spherical mirrors as well as refracting surfaces (catadioptric system) to give extremely long focal lengths with a more compact design and larger aperture than would otherwise be possible. The design of mirror lenses is such that they cannot be used with an iris diaphragm; the lens must at all times be used at maximum aperture. Exposure is varied using shutter speeds and neutral density filters.

Another type of lens in a continuing state of development for still cameras, is the variable focal length or "zoom" lens. The so-called "macro" lens, which is designed and corrected for close-up work, incorporating an extended-range focusing mechanism, is also common.

Finally, the "standard" lens for a given format has undergone many changes. Contrast, resolution and freedom from flare have all been improved. Maximum apertures of $f/2$ or $f/1\cdot4$ are normal for lenses used with the 24 × 36 mm format and $f/1\cdot2$ is not uncommon. Lenses for the 60 × 60 mm format rarely exceed a maximum aperture of $f/2\cdot8$.

A manufacturer producing a camera as the basis of a system has to ensure that an adequate range of lenses is available. Additionally, other manufacturers produce ranges of lenses with interchangeable or alternative fittings for attachment to various camera bodies.

This situation is possible now that many cameras use the same fitting for lenses instead of introducing yet another version. Many manufacturers, of course, still make cameras with their own unique fitting.

As a direct result of improvements in camera design and specifications, the mechanical complexity of lens mountings has greatly increased, to permit incorporation of features such as fully-automatic diaphragms, depth-of-field indicators, exposure-value shutters and close-focusing mechanisms.

The lens hood

The use of a properly designed lens hood with any lens, under most circumstances, will contribute significantly to the quality of results obtained. In particular, it will shield the lens from light extraneous to the subject area and reduce flare, especially in back-lit and side-lit conditions. The most common type of lens hood is conical in shape to enable it to be of maximum depth without causing vignetting. The internal finish is ridged and painted matt black. The front aperture is circular or of the same proportions as the negative format in use. Owing to the danger of vignetting by a lens hood, many wide-angle lenses are not fitted with one, nor would one be of much help, but as the focal length increases the need for an efficient lens hood becomes greater. Many long-focus lenses are now supplied with an integral, telescoping hood to encourage the user to employ it. The bellows type of lens hood is unsurpassed in its efficiency and is adjustable for a wide range of focal lengths. Optimum adjustment is easy with a single-lens reflex camera.

Filters

Camera filters of various categories are fully dealt with in Chapter 18. They are supplied as dyed gelatin, either alone or cemented between glass, or as dyed glass. The optical quality of glass filters is reflected in their price. Filter mounts may be push-on, screw-in or bayonet types. A significant design point, in many manufacturers' favour, is that a range of focal lengths of lenses may be designed to accept the same size of filter, giving considerable economies to the user. Most cameras with a built-in exposure metering system incorporate a setting device to allow for filter factors. In most circumstances, a through-the-lens metering system will compensate automatically for any filter that may be in use.

Supplementary lenses

Supplementary lenses provide a useful means of altering the focal length of a camera lens. They may be positive or negative, although positive supplementaries are most widely used. Probably the most valuable use of a supplementary lens is for close focusing with cameras having limited focusing movement. We can focus on an object inside the minimum distance for which the camera is scaled, by selecting a positive supplementary lens of focal length equal to the object distance, irrespective of the focal length of the camera lens. The camera lens is then focused for infinity and the path of the rays is as shown in Figure 11.1. This is the basis of "close-up" or "portrait" attachments.

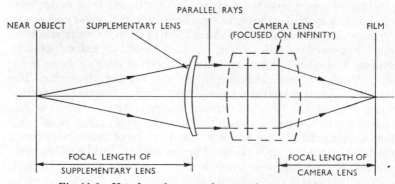

Fig. 11.1 – Use of supplementary lens as a close-up attachment

Supplementary lenses are invariably specified by their power in *diopters*, rather than by their focal length. The relation between the power of a supplementary lens and its focal length is:

$$\text{Focal length in millimetres} = \frac{1000}{\text{power in diopters}}$$

The power of a convergent supplementary lens is said to be positive, and that of a divergent lens negative. The practice of specifying supplementary lenses by their powers is convenient in that powers are additive, i.e., by adding the powers of two supplementaries we obtain the power of the combination. It is possible to purchase supplementary lenses in a range of $+\frac{1}{4}$ to $+5$ diopters. The weaker ones of $\frac{1}{4}$ and $\frac{1}{2}$ diopter strength are widely used with long-focus lenses to extend their focusing range without the need for a long focusing movement. They do not usually seriously affect the corrections of the camera lens. For very close-up work, however, where supplementaries of a considerable power would be needed, the use of extension tubes is a preferred alternative (see below). Supplementary lenses are preferably of meniscus form, because this minimizes oblique aberrations and affects definition least. For many purposes, ordinary spectacle lenses are suitable for use as supplementary lenses, although a number of supplementary lenses produced for specific lenses are achromats and have antireflection coatings.

Stereo attachments

A stereo attachment is basically a beam-splitter device using surface-silvered mirrors or glass prisms whose optical axes are separated by the interocular distance. There are limitations on the nearest subject distance. One frame of the format in use yields a stereo pair of transparencies which are then used in a stereo viewer or for projection.

Diffusion discs

For some applications, such as portraiture, it is desirable to reduce the resolution available from the lens in use and to obtain a "soft-focus" result. This may be done by using a plain glass disc that has been engraved with concentric depressions, rather like a Fresnel lens. Alternatively, the surface may be treated to give minute, rounded contours. The degree of diffusion obtained from the former type depends upon how large an aperture is used, but the latter type is independent of aperture.

Converter lenses

The purpose of a converter lens is to increase or decrease the effective focal length of the lens in use on the camera. There are two types to consider, the teleconverter lens and the afocal converter lens.

Teleconverter lens

This lens unit can be used with interchangeable lenses only, as it is positioned between the camera body and lens. It consists of a short extension tube containing a number of elements forming a negative lens group. This converts the camera lens into one of telephoto construction (Figure 8.15) with the camera lens as the converging group and the converter lens as the diverging group. Converters are generally available in $\times 2$ and $\times 3$ powers, i.e., to double or triple the effective focal length of the camera lens respectively. Acceptable results are obtained with long-focus lenses but their use with standard and especially wide-angle lenses is not recommended, because it may result in a loss of image quality. Concomitant with the increase in focal length is a loss in maximum aperture. Doubling of the effective focal length gives a loss of 2 stops in maximum aperture, i.e., a ×2 teleconverter used with a 100 mm $f/2\cdot8$ lens will give a combination of 200 mm $f/5\cdot6$, and all other marked aperture numbers are similarly doubled. The teleconverter is a very compact unit of moderate price. Most versions have a mechanical linkage to ensure that operation of an automatic diaphragm is retained. The combination will also focus down to the closest distance of the camera lens alone. Teleconverters are primarily designed for single-lens reflex cameras.

Afocal converter lens
These multiple-element lens units are generally used with noninterchangeable lenses because they are used in front of the camera lens. The term *afocal* indicates that they have no focal length of their own, i.e., parallel light incident on the unit emerges still parallel. However, when such a converter is used with a camera lens the effective focal length of the combination may be greater or less than that of the camera lens alone, depending upon the construction of the converter. The "wide-angle converter" and the "telephoto converter" decrease and increase the focal length of the camera lens by factors of approximately 0·5 and 1·5 respectively. A common use is with twin-lens reflex cameras, which usually have noninterchangeable lenses. Unless the converters are of high optical quality and cost the results are disappointing. Large apertures give poor resolution and small apertures give vignetting. A medium aperture is best. No change in the marked apertures of the camera lens is necessary. Reflex focusing is essential. With the telephoto converter in use there is a loss of focusing range, in that the nearest distance that can be brought into sharp focus is increased.

Extension tubes and bellows
Like a supplementary lens, extension tubes and bellows provide a means of focusing a camera with limited focusing movement on close objects. Unlike supplementary lenses, however, these are intended for use only on cameras having interchangeable lenses. The extension tube is a tube of similar diameter to the lens mount with suitable fittings for attaching the lens to one end and the camera body to the other. These tubes are usually made in a range of lengths which can be used singly or in combination with one another. For single-lens

reflex cameras, automatic extension tubes are made which transmit the operation of the automatic diaphragm mechanism from the camera body to the lens; otherwise, this facility is lost.

Any length of extension tube in conjunction with the focusing movement on the lens mount imparts a limited focusing range. Also, at long extensions, the narrow diameter of the tube may cause vignetting. For these reasons, extension bellows are preferable because they permit an extensive focusing range and allow lenses of very long focal length to be used. Many lenses have the optical part removable from the focusing mount to facilitate their use on extension bellows. Typically, a 135 mm focal length lens for the 24 × 36 mm format with bellows may have a focusing range from infinity down to same-size reproduction.

Extension tubes and bellows are of most use with single-lens reflex cameras owing to the ease of focusing, but often reflex attachments may be used with other cameras. The tubes and bellows are normally supplied with data in chart or calibration form giving the necessary information on the increase in exposure required with a range of focal lengths at various magnifications.

The automatic diaphragm operation of a lens is usually lost when extension bellows are used so the lens has to be stopped down manually. Some lenses, however, have a cable release socket to operate the diaphragm and can therefore be used with a double cable release. For extreme close-ups, or photomacrography, the optical performance of a lens may be impaired because corrections are normally computed for work at infinity. A lens reversing ring attached to the bellows will often improve results.

The shutter

In terms of delicacy, the camera shutter is usually ranked just after any exposure metering system that may be incorporated in the camera. The quality and type of the shutter contribute significantly to the performance of the camera. The function of a shutter is to expose the sensitised material to the action of light for a given time. A perfect shutter should expose each part of the film equally, and preferably at the same time, i.e., it should allow the cone of light passing through the selected aperture to fall upon the film for the entire duration of the exposure, it should be silent in operation, there should be no jarring or vibration and it should require little effort to set it in motion.

The two main types of shutter in use today are the *diaphragm*, or *between-lens, shutter* and the *focal-plane shutter*; both may be purely mechanical in operation or may combine mechanical and electrical features.

Between-lens shutters

The ideal position to intercept the light transmitted by the lens is in the plane of the diaphragm. The beam of light is at its narrowest near the diaphragm and the minimum amount of shutter travel is therefore required if the shutter is in this position. The sensitive material is also evenly exposed at all stages in the opening of the shutter.

Simple cameras often use single-bladed between-lens shutters but the majority of cameras use multi-bladed shutters. The blades, or sectors, open like the leaves of an iris diaphragm. In lower priced cameras an "everset" or "self-setting" type of multi-bladed shutter is used. In this, a single control is depressed to compress the spring and release the shutter in one movement. Mechanical limitations mean that a speed range of only 1/30th to 1/125th second is obtained.

More expensive mechanical between-lens shutters are of the "preset" type. In these, two movements are required: one for tensioning (cocking) the operating spring and one for releasing the shutter. In many cameras the cocking operation is performed by the film advance mechanism. Preset shutters such as the Compur, Copal and Prontor types commonly provide for exposures ranging from 1 second to 1/500th second, a speed of 1/1000th second being provided by one type. The shutter blades pivot about their ends (or, rarely, centre) and for all but the highest speeds open with constant velocity. An additional spring mechanism causes the blades to open very quickly and close almost immediately at the highest speeds, while the slower speeds are usually controlled by engaging a gear train to retard the blade closing mechanism.

On older shutters, the conventional series of shutter speeds was 1, $\frac{1}{2}$, 1/5, 1/10, 1/25, 1/50, 1/100, 1/250 and 1/500th second. In current models, it is 1, $\frac{1}{2}$, $\frac{1}{4}$, 1/8, 1/15, 1/30, 1/60, 1/125, 1/250 and 1/500th second, to give a progression of exposures similar to that provided by the standard series of lens aperture numbers, i.e., with each step double or one half of the next. This has been done primarily to permit the introduction of a mechanical interlock between the aperture and shutter speed controls, in order to keep the two in reciprocal relation. This ensures that as the shutter speed is adjusted, so the iris diaphragm is automatically opened or closed to keep the exposure the same. The advantages of this are obvious.

Shutter speeds are usually set by click stops on the selector ring although the design of the shutter may permit intermediate values to be set. For reasons of economy many shutters do not have speeds below 1/30th second. Large diameter lenses used in large format cameras impose a limit of about 1/200th second as a top speed in their shutters.

In recent years the mechanism of some between-lens shutters has been made to include electrical as well as mechanical operations. Such shutters are generally called *electronic shutters*. In these, the blades are still opened by a spring mechanism but the closing operation is retarded by an electromagnet, controlled by a timing circuit. A typical capacitor-resistor circuit as used is shown in Figure 11.2. Switch S is

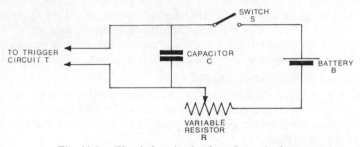

Fig. 11.2 – The timing circuit of an electronic shutter

closed by the shutter blades opening and battery B begins to charge capacitor C through a variable resistor R. The time taken to reach a critical voltage depends upon the value of R, but when it is reached the capacitor discharges to operate a transistorised trigger circuit T which releases the electromagnet holding the shutter blades open. The alteration of shutter speed normally means switching in a different value of R. A great convenience, however, for automatic cameras, is for R to be the CdS photoresistor monitoring the subject luminance and giving a continuously variable speed range from many seconds to about 1/250th second exposure. Even the light reflected from the subject during the burning of a flashbulb may be monitored in this way by some camera exposure systems. A visible signal normally gives a warning when the exposure time is longer than 1/30th second, necessitating the use of a tripod.

As the blades and drive of an electronic shutter are mechanical, it cannot improve on earlier designs in terms of performance at higher speeds or greater efficiency. It does, however, lend itself to automation and remote control. A control box for selecting shutter speeds and apertures may be used on a long cable for linking to electronic shutters in technical camera lenses.

Returning to the conventional between-lens shutter, we may note some other items usually incorporated in the mounting. In addition to the usual shutter speed and aperture scales, an interlocked shutter bears a third scale of *exposure values* (page 327). The numbers on this scale range from, e.g., 2 to 18, the change from one number to another corresponding to an alteration in the luminance of the scene by a factor of 2. This scale is normally used with a specially scaled exposure meter. A "self-timer" or delayed-action device is often fitted, by means of which the release of the shutter can be delayed for some 5 to 15 seconds. On many shutters fitted to lenses for technical cameras there is a "press-focus" button which opens the shutter on a time setting irrespective of the shutter speed set. This facilitates focusing and eliminates constant resetting of shutter speeds.

One of the great advantages of between-lens shutters is the ease of flash synchronization of all types and this is discussed fully on page 196.

Efficiency of a between-lens shutter
However rapidly the blades of a between-lens shutter are made to move they take a measurable time to uncover the lens fully. If we plot light transmitted by the shutter against time, we obtain a curve of the type shown in Figure 11.3.

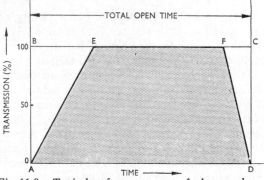

Fig. 11.3 – Typical performance curve of a between-lens shutter

The *efficiency* of a shutter is defined as the ratio of the quantity of light actually transmitted by the shutter to the quantity of light that would have been transmitted had the shutter been fully open for the *total open time*. In Figure 11.3, the efficiency is given by the ratio of the shaded area *AEFD* to the area *ABCD*. In the example shown it is about 80 per cent. The product of the total open time and the efficiency is termed the *effective exposure time*.

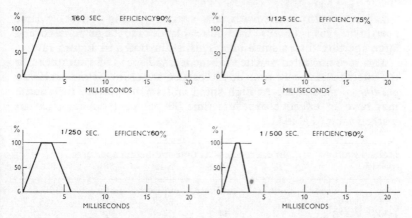

Fig. 11.4 – Performance curves of a between-lens shutter at different speeds

The efficiency of a between-lens shutter varies with the shutter speed, being at its lowest at high speeds. This is made clear by Figure

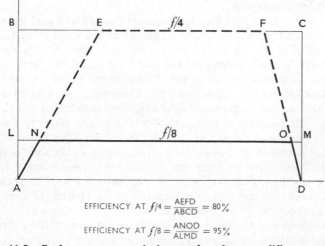

EFFICIENCY AT $f/4 = \dfrac{\text{AEFD}}{\text{ABCD}} = 80\%$

EFFICIENCY AT $f/8 = \dfrac{\text{ANOD}}{\text{ALMD}} = 95\%$

Fig. 11.5   Performance curves of a between-lens shutter at different apertures

11.4, where it is seen that the opening and closing of the blades take a far greater proportion of the total open time at fast shutter speeds than at slow speeds.

Efficiency also varies with lens aperture, being lowest at large apertures. This is because the shutter blades take longer to uncover a large aperture than a small one. This is illustrated in Figure 11.5.

It is recommended practice for the *marked* speed of a shutter to be the effective exposure time at the particular setting *at the maximum opening of the shutter*. At high speed and small aperture the shutter may have an effective exposure time 50 per cent. longer than the marked value (Table 11.1).

| Marked shutter speed | Effective exposure time at different apertures | | | | |
	$f/2$	$f/2\cdot8$	$f/4$	$f/8$	$f/16$
	millisecs.	millisecs.	millisecs.	millisecs.	millisecs.	millisecs.
1/15	67	67	68·2	68·8	69·3	69·5
1/30	33	33	34·2	34·8	35·3	35·5
1/60	17	17	18·2	18·8	19·3	19·5
1/125	8	8	9·2	9·8	10·3	10·5
1/250	4	4	5·2	5·8	6·3	6·5
1/500	2	2	2·6	2·9	3·1	3·2

Table 11.1 – Performance of a good between-lens shutter

Focal-plane shutters

This type of shutter is located in the camera body and travels as nearly as possible in the focal plane. In earlier forms the focal-plane shutter consisted of an opaque blind with a slit or several slits of varying width; the slit was driven past the front surface of the film and the exposure made as it passed across. The speed of travel and width of the slit determined the exposure time. Some of these shutters gave a very wide range of shutter speeds by variations in both slit and shutter tension. The modern version uses two blinds: one starts to uncover the film when the shutter release is pressed and the other follows behind at a greater or smaller distance according to the shutter speed set. The separation between the blinds thus constitutes a slit of variable width, giving the range of exposure times. The speed of movement across the film is constant. Such a shutter is also self-capping in that the slit is closed when the shutter is being set.

Focal-plane shutters were once much used in large-format cameras to obtain high shutter speeds but reliability and flash synchronization problems caused them to be largely discontinued in such cameras in favour of between-lens shutters.

Some 60 × 60 mm format single-lens reflex cameras use a focal-plane shutter with the advantage of easy interchangeability of lenses, but once again flash synchronization causes problems, especially for electronic flash. For 24 × 36 mm format cameras the focal-plane shutter has reached a high degree of development. A top speed of 1/2000th second is now common and certain shutters synchronize with electronic flash at speeds as high as 1/125th second. Details of flash synchronization are on page 198.

Speed selection is by a click-stop dial. Electronic versions of focal-plane shutters are now common, with the mechanical escapement replaced by a transistorised timing circuit.

With focal-plane shutters, different parts of the film are exposed at different times. With fast-moving objects, therefore, distortion may result, depending upon the relation between the direction of movement of blind and object. In any given circumstances, this distortion is constant for a given speed of travel of the slit.

Efficiency of a focal-plane shutter
If the blind of a focal-plane shutter were in actual contact with the film, each part of the film would be exposed in turn to the entire lens aperture for the whole time that the slit took to pass. In practice, the blind must be some way in front of the emulsion surface, and consequently the slit takes a finite time to uncover the lens aperture. The

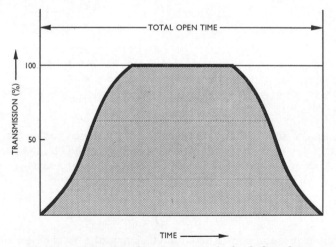

Fig. 11.6 – Typical performance curve of a focal-plane shutter

performance curve of a focal-plane shutter is therefore of the form shown in Figure 11.6.

The efficiency of a focal-plane shutter is defined in the same way as that of a between-lens shutter; i.e., it is the ratio of the quantity of light actually transmitted by the shutter to the quantity of light that would have been transmitted had the lens aperture been fully uncovered for the total time that a point on the film receives any light.

Efficiency is given by the equation:

$$\text{Efficiency} = \frac{w}{w + d_1}$$

where w is the width of the slit, and d_1 the diameter of the cone of light proceeding from the lens to a point in the image plane, measured in the plane of the blind (Figure 11.7).

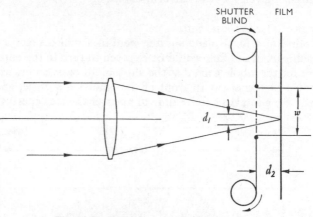

Fig. 11.7 – Efficiency of a focal-plane shutter

It can be shown that if the lens-to-film distance equals the focal length, $d_1 = d_2/N$, where d_2 is the distance from the blind to the film and N the f-number of the lens. Efficiency then becomes:

$$\frac{w}{w + \dfrac{d_2}{N}}$$

This expression shows that the efficiency of a focal-plane shutter depends upon the width of the slit (the wider the slit the greater the efficiency), upon the distance of the blind from the film (the closer the blind to the film the greater the efficiency) and upon the lens aperture (the smaller the aperture the greater the efficiency).

As with the between-lens shutter, the effective exposure time of a focal-plane shutter is the product of total open time and efficiency. Now, every ray from the lens to a point on the film will be allowed to pass for the same period of time, whatever the distance of the blind from the film. Thus, the effective exposure time is seen to be independent of the location of the blind, being determined by the equation:

$$\text{Effective exposure time} = \frac{w}{v}$$

where w is the width of the slit and v its linear velocity. Since, however, efficiency varies with blind-to-film distance, it is apparent that the total open time of the shutter must also vary with this distance. For stopping motion, therefore, the blind should be as close as possible to the film, since efficiency is then greatest and total open time – for a given effective exposure time – is smallest.

As the formula above shows, the effective exposure time is independent of the lens aperture. Since, however, lens aperture affects the efficiency it also affects the total open time; therefore, the smaller the aperture (giving greater efficiency) the smaller the total open time.

Choice of shutter type

For any given camera it is not usually possible to choose between a between-lens shutter and a focal-plane shutter. One or the other type is usually a fundamental feature of the camera design. Formerly, a focal-plane shutter was essential if the camera was to be fitted with interchangeable lenses. The introduction of interchangeable lenses that are either fitted with a between-lens shutter or fit into a similar shutter retained in the camera body has altered this situation.

Some of the latter type, however, have restrictions on the range of focal lengths available and on close-up work. In general, a focal-plane shutter offers greater efficiency at its higher range of shutter speeds than a between-lens shutter, but efficient synchronisation for flash photography is more difficult.

Some other types of shutter

Apart from the between-lens and focal-plane types a number of obsolete and specialised shutters may still be found in cameras and lenses.

The lens cap

This can serve as an excellent vibration-free shutter in many situations where time exposures may be given.

The roller-blind shutter
This was attached to the front or rear of a lens and operated rather in the manner of a focal-plane shutter. The top speed available was about 1/100th second.

The bellows shutter
This type consisted of two collapsible pneumatic bellows which formed a hemisphere when inflated. Fitted inside a camera bellows it was practically noiseless and much favoured for portraiture.

The louvre shutter
This type in operation resembled the slats of a venetian blind and opened and closed by a reversing action through 90°. Commonly fitted to aerial cameras, it had the advantage over the focal-plane shutter that it gave no distortion of the image.

Releasing a shutter
The method of releasing the shutter on a hand-held camera is important because if operated carelessly it may impart a jolt to the camera, resulting in a loss of definition. Similar effects may occur if the release mechanism has high inertia or is in an awkward position relative to the hand. Usually the button used for releasing the shutter is located on the camera body in a position to minimise camera shake. This body release may often also serve to operate a reflex mirror, automatic diaphragm or an exposure metering mechanism before the shutter is actually released. The button usually has an internal thread to accept a cable release. Some shutters are released by pressure on a small lever on the shutter casing; these also usually have provision for a cable release. Several cameras accept a motor drive which, when the release is depressed, will advance the film and release the shutter at rates of up to several frames per second. Remote control units for shutter release actuated by radio or electrical impulses are commonly available.

The diaphragm
For a number of reasons, which were discussed in earlier chapters, the beam of light passing through a photographic lens is limited by means of a diaphragm or stop in which is an aperture usually approximately circular in shape. In some simple cameras the aperture is fixed in size. In others the diaphragm consists of a disc bearing several circular apertures and capable of rotation so that any one of the apertures may be brought into position in line with the lens. This arrangement of fixed apertures is often used in fish-eye lenses as well. For

some graphic arts purposes the lens aperture must be known very precisely; interchangeable metal plates each with a different aperture are then used. Such fixed apertures are known as *Waterhouse stops*.

Such an arrangement is limited in scope and so the majority of lenses are fitted with *iris diaphragms,* the leaves of which may be varied, forming an approximately circular aperture of a continuously variable diameter. When the camera shutter is of the between-lens type the diaphragm is normally part of the shutter assembly.

The diaphragm is operated by a rotating ring, usually with click stops at half-stop intervals, calibrated in the standard series of f-numbers (page 69). The interval between marked values will be constant if the diaphragm blades are designed to give such a scale, otherwise, on older lenses with multi-bladed diaphragms the scale is a square-law one with cramping together of calibrations at the small aperture end, $f/11, f/16$ etc.

The maximum aperture of a lens is not necessarily a fixed value on the scale but may be an intermediate value, e.g., $f/3 \cdot 5$. The minimum aperture for lenses on small-format cameras is seldom less than $f/16$ or $f/22$, but for lenses on large-format cameras, minimum values of $f/32$ to $f/64$ are common.

As noted earlier, many cameras have the aperture and shutter speed settings linked together to give a single number scale calibrated in *exposure values,* for use in conjunction with specially calibrated exposure meters.

With the increase in use of the single-lens reflex camera came a demand for automatic selection of the chosen aperture just prior to exposure. This would permit viewing and focusing at full aperture until the shutter was released.

On the earliest forms of these cameras, the lens had to be stopped down by reference to the scale. The introduction of click-stops assisted in this process. Then a pre-setting device was introduced which, by means of a twist on the aperture ring, stopped the lens down to the pre-selected aperture and no further. The next step was to introduce a spring mechanism into this type of diaphragm that was triggered by the shutter release. Operation was easier and the sequence speeded up but the spring had to be reset after each exposure and the diaphragm re-opened to its maximum value. This was known as the *semi-automatic diaphragm.* Finally, with the advent of the instant-return-mirror came the *fully-automatic diaphragm.* An actuating lever or similar device in the camera, when operated by the shutter release, closed the diaphragm down, usually against a spring, during the shutter operation. When the shutter closed the diaphragm was released and re-opened to coincide with the return of the reflex mirror to permit full-aperture viewing again. A manual override is normally fitted for depth-of-field inspection. Certain cameras with through-the-lens metering (page 191) necessitate exposure measurement being carried out at the desired working aperture, so this mechanism is essential.

Extension tubes usually transmit the actuation pressure for diaphragm operation but extension bellows do not and manual operation or a double cable release is required.

As the lens focal length increases the problems of fitting a fully-automatic diaphragm increase; the diaphragms of most very long-focus lenses, therefore have to be set manually. A limited number employ electromagnetic diaphragm operation.

In general, the lenses fitted to large-format technical cameras are manually operated, although some pre-setting devices are available. When an electronic shutter is fitted to such a lens, the diaphragm opening may be selected from a remote control box and operated electrically.

Function of viewfinder

The function of the viewfinder is to indicate the limits of the field of view of the camera lens in use and to enable the user to select and compose the picture. Normally, apart from simple cameras, the viewfinder also incorporates a method for focusing the lens by means of a rangefinder or a ground-glass screen. The type of viewfinder used often determines the shape and size of a camera, as with the twin-lens reflex type, and the popularity of a camera may be related to the ease of use of the viewfinder, especially if spectacles are worn.

Simple viewfinders

The simplest finders, as fitted to early box cameras and as a supplement to the ground glass screen of a technical camera, employed a positive lens of about 25 mm focal length, a mirror inclined at 45° and a ground glass upon which the image was viewed. This finder was used at waist level and the illumination of the image was poor.

This early type of finder has been superseded by the "brilliant" finder which employs in place of the ground glass a second positive lens, of such a power as to image the first lens in the plane of the viewer's eyes, giving greatly improved illumination. Such finders are still occasionally found on simple cameras.

The need for a simple finder for use at eye level introduced the wire frame finder. A wire or metal open frame, in the same proportions as the negative format, was viewed through a small "peep-sight" to define the subject area. This type of finder is often available as an accessory and is most compact when collapsed. Refinements to the simple design gave exact delineation of the subject area and parallax compensation. Once much favoured for use on press cameras of the large format type, its use is now mainly confined to technical, aerial and underwater cameras.

Direct-vision optical viewfinders

At one time most small- and medium-format cameras employed a "direct-vision" finder for use at eye-level. In the simplest optical type, a strongly diverging lens is used to form a virtual image which is viewed through a weak positive lens. This type of viewfinder – sometimes termed a Newton finder – is, in effect, a reversed Galilean telescope, the two lenses combining to produce a bright virtual image, erect and the right way round. A great improvement on this viewfinder type – the Albada finder – has a mask bearing a white frame line in front of the positive lens, and the negative lens has a semisilvered rear surface. As a result, the white line is seen superimposed on the virtual image (Figure 11.8). The view through the finder extends beyond the frame line so that objects outside the scene can be

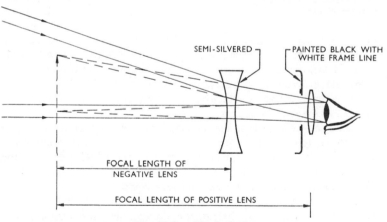

Fig. 11.8 – Albada finder

viewed. This is a great aid in composing, especially if the subject is in motion. The eye may be moved laterally without altering the boundary of the scene. This type of finder has been considerably refined in recent years, e.g., in the Leica M series of cameras, where different frames for lenses of various focal lengths may be brought into use in turn. Other refinements are compensation for viewfinder parallax error by movement of the frame with the focusing mechanism and a reduction in the mask area when focusing at closer range. Unfortunately, this finder, while excellent for wide-angle lenses, is unsatisfactory for lenses longer than 135 mm focal length for the 24 × 36 mm format. The subject area covered may, in this case, be indicated by a small frame of an approximate size to the range-finder image in the same viewfinder. The increasing viewfinder error makes this type of finder unsuitable for close-up work.

The image size as seen in such a viewfinder is usually about 0·7 × to 0·9 × life-size. Simpler cameras with a non-interchangeable lens often have a finder giving a life-size image so that both eyes may remain open, giving the impression of a frame superimposed on the scene.

For technical cameras, the advanced type of range-viewfinder is often used and a zoom-type Albada viewfinder is available for use with a variety of lenses.

Ground glass screen viewfinders

Many of the earliest types of camera used a plain ground glass screen upon which the image from the lens was composed and focused, and then replaced by a plate or film holder in order to make the exposure.

This system is still in use on technical cameras, where the inverted and laterally reversed image on the ground glass screen usually causes no inconvenience. The advantages of exact assessment of subject area covered by the lens, and accurate focusing, offset the disadvantages.

For the majority of small- and medium-format cameras a reflex system is used, where a surface-silvered mirror inclined at 45° to the optical axis gives an image on a ground glass screen. The image is the same size as it will appear on the negative, and upright, but is still laterally reversed. Viewing and focusing is by a separate lens on the twin-lens reflex camera and by the actual camera taking lens on the single-lens reflex type. Focusing is carried out at waist level using the unaided eye or a flip-up magnifier in the viewfinder hood. Unlike the single-lens reflex type, the twin-lens reflex camera suffers from field-of-view error, and a mask or indicator in the viewfinder, provided to compensate for this defect, may be coupled to the focusing mechanism.

The presence of the mirror in the viewfinder system of a single lens reflex camera has led to a number of refinements in camera design. The most common requirement is for an instant-return mirror (with an adequate braking system to avoid camera shake). Cameras without this facility have the viewfinder blanked out until the mirror is returned to the viewing position when the film is advanced to the next frame. The mirror may be locked up to enable certain wide-angle lenses to be used. An accessory optical viewfinder is then needed. A common practice in single-lens reflex cameras is to introduce a deliberate viewfinder error in that the area as seen on the ground glass screen may be less, by about 10 per cent. per dimension, than the area included on the negative. The reason usually quoted is to overcome differences in aperture size in transparency mounts. One or two cameras, however, do indicate the actual area included on the negative.

While a ground glass screen gives positive indication of correct focus, a plain screen is not always preferred, because it gives a rather dim image with a rapid fall-off in illumination towards the corners. Evenness of illumination is improved if the screen is etched on the flat base of a plano-convex lens or if a fresnel screen is used, but only at the expense of accurate focusing. Small format cameras, therefore, usually have a supplementary focusing aid incorporated in the centre of the screen. This may be a clear spot with cross-hairs in order to assist in focusing the aerial image, split-image rangefinder (Figure 11.11), or a microprism screen. Many cameras have interchangeable viewing screens to suit the user. With all these screens, however, if the reflex mirror is of inadequate dimensions, there will be a progressive loss of illumination on the top of the screen with increase in focal length of camera lens. This cut-off is not obtained on the negative, of course.

With all reflex systems the lateral reversal of the image is most troublesome for certain types of photography, especially when the subject is moving. Direct-vision can often be obtained by pushing down the front flap, but focusing is then not normally possible. Fortunately, the introduction of the pentaprism viewfinder for both 24 × 36 mm and 60 × 60 mm formats has given a method of focusing an upright, right-way-round and magnified image (Figure 10.4) and has been a major cause of the popularity of the single-lens reflex camera. These prism finders are sometimes interchangeable with waist-level finders and many have provision for eyepiece correction lenses to obviate the use of spectacles, if normally worn. The viewfinder prism may also incorporate a through-the-lens exposure metering system for measurements from the ground glass. With the introduction of such exposure measurement systems the viewfinder of many such cameras has acquired more functions. Warning signals may appear to indicate, typically, that an exposure time longer than 1/30th second is needed. The shutter speed or aperture in use may be shown on an adjacent, illuminated scale. The exposure meter needle and matching pointer to give correct exposure may also be visible, see Figure 11.14.

The focusing mechanism

While many lenses can be used satisfactorily as fixed-focus objectives, relying upon depth of field to give adequate sharpness, the situation alters when using lenses of large aperture or long focal length, and for close-up work. To ensure that the subject may be sharply focused at the focal plane of the camera it is then necessary to have a means of altering the lens-to-film distance and to have a visual indication of focus linked to the focusing mechanism.

Front cell focusing

For reasons of economy in simple cameras, and those fitted with between-lens shutters, focusing may be achieved by varying the focal length of the lens and not by varying the lens-to-film distance. This is achieved by mounting the front element in a cell with a coarse pitch screw thread. Rotation of the cell alters the separation between the front element and other glasses of the lens. A slight alteration in separation causes an appreciable change in focal length, giving a useful focusing range. Close focusing is not possible because the lens aberrations that would then be introduced would badly affect performance. A distance scale is engraved on the rotating cell.

Movement of entire lens

This is the best method of focusing and is achieved in various ways. Technical cameras of the baseboard type employ a rack-and-pinion or friction device to move the lens panel for focusing by ground glass screen or rangefinder. Back (as well as front) focusing is common on the monorail type and is most useful in applications such as copying, because back focusing alters the focus only, whereas front focusing alters the size of the image as well as its focus.

Small-format cameras generally use helical focusing, where rotation of an annular ring on the lens barrel moves the lens bodily in an axial direction. Rotation of the lens is undesirable as the various scales would not be fully visible at all times.

The operation of visually focusing the subject is achieved by use of a visual rangefinder system or a ground glass screen. In the majority of cameras the rangefinder is coupled to the focusing mechanism, but built-in, uncoupled rangefinders are occasionally encountered.

Rangefinders

Coincidence-type rangefinders usually employ two windows some distance apart, through each of which an image of the object is obtained. Both pictures are viewed together, one directly and the other after deviation by a system of mirrors (Figure 11.9). If the second

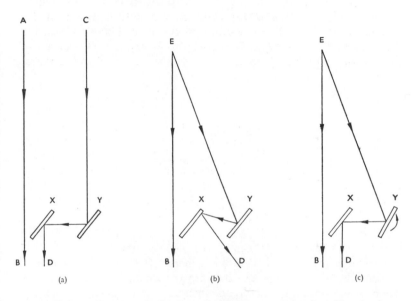

In (a), AB and CD are two rays proceeding from the same point on a distant object. AB reaches the eye directly and CD after deviation by two mirrors X and Y. The images coincide.

In (b), the object is nearer, at E. The mirrors are in the same position as in (a) but the images are no longer coincident.

In (c), mirror Y has been rotated to bring the images into coincidence. The degree of rotation is a measure of the distance of E.

Fig. 11.9 – Principle of the visual rangefinder

beam is directed through two successive right angles, and if the objects in the field of view are a long way away, the two fields will be identical. If they are arranged to fall one upon another they will coincide exactly. Alternatively, if the system is a split field one, the two halves will link up. If the rangefinder is directed at nearer objects the two fields will not be identical, but they can be made so by altering the degree of deviation of the second beam. For a given distance between the windows (base length), the amount by which one beam must be redirected to bring the two images into coincidence is a measure of the distance of the object.

In many rangefinders the variable deviation is brought about by altering the angle of a hinged mirror, as in Figure 11.9. Unfortunately, the adjustment is a rather coarse one, the complete range from 1 metre to infinity being represented by an angle of rotation of only about 3°. The difficulty is overcome in certain cameras by using, instead of a hinged mirror, two rotating wedges as shown in Figure 11.10. The

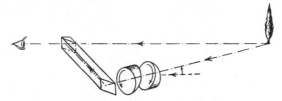

Fig. 11.10 – Rotating wedge coincidence adjustment

range from 1 metre to infinity is then represented by a rotation of almost 90°.

Operating upon a different principle, because it has no moving parts, is the so-called *split-image rangefinder* fitted to the focusing screens of many single-lens reflex cameras. It consists of two small semicircular glass prisms inserted into the focusing screen itself. As will be seen from Figure 11.11, any image which is not exactly in focus on the central area of the focusing screen appears split into two displaced halves. These join up as the image is brought into focus, in the same way as the two halves of the field in a conventional coincidence-type rangefinder. An array of minute prisms operating in this manner is termed a *microprism grid* and gives a distinctive appearance to an unsharp image.

The ground glass screen
Use of the ground glass screen has been dealt with under the section relating to viewfinders (page 182). It has the great advantages of giving a positive indication of focus and allowing the depth of field to be estimated. No complex linkage between lens and viewfinder is necessary, only a mirror if reflex focusing is used.

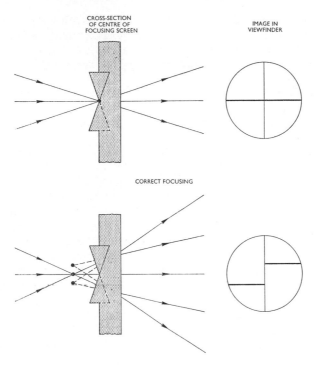

CROSS-SECTION
OF CENTRE OF
FOCUSING SCREEN

IMAGE IN
VIEWFINDER

CORRECT FOCUSING

INCORRECT FOCUSING

Fig. 11.11 – Principle of the split-image rangefinder

Both rangefinder and ground glass screen methods have their particular advantages and disadvantages. The coincidence-type rangefinder may normally be employed to focus a lens from infinity to about 1 metre; closer focusing to about 0·5 metre requires accessory optical devices of limited use. The rangefinder mechanism must be robust to withstand occasional knocks. The accuracy of the distance setting is determined by the base length, which determines the longest focal length of lens that may be used. Typically this is 135 mm focal length for the 24 × 36 mm format; after this, ground-glass focusing must be used with a reflex attachment. However, a rangefinder is very useful for focusing wide-angle lenses of short focus, which are difficult to focus on a ground-glass screen owing to their great depth of field. A rangefinder is also most easy to use in poor or adverse light conditions.

A ground glass screen may be used to focus any lens that could be fitted to the camera, but the accuracy of focusing depends partly upon eyesight. Consequently, a supplementary device such as a microprism is useful. In use, a magnifier and hood to screen extraneous light from the screen are essential. Even with these aids, the focusing of long focus lenses of small aperture in poor light is still difficult.

Focusing scales

The majority of lenses are focused without reference to the distance scale engraved in metres (and also, usually, feet) on the focusing knob or ring, when the rangefinder or ground glass screen is used. It is essential to retain these figures, however, for two reasons. First, for reference when flash is being used, so that the aperture may be correctly set according to the flash guide number. Certain lenses incorporate a degree of automation in that the flash guide number may be set on a scale on the lens barrel. The aperture is then made to alter automatically in accordance with the focusing and thus gives constant exposure as the distance from the flash-gun (on the camera) to the subject is varied. Secondly, the distance figures give the depth-of-field by reference to the appropriate scale. Many cameras have automatic depth-of-field indicators linked to the aperture scale as well as to the focusing mechanism.

As the focal length of a lens determines the amount of extension necessary for focusing upon a nearby subject, the closest marked distance on a focusing scale varies with the lens. The small extension required with wide-angle, short-focus lenses means that many have provision for focusing down to a few centimetres. The standard lenses fitted to 24 × 36 mm format cameras commonly focus down to approximately 0·5 metre without supplementary devices.

Some standard lenses (usually of special design), termed *macro lenses*, are provided with a focusing mount with sufficient extension to permit continuous focusing down to 1 : 1 reproduction. Such lenses usually also have an additional scale of exposure increase factors on the lens mount. It is interesting to note that in certain lenses which may be focused closer than normal, the focusing mechanism is linked to the iris diaphragm which is opened to compensate for the increase in exposure required. Long-focus lenses fitted to 24 × 36 mm format cameras seldom focus closer than about 2 to 10 metres (depending on focal length) without recourse to extension tubes or bellows. In the case of technical cameras, the long extension of the bellows and the possibility of increasing it by an additional bellows, makes for a very versatile focusing system. Often a "bag" bellows is required with short-focus lenses, because the ridged type will not compress sufficiently to allow focusing to infinity.

Finally, the ease of use of a focusing mechanism on a camera or lens should be considered. Focusing rings, knobs and levers of varying sizes and width are found on lenses and camera bodies. On most of these the amount of friction, ease of gripping and direction of rotation to focus down from infinity are different. This may cause difficulties in changing from one lens or camera to another until the necessary mental adjustment is made. Many lenses have two or three raised rings on the lens barrel to alter aperture or shutter speed, focus and perhaps focal length if the lens is of a zoom type. These lens rings have to be most carefully designed so as not to confuse functions. Zoom lenses often have a "trombone" mechanism where rotation of a broad ring alters focus, and sliding it axially alters focal length. There is room for improvement in all such designs.

The exposure meter

The topic of camera exposure determination is fully dealt with in Chapter 20. The incorporation of an exposure meter into a camera body is a great convenience but the range of types available, each with advantages and disadvantages, presents a problem of selection for use. With the increased use of colour materials in preference to black-and-white, the need for accurate exposure assumed increasing importance. Separate exposure meters have been in use for many years, but the operation of transfering the indicated values of shutter speed and aperture from meter to camera is felt by many to be disadvantageous. A meter built in to the camera and coupled in some way to the controls would be preferable, giving more rapid operation with one piece of apparatus. Many manufacturers considered inclusion of an exposure meter more important than a focusing device such as a rangefinder. The evolution of the built-in meter has gone through several stages of increasing complexity, but before considering these it is useful to review the salient properties of the two types of photo-electric cell in use in exposure meters.

The selenium cell meter. Light-sensitive selenium is incorporated in a barrier-layer cell. On exposure to light an electric current is generated. A sensitive galvanometer in the circuit gives a deflection according to the amount of light incident on the cell and the necessary camera exposure is derived from a dial-type calculator. Sensitivity of the system is rather limited, depending on the area of the cell exposed to light. A baffling device usually limits the acceptance angle of the cell to approximately that of the camera with normal focus lens.

The cadmium sulphide cell meter. The action of light upon a cadmium sulphide (CdS) cell is to increase its conductance, i.e., lower its resistance, and hence increase the flow of current from a battery connected across the cell. A sensitive galvanometer in the circuit is calibrated accordingly. A small, long-life battery of constant voltage must be incorporated into the meter circuit. The cadmium sulphide cell may be of very small dimensions yet of greater sensitivity than a selenium cell. The spectral response is adjusted to approximate that of the selenium cell.

Accessory exposure meters
These are separate exposure meters but are specially produced for use on a camera.

Clip-on meters. Generally these are selenium cell meters of small dimensions to clip into the camera accessory shoe. They are not coupled to the camera and are of moderate sensitivity.

Coupled clip-on meters. These are also designed to fit into an accessory shoe but have a device to couple with the shutter speed or aperture setting controls. The reading given then indicates directly the other variable once the film speed has been set. They are obtainable as selenium or cadmium sulphide cell types and with a variety of acceptance angles.

Integral exposure meters
These meters are built into the camera body and are not removable. Many camera types are available in two body versions, with or without an integral meter. Cameras with such an exposure meter may be classified into one of two groups:—

(a) with the meter cell external to the camera body.

(b) with the meter cell inside the camera body and making light measurements through the lens (TTL metering).

Integral meters with external cells
Both selenium and CdS cells are used in a variety of shapes and sizes, located in various positions on the camera. Owing to the large size of selenium cells, these are generally located in the front plate of the camera or as an annulus around the lens. The acceptance angle of the cell generally matches that of the standard lens. The CdS cell, on the other hand, being smaller, has greater freedom of position, but is generally located behind a small aperture in the front plate or in the lens mount. The acceptance angle is usually smaller than that of the normal focus lens. Provision for a small battery and on-off switch for the meter cell must be made.

Both reflected and incident light readings are possible with these cells. The linking of the meter and camera controls is dealt with in the section on automatic exposure control (page 194).

Through-the-lens exposure measurement

A direct result of the small size and great sensitivity of the CdS type of cell was the possibility of taking reflected light readings from the subject through the camera lens by a suitable cell in the camera body. In theory, this would automatically compensate for the transmission of the lens in use, for any lens extension for close focusing and for the use of filters (with limitations). Measurement could be from all or only part of the subject covered by the lens in use. Such a system is most easily incorporated in a single-lens reflex camera. Many cameras of this type are available with a variety of TTL metering systems either fixed in the camera or as an option, by means of an alternative pentaprism housing incorporating the meter system.

Several problems are encountered in the design of a TTL metering system and current camera models reflect the variety of solutions possible.

Position of the meter cell

The CdS cell or cells used can take a variety of shapes and sizes without much effect on sensitivity, allowing great flexibility in their location within the camera body (Figure 11.12). Ideally, the cell should be located as near the film plane as possible, but the presence of the focal-plane shutter hinders this. A cell on a hinged arm to locate it just in front of the shutter is a reasonably satisfactory arrangement, but in general, measurements are best made in an *equivalent focal plane*. This is a plane located at the same distance from the exit pupil of the camera lens as the film plane. One such plane is that of the ground-glass screen used for focusing. Several cameras use a beam-splitter system to divert light from part of the screen to a cell located outside the screen area. The area used for measurement purposes is delineated on the screen and shows clearly the part of the subject being measured. Another equivalent focal plane is located in the base of the dark chamber of the camera body, beneath the reflex mirror. A partially transparent area of the main mirror transmits light from the camera lens via a small subsidiary mirror down into the well of the dark chamber where a cell is located.

A simple solution to cell location is to place the cell behind all or part of the reflex mirror, allowing light to reach it by an arrangement of slits in the mirror or by making the mirror partially transparent.

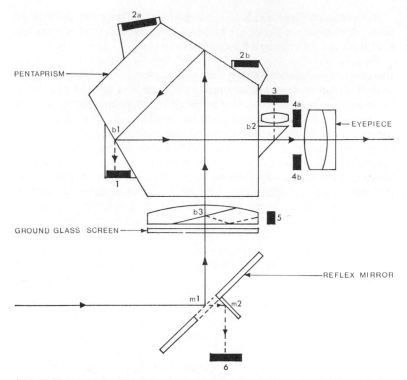

Fig. 11.12 – A selection of through-the-lens metering systems, showing the variations of meter cell position: 1, Cell giving integrated reading from ground-glass screen through pentaprism face via beamsplitter b1. *2a, 2b, Cells in series taking a form of weighted, integrated reading from ground-glass screen. 3, Cell giving reading from ground-glass screen via beamsplitter* b2. *Depending on design, fully integrated or centre-weighted readings are used. 4a, 4b, Cells about the eyepiece giving a fully integrated reading from the ground-glass screen. One cell may be used to correct for light from the eyepiece. 5, Cell reading in an equivalent focal plane via beamsplitter* b3. *Reading may be fully integrated or from a small area of screen. 6, Cell reading in an equivalent focal plane via partially transparent mirror* m1 *and supplementary mirror* m2. *A small area reading is given.*

Such an arrangement is unsatisfactory with interchangeable lenses if there is a change in position of the lens exit pupil. A different lens usually has its exit pupil nearer to or farther away from the mirror along the optical axis. The measurement area of the reflex mirror then intersects the cone of light from the lens exit pupil in a different position and samples a different cross-sectional area of the cone.

Another general solution to cell location is to position cells in the housing of the pentaprism or the eyepiece lens and use them to measure from the image on the ground-glass screen.

Such an arrangement necessitates a minimum amount of redesign of the camera and also permits an interchangeable pentaprism housing with TTL metering to be offered as part of a camera system. This latter alternative is favoured for 60 × 60 mm format cameras both of the twin-lens and single-lens reflex types. The cell or cells used are located either behind a pentaprism face or about the eyepiece lens. A single cell monitoring the whole of the screen area may be used, but generally two cells are employed to give a "weighted" reading favouring the centre of the screen. This is to offset uneven illumination of the screen caused by lenses of a variety of focal lengths.

Type of reading

The TTL metering system is based on measurement of the light reflected from the subject as transmitted by the optical system in use. The meter cell does not, however, always measure all the light from the subject area covered by the lens. Several different systems are employed (Figure 11.13). A "fully integrated" reading is a measure of

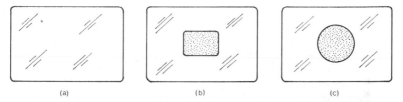

(a)   (b)   (c)

Fig. 11.13 – Types of meter readings used in cameras with through-the-lens exposure measurement: (a) Fully integrated from whole of screen area. (b) Small area or narrow angle. Only one-ninth of screen area used. (c) Weighted type. Central area contributes 60 per cent of reading; rest of screen area contributes the remaining 40 per cent.

all the light from the subject area and the exposure given is liable to all the usual variations caused by subject tonal distribution and luminance range. A "spot" reading is when a small area of the subject is measured, but, unlike the case when a photometer is used, a midtone must be selected for measurement and not a highlight or shadow only. The "small area" type of reading is an integrated reading of an area of the subject too large to be considered a spot reading but not a fully integrated one. The "weighted" reading is a compromise where the whole subject area is measured but the central portion of the subject as viewed contributes most towards the result given.

The multiplicity of methods of reading combined with the different locations possible for the meter cell give rise to the large number of variations in the TTL metering cameras on the market.

Calibration

The variety of designs raises a problem in calibration of the meter system used as there is no generally agreed method. The method used in most cases, however, is based upon "pegging" the selected area as a mid-tone.

Sensitivity

Although a cadmium sulphide cell is used, the sensitivity obtained in a TTL metering system is generally only of the same order as a good selenium cell meter for hand use. This is due to the great absorption of light by the optical and viewing system of the camera.

Operation of the meter

While it is a great convenience to have an exposure metering system in the camera, the method used to set the camera at the indicated exposure varies somewhat between makes of camera. There are a number of steps involved. First, the battery to power the CdS cell must be switched on. Then the subject must be sharply focused and the appropriate area selected for measurement. In semi-automatic models either the shutter speed or lens aperture is first selected and set, and then the other variable set as indicated by the meter. Normally this is done by aligning a pair of needles visible in the viewfinder. One needle is operated by the meter cell and the other is matched to it by adjustment of the lens aperture or shutter speed control. Often another scale is visible in the viewfinder indicating the shutter speed or aperture selected. The majority of cameras make full-aperture measurements but a few require that the lens be stopped down to the pre-selected aperture for measurement. The latter system has disadvantages.

In fully automatic cameras the aperture is pre-selected and the CdS cell operates the timing circuit of the electronic shutter for the time required.

Automatic exposure control

The provision of an exposure meter integral with the camera makes possible several methods of exposure control of varying degrees of automation.

Uncoupled. When using an uncoupled exposure meter, the exposure required is read off the meter scales and transferred manually to the shutter speed and aperture setting rings. This meter reading may be simplified as a single number, termed an *exposure value* (page 327) and the shutter speed and aperture rings are linked and calibrated accordingly.

Cross-coupled or follow-pointer. With this type of integral exposure meter the meter needle has a pointer coaxial with it, moving over the same range but connected by a linkage to the shutter speed and aperture controls. Either may be pre-selected and the other is then set for the indicated exposure by altering the setting control to match the pointer with the meter needle. No calibrations or markings are necessary on the meter scale. The two needles or pointers are often visible in the viewfinder to facilitate operations. This system is much used in TTL metering cameras (Figure 11.14). A manual over-ride is usually provided for atypical subjects and for flash work.

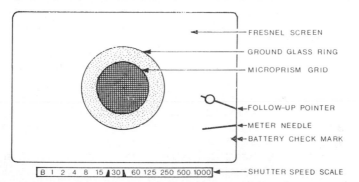

Fig. 11.14 – Typical viewfinder arrangement in a single-lens reflex camera with through-the-lens metering

Programmed shutter. The programmed shutter has a limited range of speeds, usually 1/30th to 1/500th second, and three modes of operation. One is for flash work when the meter connection is uncoupled and the shutter speed set to 1/30th second. Apertures are then set manually as required. The second is for other occasions when manual setting is desired. The third possibility is the automatic mode when both the shutter setting and the lens aperture are linked to the meter needle. The shutter is programmed so that it will remain at a fixed speed while the whole aperture range is used to match the meter needle. If the light is inadequate or excessive at the largest or smallest aperture setting respectively, then the shutter speed will change to a slower or higher speed to enable the correct aperture to be set. This method ensures that the highest possible shutter speed is used in all circumstances. There are variations in this method of programming. A typical shutter is programmed to give exposures ranging from 1/30th second at $f/2\cdot8$ to 1/500th second at $f/22$.

Some cameras have no visible calibrations for shutter speed or aperture when a programmed shutter is used; a single ring only is turned to align two pointers in the metering system.

Automatic control. The meter movement may be used to adjust automatically the iris diaphragm in accordance with a pre-selected shutter speed, but this system is not common in still cameras. The preferred method is to use a CdS meter cell in an electronic shutter timing circuit and vary the exposure duration according to a pre-selected aperture. The range may be from 30 seconds to 1/200th second in a typical shutter. A warning is given when a exposure of longer than 1/30th second is needed so that a tripod may be used.

Flash synchronization
In the early days of flash photography it was customary to set the camera on a tripod, open the shutter, fire the flash and close the shutter. As the manufacture of flashbulbs progressed, bulbs were produced which were sufficiently reliable for them to be synchronized with the camera shutter. This made it possible for flash to be used with the shutter set to give an instantaneous exposure, and the camera could therefore be hand-held. At first, a separate synchronizer was attached to the camera but it is now usual for flash contacts to be incorporated in the shutter itself.

The synchronization of between-lens and focal-plane shutters presents two different problems. With a between-lens shutter, the aim in synchronizing is to arrange for the peak of the flash to coincide with the period that the shutter blades are fully open. In all shutters there is a delay between the moment of release and the time when the blades start to open (approx. 2 to 5 milliseconds), and a further slight delay before the blades are fully open. With flashbulbs also there is a delay after firing, while the igniter wire becomes heated, before combustion occurs and light is produced. Whereas the delay with shutters is fairly constant, the delay with flashbulbs varies widely from one type of bulb to another (see Chapter 3), so that for synchronization

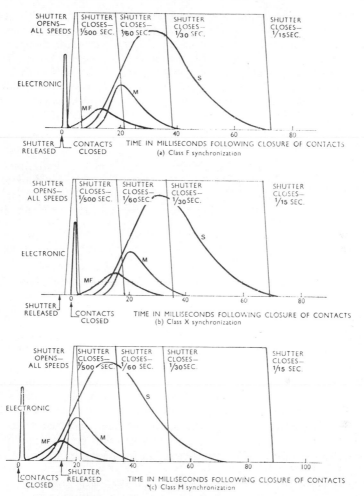

Fig. 11.15 – Flashbulb light output curves shown in relation to shutter performance curves for different types of synchronization

with different types of bulb, several different classes of synchronization have been introduced. These are as follows:

(1) Class F
With this class of synchronization the shutter is released and electrical contact is made simultaneously. Class F contacts are intended for use

with class MF and class M flashbulbs at speeds not faster than 1/40th second. They are *not* suitable for use with electronic flash tubes.

(2) Class X

With this class of synchronization electrical contact is made when the shutter blades are just fully open. Class X contacts are intended for use with electronic flash at all shutter speeds. They are also suitable for use with class MF and class M flashbulbs at speeds up to 1/30th second and with class S flashbulbs at speeds up to 1/15 second.

(3) Class M

With this class of synchronization it is arranged that the shutter blades are fully open approximately 17 milliseconds after electrical contact is made. This requires a delay mechanism, and one similar to that employed for the slower speeds in preset shutters is commonly employed.

Type of synchronization on camera	Type of flash Class MF bulbs	Class M bulbs	Class S bulbs	Electronic flash
F	Up to 1/40	Up to 1/40	Up to 1/15	—
X	Up to 1/30	Up to 1/30	Up to 1/15	All speeds
M	—	All speeds	Up to 1/60	—

Table 11.2 – Shutter speeds suitable for different types of flash synchronization with between-lens shutters

Class M contacts are intended for use with class M bulbs at all speeds – including the fastest; they are also suitable for use with class S bulbs at speeds not faster than 1/60th second. They are *not* suitable for use with class MF flashbulbs or electronic flash tubes.

The range of shutter speeds suitable for different types of flashbulb and flash synchronization is illustrated in Figure 11.15 and shown in tabular form in Table 11.2.

It is usual in inexpensive cameras for the flash contacts to be arranged to give class F synchronization; this permits the use of flashbulbs at relatively slow shutter speeds, but not electronic flash.

Cameras with multispeed shutters usually have two types of synchronization – X and M. The X setting permits the use of electronic flash and class MF bulbs at slow speeds; the M setting permits the use of class M bulbs at all speeds and class S bulbs at slow speeds. In practice, it is usual to reserve use of the M setting, which involves the operation of the delay mechanism, for exposures with class M bulbs at speeds of 1/60th and over, i.e., for exposures which cannot be made with X synchronization. A "V" setting on a multispeed shutter with both X and M synchronization gives delayed-action exposures with X synchronization. A camera with both X and M contacts is sometimes described as "fully synchronized".

Synchronization of focal-plane shutters

Synchronization of focal-plane shutters presents a special problem. Exposures with electronic flash and most ordinary types of expendable flashbulb can be made only at low shutter speeds, when the whole film is uncovered simultaneously. At faster speeds, special slow-burning "focal-plane" (class FP) bulbs are generally necessary. The emission of these bulbs rises to a plateau rather than a peak, giving almost constant output for the whole of the time that it takes the shutter blind to travel across the film.

As focal-plane shutters vary considerably in design and in the speed of travel of the shutter blinds, it is essential to consult the camera instruction book before using flash equipment with a camera fitted with a focal-plane shutter.

Unlike the fully-synchronized between-lens shutter which has only one flash connection and a two-position switch for X or M selection, focal-plane shutters may have one, two or even three flash connections. If only one, unmarked, outlet is fitted to the camera the flash delay must be selected by a separate control, usually coaxial with the shutter speed dial. A pair of outlets may be marked X and M or, more commonly, X and FP. Use of the appropriate one of these with a suitable shutter speed automatically gives correct synchronization. Shutter speeds may be colour coded to assist setting a correct speed for the type of flash in use. In general, class MF and M bulbs are used at shutter speeds up to 1/15th second using the X setting or outlet. Use of higher speeds requires a class FP bulb and use of the FP setting or outlet. Electronic flash is widely used with focal-plane shutters. Depending upon the type of shutter, synchronization may be possible up to a speed of 1/125th second. Shutters with blades travelling vertically generally synchronise at the higher speeds of 1/60th and 1/125th second, but this is restricted to 24 × 36 mm format cameras. Synchronization of class MF and class M bulbs is also extended to 1/60th second in such cameras.

CHAPTER 12

Camera Movements

ON technical cameras, and to a lesser extent on certain other types of cameras, provision is made for movement of the lens axis relative to the film plane. The purpose of such camera movements is to permit control of the centring, focusing and "shape" of the image on the film. The movements are made on the lens panel and on the camera back and can be grouped under three main headings:

(1) Sliding lens panel.
(2) Swinging and tilting camera back.
(3) Swinging and tilting lens panel.

Sliding lens panel
A lens board which is free to slide vertically (up and down) permits the movements of *rising front* and *falling front*. If it is free to slide horizontally, i.e., sideways, the movement is described as *cross front*.

The function of these movements is to permit the image to be *centred* on the film without moving the camera; the shape and focus of the image are not affected by the movements.

The rising front is an indispensable movement in architectural photography. When photographing buildings – especially tall ones – we frequently have to tilt the camera up (assuming that there are no movements on it) in order to include the whole of the building in the picture. The result is that vertical lines in the picture converge to the top, producing an effect which usually appears unnatural. The reason for the convergence is that the top of the building is farther from the camera than the bottom, and therefore appears smaller on the film. We can avoid converging verticals in the negative only by keeping the film plane parallel to the building, i.e., vertical, when the greater distance of the top of the building is offset by the greater distance from the lens to the image of this part. However, if we do keep the camera level, we shall (unless we go back a long way – which even if practicable may result in an unacceptably small image) lose the top of the building again. The rising front provides the solution to this problem. With its aid we can keep the camera level to obtain a distortion-free image, and move this image across the film until the whole building is included on the negative. See Figure 12.1.

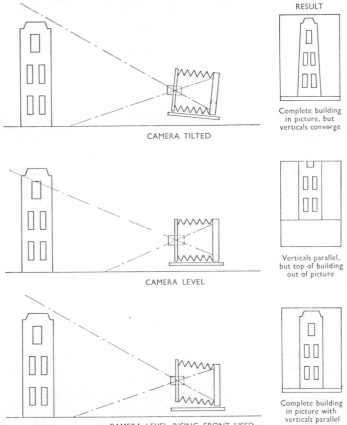

Fig. 12.1 – Use of rising front in architectural photography

If a photograph is to be taken looking down from a high viewpoint, as is often the case when photographing small objects, the *falling front* movement can be introduced to prevent, in this case, *diverging* verticals.

When distortion cannot be avoided in the negative, e.g., because the required camera movements are not fitted, a certain amount of correction of distorted verticals can be obtained by introducing an equal and opposite distortion at the enlarging stage (page 385). However, the degree of distortion that can be corrected satisfactorily in the enlarger is usually quite small and there is always a danger of foreshortening or elongating the image. For these reasons, every effort should be made at the camera stage to avoid distorted verticals.

Whereas a sliding front is essential in architectural work, use of this movement is by no means confined to architecture. In copying, for example, it is usually desirable to fill the negative area to make the most use of the photographic material, and accurate centring of the image is therefore normally required. The movements of rising and cross front provide a ready and positive means of making final adjustments to this centring, avoiding the need for the tedious process of making small adjustments to the position of the camera as a whole, or of the copy on the easel.

A cross front may be used to obtain a square view of the front of a building when it is impossible to set up the camera in a central position, e.g., because of an obstruction such as a tree. The movement is also useful for centring the image on any occasion when the position of the camera is restricted by limitations of space, to avoid an undesirable background, or to avoid reflections from a shiny surface such as an oil painting.

Swinging and tilting camera back

The movement by which the camera back is permitted to swing from side to side about a vertical axis is termed *swing back*, and the movement by which the back is permitted to tilt backwards and forwards about a horizontal axis is termed *tilting back*. The functions of these movements are two-fold:

(1) They permit control of parallel or converging lines in the image; i.e., they control the *shape* (parallelism) of the image.

(2) They can be used to control the region of sharp *focus*, e.g., to enable sharp focus of an object in depth to be obtained over the entire negative area.

The centring of the image is not usually seriously affected by these movements. Whether it is affected at all depends on the location of the axes about which the camera back is made to pivot.

As with the movements provided by the sliding front, the movements on the camera back – tilting back in particular – are especially valuable in architectural work. In this field, the tilting back may be used to provide, in effect, additional "rising front", for, when the rising front movement provided proves insufficient for a given subject, the camera may be tilted upwards to include the view required and the back tilted forwards to bring the film into the vertical plane again, to avoid converging verticals.

Sometimes the swing and tilting back movements are useful not for preventing distortion of the image but to *introduce* distortion for artistic or commercial effect (e.g., to make cars look longer than they really are, to make toys appear massive and realistic, to emphasize vertical lines in clothing or to make a short fashion model appear tall).

As far as control of focus is concerned, the movements on the camera back are valuable for increasing the effective depth of field in a variety of types of work. Examples are:

(a) When taking "group" photographs – to ensure that people in the front and back rows are in focus simultaneously.

(b) In studio portraiture – to bring, for example, a shoulder into sharp focus simultaneously with the face, without stopping down.

(c) In the commercial photography of small objects, where depth of field is usually very small.

It is a help in deciding which way to move the swing or tilting back to control focus to bear in mind that the farther the subject (or part of the subject) is from the camera the nearer must the film be to the lens. Another rule which helps in this connection is given on page 205.

It is important to note that, when swing or tilt is imparted to the camera back, both the shape and focus of the image are affected simultaneously. Thus, if we tilt the back to avoid convergence of verticals it will frequently be more difficult than before to obtain sharp focus over the entire subject. In such circumstances we shall normally have to stop down to increase depth of field, unless we can tilt the lens panel as described below. In the same way, when we swing or tilt the back to control the focus over an object we shall also alter its shape. Control of focus by movement of the camera back is therefore usually permissible only when the correct shape of objects is unimportant, as for example in landscape work and other subjects which do not include manifestly straight lines in their composition. As we shall see in the following section, the swing *front* permits control of overall focus without affecting the shape of the image.

Swinging and tilting lens panel

The third important group of movements are *swing front* – achieved when the lens panel is made to swing from side to side about a vertical axis – and *tilting front* – achieved when the lens panel tilts backwards and forwards about a horizontal axis. These movements affect overall *focus* of the image without altering its shape. Centring of the image may be affected to some extent, depending on the location of the axes about which the lens panel moves. The fact that the shape of the image is not altered makes the front swing and tilt very valuable for controlling focus when the "shape" of objects is important and use of the swing back for this purpose is inadmissible.

Apart from the effect on the shape of the image, there is one other difference between the use of swing (or tilting) front and swing (or tilting) back to control focus. When the front movement is used the image moves to the edge of the field; with swing back this does not happen. Thus, use of swing front to control focus is quickly limited by the covering power of the lens, and, even within this limit, definition may fall off because the edge of the field is being employed. This limitation applies, of course, not only to swing front but to any movement – including, e.g., rising front – which results in the image moving to the edge of the field. Hence, if movements are to be used freely, a lens with very good covering power is required (page 84).

In architectural photography we have already seen that when the tilting back is used to obtain increased "rising front", difficulty is found in obtaining overall sharp focus. If, however, a tilting front movement is available this difficulty can be overcome, without stopping down, by tilting the lens panel forwards until the lens axis is again at right angles to the film. This is illustrated in Figure 12.2.

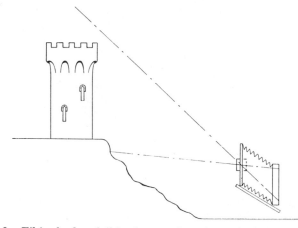

Fig. 12.2 – Tilting back and tilting front used together to give increased rising front

It may sometimes happen that the camera has sufficient rising front but the covering power of the lens is inadequate. The swing front can then be used to bring the film within the normal angle of covering power of the lens, it being assumed that in this instance sufficient depth of field can be obtained merely by stopping down.

A *swing* front is a less usual movement than a tilting front. Usually a swing back can be safely used to control overall focus in this direction (i.e., from left to right of the picture), for, although "converging horizontals" are introduced by using the swing back, these are not usually objectionable – certainly by no means as objectionable as converging verticals.

Condition for overall sharp focus
When the movements of swing or tilting front or back are used to obtain sharp focus over the whole of the negative area of an object with depth, the optimum position of the various parts of the camera for overall focus is obtained when lines lying in the plane of the subject, lens panel and film plane meet in a single point. This is illustrated in Figure 12.3.

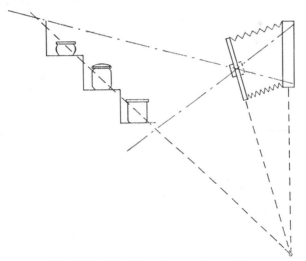

Fig. 12.3 – Condition for overall sharp focus

In the special case where the subject plane, lens panel and film plane are all parallel, the lines can be considered to meet at infinity.

Drop baseboard
On a camera provided with front focusing only, use of a wide-angle lens may result in a cutting off of the lower part of the field by the

baseboard – which projects in front of the lens. (Where back focusing is provided, the trouble can be avoided by keeping the lens board well forward.) To avoid this cut-off, provision is sometimes made for the baseboard to drop down until it is clear of the field (Figure 12.4). This movement is standard on technical cameras of the folding type with hinged baseboard.

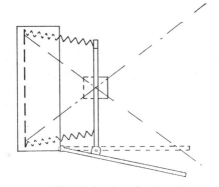

Fig. 12.4 – Drop baseboard

Reversing and rotating backs

A *reversing back* is a standard movement on most stand cameras and reflex cameras; i.e., the camera back may be positioned with the film or plate in either the horizontal or the vertical position. Occasionally, the back is made so that it can be revolved to any desired position; this is termed a *rotating back*.

CHAPTER 13

The Sensitive Material

MANY light-sensitive substances are known, widely varying in their sensitivity. In the manufacture of photographic materials, reliance is placed almost entirely upon the light sensitivity of the *silver halides*, the salts formed by the combination of silver with members of the group of elements known as the halogens – bromine, chlorine and iodine.

Photographic materials are coated with suspensions of minute crystals of silver halide in a binding agent – nowadays almost invariably gelatin. These photographic suspensions are called *emulsions*, although they are not emulsions in the true sense of the word. The crystals are commonly referred to as *grains*. In materials designed for the production of negatives, the halide employed is usually silver bromide, in which small quantities of iodide are also normally present. With papers and other positive materials the halide used may be silver bromide, silver chloride or a mixture of the two. The use of two silver halides in one emulsion results not in two kinds of grains but in grains in which both halides are present, although not necessarily in the same proportion in all grains. Photographic materials containing both silver bromide and silver iodide are referred to as iodobromide materials, and materials containing both silver chloride and silver bromide as chlorobromide materials.

A property which makes the use of the silver halides particularly attractive in photography is that they are *developable*. By this we mean that the effect of light in producing an image can be multiplied by using a developing solution. The gain in sensitivity achieved in this way is of the order of a thousand million times. The image produced when photographic materials are exposed to light is, in fact, normally invisible, the visible image not being produced until development. The invisible image is termed a *latent* ("hidden") *image*. Photographic materials in which the image is produced in this way are sometimes termed *development*, or *developing-out*, *materials*.

For special purposes, silver halide emulsions are sometimes produced in which the action of light alone is relied upon to produce the visible image. These are referred to as *printing-out materials*. They are necessarily very much slower than development materials, and their use is nowadays confined to the preparation of certain types of contact printing and oscillograph trace recording papers.

The emulsion binder

For the proper working of a photographic material, the silver halide grains must be evenly distributed and each crystal should preferably be kept from touching its neighbour, the sensitive layer must be moderately robust so that it may be able to resist abrasion and slight rubbing, and the grains in the layer must be accessible to processing solutions. There are few emulsion binders which meet all these requirements.

One of the first binding agents to be used was collodion, a syrupy, transparent fluid prepared by dissolving pyroxyline (gun-cotton) in a mixture of ether and alcohol. Collodion is still occasionally used today in the photomechanical trades. Collodion plates, however, have normally to be exposed and processed while still wet, i.e., within a few minutes of coating; hence the name *wet collodion plates*. If allowed to dry, the plates suffer a considerable loss of sensitivity. The usefulness of wet collodion plates is therefore seriously restricted.

Collodion, although of historical interest as an emulsion binder, has been replaced in general use by gelatin. Two great advantages of gelatin over collodion are that no expensive solvents are required when gelatin is used and, more important, that it acts as a sensitiser, the speed of a gelatino-bromide plate being some 20 times greater than that of a corresponding collodion plate. Plates coated with gelatino-bromide emulsions are sometimes termed *dry plates*, to distinguish them from wet collodion plates.

Gelatin has remarkable properties as a binding agent:

(1) Dispersed with water, it forms a convenient medium in which solutions of silver nitrate and alkali halides can be brought together to form crystals of insoluble silver halides. These crystals remain suspended in the gelatin in a fine state of division.

(2) As already stated, no expensive solvents are required when gelatin is used. Warmed in water it forms a solution which will flow, and further, by cooling an aqueous solution of gelatin it can be set to a firm jelly. Thus it is possible to cause an emulsion to set firmly almost immediately after it has been coated on the base. Thereafter, all that remains to be done is to remove the bulk of the water in a current of

warm air, and the resulting emulsion surface is reasonably strong and resistant to abrasion.

(3) When wetted, gelatin swells and allows processing solutions to penetrate.

(4) Gelatin is an active binding agent, containing "impurities" which profoundly influence the speed of emulsions made from it. By reason of certain of its constituents gelatin acts as a sensitiser and thus influences the speed of an emulsion. It is also believed to act as a bromine acceptor. The action of light predisposes silver halide grains to break down to silver with the liberation of bromine, development causing the breakdown to proceed in the places where the grain has been weakened. After exposure, and before development, there is a tendency for the silver and bromine which have been separated by the action of light to recombine; in other words, for the effect of the exposure to be undone. By "accepting", i.e., combining with the liberated bromine, gelatin prevents this back-reaction and so enables the full effect of the exposure to be achieved.

Manufacture of photographic materials

Over the years, great progress has been made in the production of emulsions – a result of the policy adopted by all the leading photographic manufacturers of maintaining their own research establishments which work in close association with the production units. Each firm has developed its own particular methods, many of which are naturally regarded as confidential, but the general principles on which emulsion-making rests are well established, and these will at least serve to illustrate the complexity of the whole process.

The principal materials used in the preparation of the emulsion are silver nitrate, alkali halides and gelatin, and all these must satisfy stringent tests. The gelatin must be carefully chosen, since it is not a simple chemical but a complex mixture of substances obtained from the hides and tendons of animals, and, although silver salts form the actual sensitive material, gelatin plays a very important part both physically and chemically, as already explained. Gelatins vary greatly in their photographic properties. The "blending" of gelatins originating from different sources helps in producing a binder with the required properties and in obtaining consistency. The general way to test a blend of gelatin for performance is to use some of it to make an emulsion and to test this to see whether it possesses the desired photographic properties.

The emulsion-making process, reduced to its essentials, consists of the following stages:

(1) Solutions of silver nitrate and soluble halides are added to gelatin, where they react to form silver halide and a soluble nitrate. This stage is called *emulsification*.

(2) The emulsion thus formed is subjected to heat treatment in the presence of the gelatin in a solution in which the silver halide is slightly soluble. During this treatment the crystals of silver halide grow to the size and distribution which will determine the characteristics – in particular speed, contrast and graininess – of the final material. This stage is known as the *first* (or *Ostwald*) *ripening*.

(3) The emulsion is them *washed* to remove the by-products of emulsification. In the earliest method of doing this the emulsion was cooled (chilled) and thereby caused to set to a jelly, shredded or cut to a small size and then washed in water. In modern practice, washing is achieved by causing the emulsion to settle to the bottom of the vessel, by the addition of a suitable coagulant to the warm solution. The liquid can then be removed by decanting or some other means.

(4) The emulsion is subjected to a second heat treatment in the absence of a silver halide solvent. No grain growth occurs (or should occur) during this stage, but sensitivity nuclei are formed on the grains and maximum sensitivity (speed) is reached. This stage is known as the *second ripening*, or *digestion*.

(5) Sensitising dyes (see Chapter 16), stabilizing reagents, hardeners, spreaders, etc., are now added.

All these operations are capable of almost infinite variation, and it is in the modification of these steps that much progress has been made in recent years, and emulsions of extremely diverse characteristics produced.

The support

The finished emulsion is coated on to a support, usually referred to as the "base". The commonly used supports are film, glass and paper. Negative emulsions are normally coated either upon film or upon glass (plates); paper base is usually reserved for positive emulsions. There are, however, important exceptions to this (see page 6).

Film base

The base used in the manufacture of films is usually a cellulose ester – commonly triacetate or acetate-butyrate. Cellulose nitrate (celluloid) also was at one time widely used, but its use has now been almost entirely discontinued on account of its flammability. Cellulose triacetate and acetate-butyrate are not, strictly speaking, non-flammable, but they are slow-burning. These "safety" bases have the additional advantage that they keep well, whereas nitrate base disintegrates on prolonged storage. Early acetate film bases would not stand up to wear and tear or the effect of processing solutions so well as nitrate base, but triacetate and acetate-butyrate bases do not suffer from these disadvantages.

Until World War II, film bases were made almost exclusively from cellulose derivatives. Since then, and particularly in the past decade, new synthetic resins have appeared which offer important advantages in film properties, particularly dimensional stability; this makes them of especial value in the fields of graphic arts and aerial survey.

The first of these new materials used at all widely was polystyrene, but the most outstanding dimensionally stable base material to date is polyethylene terephthalate, a polyester, and the raw material of Terylene fabric. As a film, polyethylene terephthalate has exceptionally high strength, much less sensitivity to moisture than cellulose derivative films and an unusually small change of size with change of temperature. Being insoluble in all common solvents, it cannot be fabricated by the traditional method of "casting", i.e., spreading a thick solution of the film-former on a moving polished band or drum, evaporating off the solvent, and stripping off the dry skin. Instead, the melted resin is extruded, i.e., forced through a die, to form a ribbon which is then stretched, while heated, to several times its initial length and width. A heat-setting treatment locks the structure in the stretched condition, and the film is then stable to heat throughout the range of temperatures encountered by photographic film. Polystyrene is extruded in a somewhat similar manner.

The most recent of the new materials, bisphenol–A polycarbonate, another polyester, is of interest in that while it compares with polyethylene terephthalate in several of its physical properties, it is soluble in some solvents and can be made by the same casting technique as cellulose derivative films.

Film base is of different thickness according to the particular product and type of base, most bases in general use coming within the range of 0·08 mm to 0·25 mm. Roll films are generally coated on 0·08 mm base, miniature and cine films on 0·13 mm base and flat films on 0·10 mm to 0·25 mm base. Polythylene terephthalate base can usually be somewhat thinner than the corresponding cellulosic base because of its better strength characteristics.

Glass plates

Plates came before films, and, although they have now to a large extent been replaced by films, they are still used in certain branches of photography, because of certain inherent advantages. The first thing which characterizes the glass plate is its rigidity. During processing, glass plates undergo no significant changes in dimensions, a feature which is particularly valuable in scientific work when accurate evaluation of image size is important. Similar conditions apply in photogrammetry and in many graphic arts processes, although the dimensional stability of modern safety film bases is such that the use of plates is now rarely *essential* in these fields. A further advantage of using plates is that no pains need be taken to ensure that the sensitive material lies flat in the camera; there is not the possibility of cockling which is frequently present with film. Plates are, of course, at a disadvantage as regards the possibility of breakage, weight, space taken up for storage and the fact that each must be loaded in the darkroom in a special dark-slide.

Paper base
The paper used for the base of photographic papers must be exceptionally pure. Photographic base paper is, therefore, manufactured at special mills where the greatest care is taken to ensure its purity. Before it is coated with emulsion, the base is usually coated with a paste of gelatin and a white pigment known as "blanc fixe", or baryta (barium sulphate), the purpose of which is to provide a pure white foundation for the emulsion, giving maximum reflection. Baryta is chosen because it is a pure white pigment which is highly insoluble and is without any harmful action on the emulsion.

Since baryta-coated papers cannot be folded or creased when dry without the risk of cracking at the fold, paper base intended for airmail and document papers is not usually baryta-coated.

Coating the emulsion on the base
The finished emulsion is coated on to the film, glass or paper base by flowing it over a weir or applying it with a roller. Before coating, the base must be suitably prepared to ensure good adhesion of the emulsion. Glass for photographic plates is prepared by coating it with a very thin *substratum* of strongly hardened gelatin; film base is similarly coated with a substratum. Film base is also usually coated with an anticurl and antihalation backing layer (page 220) before being coated with emulsion (Figure 13.1). Plates are usually backed after the emulsion has been coated.

The coated material is chilled to set the emulsion, after which, with films and papers, a protective layer – termed a *nonstress supercoat* – is applied to reduce the effects of abrasion, and drying is then carried out. With papers, the supercoat also serves to give added sheen or "lustre" and, in the case of glossy papers, assists in glazing.

Plates are coated on glass of various sizes, but not usually smaller in size than about 150 × 150 mm. Small plates are prepared by coating larger sheets of glass and cutting them.

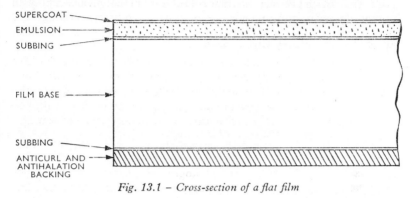

Fig. 13.1 – *Cross-section of a flat film*

Film base is coated as large rolls, commonly a little over 1 metre wide by 300 metres or thereabouts long, and when dry is "slit" and "chopped" into the required sizes. Papers, too, are coated as large "parent" rolls. These may be up to 1000 metres long for single-weight papers and 500 metres long for double-weight.

"Festoon" drying is one of the methods commonly adopted for the drying of films and papers, the coated material being passed through a drying tunnel in a series of festoons supported on crossbars travelling on an endless chain (Figure 13.2).

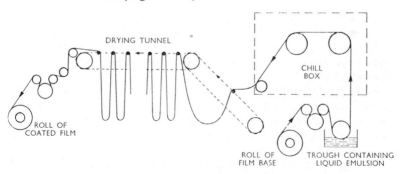

Fig. 13.2 – *A film coating machine shown diagrammatically*

With fast negative materials it is sometimes impossible to obtain the desired properties in any *single* emulsion. Two emulsions may then be prepared which together exhibit the desired characteristics. These may be mixed and coated in the same way as a single emulsion, or they may be applied as two separate layers, an "undercoat" and a "top-coat", the choice between the two procedures being governed largely by manufacturing convenience.

Sizes of films, plates and papers

Flat films and plates are supplied in a great number of sizes. (See, e.g., British Standards listed in the Appendix.) The sizes in most common use and the names by which certain of them are known are as follows:

82 × 108 mm (quarter-plate)
90 × 120 mm
102 × 127 mm
120 × 165 mm (half-plate)
165 × 216 mm (whole-plate)
203 × 254 mm

Roll films are made in spools of several sizes, identified by code numbers. The most popular sizes are as follows:

Spool No.	Number of pictures	Nominal picture size
120, 620*	8	60 × 90 mm
	12	60 × 60 mm
	16	45 × 60 mm
127	8	40 × 65 mm
	12	40 × 40 mm
	16	30 × 40 mm

* No. 620 spools differ from No. 120 spools in having a core of smaller diameter. They can thus be accommodated in smaller camera bodies.

Where more than one picture size is given in the list above, the picture size achieved in any given instance depends upon the design of the camera used.

Roll films 35 mm wide, perforated at each edge, are commonly termed "miniature" films. They are normally employed to yield images measuring 24 × 36 mm, a 1·64 metre length of film yielding 36 exposures and a 1·03 metre length, 20 exposures. Roll film 35 mm wide is also employed in "quick-loading" cartridges of various types. Some of these employ perforated film and yield 12 exposures of the standard 24 × 36 mm size; others employ unperforated film to give 12 or 20 28 × 28 mm images. Cameras are also available yielding 18 × 24 mm images on perforated 35 mm film. these are usually referred to as "half-frame" cameras.

Papers are supplied in packets for amateur use, in boxes for professionals and in continuous rolls for photographic "publishers" and photofinishers. As with films and plates, a wide range of sizes is available. (See, *e.g.*, British Standards listed in the Appendix.)

Packing of films, plates and papers

Flat films are normally packed facing all one way, interleaved with paper to minimize the risk of abrasion of films in contact, and to prevent possible interaction of the backing of one film with the emulsion of the next. Most types of flat film are notched in manufacture to facilitate identification of the emulsion side in the darkroom. When such films are held with the notch at the right-hand end of the top (short) side the emulsion is facing the user.

Plates are usually packed in pairs, emulsion to emulsion, the emulsion surfaces being prevented from touching by slips of card or by interleaving paper.

Sheets of paper are usually packed with the emulsion surfaces of all sheets – except the top one – facing the same way. The top sheet faces the rest.

CHAPTER 14

The Structure
of the Photographic Image

WE have seen that a photographic emulsion consists of fine silver halide crystals, or "grains", embedded in gelatin. When an emulsion is exposed to light and processed, an image of metallic silver is formed. When chemical development – the more usual of the two forms of development – is employed, this image is made up of grains of silver formed from the grains of silver halide present in the unexposed emulsion, the silver grains approximating quite closely in size and in position to the silver halide grains from which they were formed (see Chapter 23).

Grain size
The silver halide grains of an emulsion are not all of the same size; any single emulsion exhibits a range of grain sizes. The extent of this range depends upon the method of manufacture and is an important property of the emulsion. The larger grains in any given emulsion are in general more sensitive than the smaller ones. This is probably because the larger grains absorb more light, owing to their larger area. It would therefore be expected that an emulsion with a wide grain size distribution would have a wide range of response to light, i.e., low contrast; and an emulsion of restricted grain size distribution would be expected to have a narrow range of response to light, i.e., high contrast. In practice, this is generally the case.

The production of an emulsion containing large grains, i.e., a fast emulsion, is usually associated with the presence of other grains of a wide range of smaller sizes. For this reason, high emulsion speed is generally associated not only with large grain size but also with relatively low contrast. On the other hand, it is usually possible to obtain a restricted grain size distribution only if all the grains are small. Hence high contrast is usually associated with low speed and fine grain.

Graininess

The individual grains of a photographic emulsion are too small to be seen by the naked eye, even the largest grains being only about 2 micrometres in diameter. A magnification of about 50 times is needed to reveal the presence of individual grains. A grainy pattern can, however, usually be detected in photographic negatives at a much lower magnification, sometimes at as low as only three or four diameters. There are two main reasons for this:

(1) Because the grains are distributed at random over an area, and because the emulsion contains many "layers" of grains, they form a distribution in which a random irregular pattern is formed which is much more apparent than the individual grains.

(2) Not only may the grains *appear* to be "clumped" because of the way in which they are distributed in the emulsion, but they may actually *be* clumped together – even in physical contact – as the result either of manufacture or of some processing operation.

Now, a photographic image does not simply consist of black grains with white spaces in between, as it would if all the grains lay in the same plane. Instead, because the emulsion has a definite thickness and the grains are not all at the same level, light percolates between grains, and the result is that each small portion of the image is characterized by a variation of density.* This local variation of density in an image is referred to as *graininess*. It is graininess, not individual grains, which the eye sees when a negative is examined under a magnifying glass.

The graininess of negatives causes no trouble if these are used solely for the preparation of contact prints or enlargements at a low magnification. If, however, a considerable degree of enlargement is employed the grainy structure of the negative becomes visible in the print. It is usually most apparent in large and uniform areas of middle tone. Prints in which the graininess of the negative is plainly visible are generally objectionable. Hence, when a considerable degree of enlargement is required, it is desirable to keep the graininess of the negative to a minimum. (Here we may note that the graininess of the paper emulsion itself is not visible because this is not enlarged.)

Factors affecting the graininess of negatives

The following are the most important factors affecting the graininess of negatives:

(1) *The original emulsion employed.* This is the most important factor. A large average grain size generally means high graininess;

---

* For a definition of the term density as used in photography see Chapter 15.

small grain size low graininess. Hence, fast films tend to be more grainy than slow ones.

(2) *The developing solution employed.* By using fine grain developers it is possible to obtain an image in which the variation of density over microscopic areas is somewhat reduced (see Chapter 23).

Factors (1) and (2) are closely related, for just as use of a fast emulsion is usually accompanied by an increase in graininess, so use of a fine grain developer often leads to some loss of emulsion speed. Consequently, it may be found that use of a fast film with a fine grain developer offers no advantage in *effective* speed or grain over a slower, finer grained film developed in a normal developer. In fact, in such a case, the film of finer grain will yield better resolution and in consequence is normally to be preferred.

(3) *The degree of development.* Since, as we have already seen, each small area of the image contains variations in density, its structure will be more apparent in a contrasty image than in a soft one. It should, however, be noted that although very soft negatives are less grainy than negatives of normal contrast, they require harder papers to print on, and final prints from such negatives usually exhibit similar graininess to prints made from negatives of normal contrast.

(4) *The exposure level, i.e., density level.* Graininess increases with the density of the negative. This follows from a consideration of the behaviour of random distributions. As a result, over-exposure results in a rapid increase in graininess.

It may here be remarked that *excessive* over-exposure, besides giving high densities – which in themselves tend to be grainy – tends to give low contrast in the highlights. To obtain the necessary contrast when printing from such excessively over-exposed negatives, it may be necessary to use a hard printing paper and this will also accentuate graininess.

(5) *The sharpness of the negative.* The sharper the image on the film, the greater will be the detail in the photograph and the less noticeable the graininess.

Factors affecting the graininess of prints
The graininess of a print is primarily a function of the graininess of the negative and the degree of enlargement. It is also influenced by the optical system employed for printing (see Chapter 22).

Irradiation and halation
Light falling on an emulsion is affected in a number of ways, as shown diagrammatically in Figure 14.1a. A small part of the light is

reflected from the surface of the emulsion layer back towards the lens and, so to speak, passes out of the picture. Part is absorbed by the

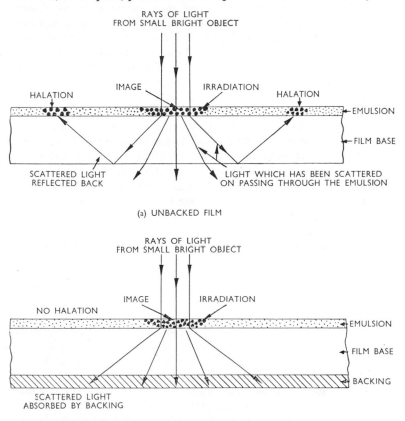

Fig. 14.1 – Irradiation and halation

silver halide grains without appreciable deviation from its original direction, and goes to form the image proper, and part is scattered in all directions in the emulsion. In very bright areas of the image a further part passes through the emulsion into the base.

It is evident that the light scattered within the emulsion will in turn be partly absorbed by the silver halide grains and partly passed on through the emulsion. The absorbed part of the scattered light produces the effect called *irradiation*, the extent of which depends on the degree to which the light is scattered and on how far away from the boundary of the image proper the scattered light is able to penetrate.

The light which passes through the emulsion enters the base, and, according to the angle at which it meets the air-base surface, may pass out of the base or may be reflected back as the result of total internal reflection (page 49). The reflected light will eventually reach the emulsion again and form an image a little distance from the image proper. This secondary image is termed *halation*. Halation takes various forms according to the nature of the object, and, for a small bright object, takes the form of a complete circle or "halo". Although halation is most readily observed where individual points of light are present, it can also be troublesome with extended areas of exceptional brightness. Here, the halos formed by each point of a bright area combine in such a way that they overlap the images of adjoining darker areas. A once familiar example of this was the tendency for twigs and the thinner branches of trees to disappear when photographed against the sky.

Irradiation and halation are both most serious with small images, and are most pronounced when the image is heavily exposed. They are thus commonly observed on images of naked light sources. Halation is most serious when the emulsion is coated on glass, since the rear reflecting surface is then further from the emulsion than with film base. With plates, the image due to halation may therefore be completely separated from the true image.

Irradiation can be minimized by use of a thin emulsion of fine grain. When irradiation must be kept to an absolute minimum a dye may be incorporated in the emulsion to keep the image on the surface and absorb any scattered light. An amber dye is used for this purpose in some recording films. A similar effect can be obtained without use of a dye by making the exposure by ultra-violet radiation, since a photographic emulsion is relatively opaque to this. This principle is employed in some sound recording systems. Any technique which minimizes irradiation also minimizes the risk of halation.

Halation can be almost entirely prevented by the use of a suitable light-absorbing substance behind the emulsion layer. With plates an *anti-halation backing layer* is applied to the reverse side of the glass from the emulsion. With flat films and roll films a dye is added to the gelatin with which the backs of these films are coated to prevent curl (Figure 14.1b). Backing dyes must be chosen to have optical properties such that any light passing into the base is not reflected by the back surface, but passes through into the "backing" and is absorbed there. The dyes must also be such that they have no harmful effect on the emulsion during storage, and must be capable of rapid and complete bleaching by processing solutions to allow of the negatives being printed easily. The use of backed materials is recommended for all types of general photography.

As films used in 35 mm miniature cameras and cine cameras are made without an anti-curl gelatin layer, the backing dye for these films is usually incorporated in the film base itself. The anti-halation action of this dye is rather different from the ordinary backing layer. Instead of preventing reflection at the back surface of the base, the dye absorbs the light passing through the base, both on its outward journey and on its return, thus appreciably reducing its intensity. The dye used in such films is permanent and its density must therefore be chosen to be sufficient to prevent halation without unduly prolonging the time needed for printing.

A rather curious fact about anti-halation treatment is that when comparative sensitometric tests are made in the laboratory, a backed material always shows lower contrast than the same material without backing. This is due to the elimination by the backing of the light reflected from the back of the support, which, being strongest in the most heavily exposed regions, reinforces the higher densities when backing is absent. In practical photography, on the other hand, backed materials usually appear to give greater contrast, an effect which is explained by the improved definition of fine detail and the sharper rendering of boundaries between areas of contrasting brightness, due to the elimination of halation.

Resolving power
The ability of an emulsion to record fine detail is referred to as its *resolving power*. The resolving power of a given emulsion depends principally upon its grain size, graininess, contrast and turbidity. *Turbidity* is the property of a material as a result of which light reaches areas which have received no direct exposure, e.g., through reflection, refraction or diffraction within the image. It depends, amongst other things, on the grain size distribution in the emulsion, the ratio of silver to gelatin and the coating weight.

Resolving power is generally expressed as the number of black lines per millimetre that can be distinguished as separated in a photographic image. In measuring the resolving power of a film a *resolving power test chart* consisting of parallel lines separated by spaces of the same width as the lines is photographed, using a lens of very high resolution, at a great reduction in size. The chart usually contains several groups of lines of diminishing width (Figure 14.2). After the film has been developed, the negative is examined with the aid of a microscope and the resolving power is determined from the finest group of lines which is just resolved.

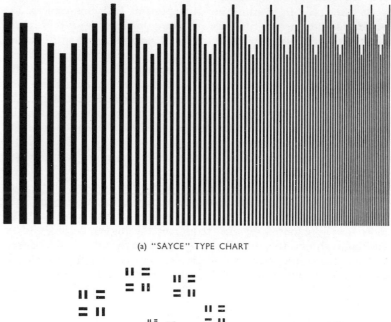

(a) "SAYCE" TYPE CHART

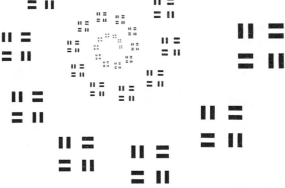

(b) "COBB" TYPE CHART

Fig. 14.2 – Typical resolving power test charts

The number obtained when determining the resolving power of any given emulsion is influenced by a number of factors. These include the arrangement of the lines on the test chart, the contrast of the chart, the wavelength of the light used in making the exposures, the exposure and the development. Resolving power falls off at very low and very high levels of exposure. It increases with the contrast of the test object. The resolving power of high-speed panchromatic emulsions is usually in the region of 40 to 60 lines per millimetre, and that of process emulsions in the region of 150 to 200 lines per millimetre, these figures being related to recommended processing, optimum exposure and a test chart contrast of 30 to 1.

The resolving power of a photographic system depends upon the resolving power of the lens (page 121) as well as upon the resolving power of the film. The following empirical relationship appears to hold good in many cases:

$$\frac{1}{R_{F+L}} = \frac{1}{R_F} + \frac{1}{R_L}$$

where R_F, R_L and R_{F+L} are the resolving powers in lines per millimetre of the film, the lens and the lens-film combination respectively. When measuring the resolving power of a film it is customary to select a lens with resolving power so high that the term $1/R_L$ is negligible in comparison with $1/R_F$.

Sharpness

The appearance of the edges of well-resolved detail in a photograph is termed *sharpness*. When a film is exposed while partially shielded by a knife-edge, the image after development does not change abruptly at the knife-edge from a high density to clear film. Instead, there is a measurable density gradient across the boundary. One reason for this is the turbidity of the emulsion, which results in the diffusion of light beyond the knife-edge. Adjacency effects in development (page 421) may also affect the image at the boundary. The quantities *acutance* and *contour sharpness* have been defined in the U.S.A. and Germany respectively as expressions of sharpness in terms of this density gradient.

Photographic definition

The term *photographic definition* is used to describe the clarity of detail in a photograph. Definition is a subjective concept because it results from the impression made by a photograph on an observer. It appears to depend upon the combined effects of resolving power, sharpness, graininess and tone reproduction.

CHAPTER 15

Sensitometry

THE scientific study of the response, or sensitivity, of photographic materials to light is termed *sensitometry*. It is concerned with the measurement of the exposure that a material has received and with the measurement of the resultant blackening.

It is perfectly possible to produce photographs without any knowledge of sensitometry, but to obtain the *best* performance out of photographic materials, under all conditions – abnormal as well as normal – an understanding of the principles governing the response of materials is invaluable. A knowledge of at least an outline of sensitometry is therefore highly desirable for anyone wishing to make use of any of the specialized applications of photography in science and industry. The present Chapter is concerned solely with black-and-white photography, but it will also provide a useful starting point for anyone wishing to study the behaviour of colour materials.

Since sensitometry is concerned with the measurement of the "performance" of photographic materials, it involves the necessity for the correct use of terminology in defining the quantities that are measured. The impression that a photograph makes on us depends on physiological and psychological factors as well as on physical factors, and for this reason the success or otherwise of a photograph cannot be determined from any single measurement or even a series of measurements. This does not mean, however, that we can learn nothing from a study of the factors which *are* amenable to measurement; it simply means that we must not forget that there are limitations to the help that sensitometry can give us.

Subject

As far as the camera is concerned, a subject consists simply of a number of areas of varying luminance. This holds good whether the subject is a portrait or a landscape, a pictorial or a record shot. In the same way, a photographic print consists simply of areas of varying luminance. Luminance is measured in candelas per square metre.

The variations in luminance in a subject are due to the different reflection characteristics exhibited by different areas of it, to the different angles at which they are viewed,* and to variation in the illumination which they receive. The ratio of the maximum to the minimum luminance in a subject is defined as its *luminance range*

It may surprise us at first to realise that an effect such as a sunset, or the rippling of wind over water, can be reduced merely to "areas of varying luminance". Yet, so it is in the camera, and so it is in the eye – with the difference that the mind draws not only on the eyes for its impression but on the other senses too, and, most important of all, on past experience. (Thus, when we look at an apple, for example, we see more than just light and shade. Our past experience of apples – their size, their weight, their taste – all comes to the aid of the eyes in presenting to the mind a picture of an apple.)

Our final goal in sensitometry is to relate the luminances of the subject with the luminances of the print. This involves the study first of the response of the negative material, then of the response of the positive material and finally of the relation between the two. We shall consider each of these in turn, beginning with the negative material, i.e., the film or plate.

It is customary to refer to the bright areas of a scene as the "highlights" and the dark areas as the "shadows". To avoid confusion, it is desirable that the same terms should be applied to corresponding areas both in the negative and in the print, even though in the negative the "highlights" are dense and the "shadows" clear.

Exposure

When a photograph is taken, light from the various areas of the subject falls upon the sensitised film for a certain time. The effect produced upon the film is proportional to the product of the illumination I and the exposure time t. We express this by the equation:

$$E = I \cdot t$$

where E is the *exposure* (see also page 65).

As the luminance of the subject varies from area to area, it follows that the illumination on the film varies similarly, so that the film receives not one exposure over the entire surface but an infinite number of different amounts of light energy, i.e., a range of exposures.

---

* A surface which diffuses light fairly completely, such as blotting paper, looks equally bright no matter from which direction it is viewed, but a surface which reflects light in mirror fashion may look very bright or very dark, according to the angular relationship between source, surface and eye.

In ordinary photography, the exposure time is constant for all areas of the film, variation in exposure over the film being due solely to variation in the illumination that it receives.

Illumination is measured in lux (lumens per square metre) (page 39), and time in seconds, so that exposure is expressed in lux seconds.

It should be noted that the use of the word "exposure" in the sense in which we are using it here is quite different from its everyday use in such phrases as, "I gave an exposure of 1/60th sec. at $f/8$". We can avoid confusion by distinguishing the latter as *camera exposure* (page 331).

Blackness of the image

When a film has been processed, areas of the image which have received different values of illumination, are seen to have differing degrees of blackening. The blackness of a negative, i.e., its light-stopping power, can be expressed numerically in several different ways. The following three ways are of interest in photography:

(1) *Transmission*

The transmission, T, of an area of a negative is defined as the ratio of the light transmitted, I_t, to the light incident upon the negative, I_i. Expressed mathematically:

$$T = \frac{I_t}{I_i}$$

Transmission is always less than 1 and is normally expressed as a percentage. Thus, if 10 units of light fall upon a negative and 5 are transmitted, the negative is said to have a transmission of $5/10 = 0.5$, or 50 per cent. Although transmission is a useful concept in certain fields, in sensitometry it is not the most expressive of units because it *decreases* as blackness *increases*.

(2) *Opacity*

Opacity, O, is defined as the ratio of the light incident upon the negative, I_i, to the light transmitted, I_t. That is:

$$O = \frac{I_i}{I_t}$$

It is apparent, therefore, that opacity is the reciprocal of transmission, i.e.:

$$O = \frac{1}{T}$$

Opacity is always greater than 1 and *increases* with *increasing* blackness. From this point of view, it is a more logical unit to use in sensitometry than transmission.

(3) *Density*

Density, D, is defined as the logarithm* of the opacity, O. That is:

$$D = \log O = \log \frac{1}{T} = \log \frac{I_i}{I_t}$$

Density is the unit of blackening employed almost exclusively in sensitometry. It shares with opacity the property of increasing with increasing blackness, and has the following practical advantages over opacity:

(a) The numerical value of density bears a simple relation to the amount of silver present. For example, if the amount of silver present in a negative of density $1 \cdot 0$ is doubled, the density will be increased to $2 \cdot 0$, i.e., will also be doubled. The opacity, however, will increase from 10 to 100, i.e., tenfold.

(b) The final aim in sensitometry is to relate the print to the subject. Blackness in the print depends on the way the eye assesses it, and is

Density	Opacity	Transmission (per cent.)	Density	Opacity	Transmission (per cent.)
0·0	1	100	1·6	40	2·5
0·1	1·3	79	1·7	50	2
0·2	1·6	63	1·8	63	1·6
0·3	2	50	1·9	79	1·25
0·4	2·5	40	2·0	100	1
0·5	3·2	32	2·1	126	0·8
0·6	4	25	2·2	158	0·6
0·7	5	20	2·3	200	0·5
0·8	6·3	16	2·4	251	0·4
0·9	8	12·5	2·5	316	0·3
1·0	10	10	2·6	398	0·25
1·1	13	7·9	2·7	501	0·2
1·2	16	6·3	2·8	631	0·16
1·3	20	5	2·9	794	0·12
1·4	25	4	3·0	1000	0·1
1·5	32	3·2	4·0	10,000	0·01

Table 15.1 – Density, opacity and transmission

* An explanation of logarithms is given in the Appendix

therefore essentially physiological. The law governing the effect produced in the eye when stimulated is not a simple one, but over a wide range of viewing conditions the response of the eye is approximately logarithmic. Thus, if we examine a number of patches of a print in which the density increases by equal steps, the eye accepts the steps as of equal blackness increase. From this point of view, therefore, a logarithmic unit is the most satisfactory measure of blackening.

Table 15.1 gives a conversion between density, opacity and transmission.

When it is desired to distinguish between densities of images on a transparent base and those of images on an opaque base, the former are referred to as *transmission densities* and the latter as *reflection densities* (page 248).

Effect of scatter in negative

We saw in Chapter 14 that when light passes through a negative it is partially scattered. One result of this is that the numerical value of density depends upon the spatial distribution of the incident light, and on the method adopted for the measurement of both this and the transmitted light. Three types of density have been defined; these are illustrated in Figure 15.1.

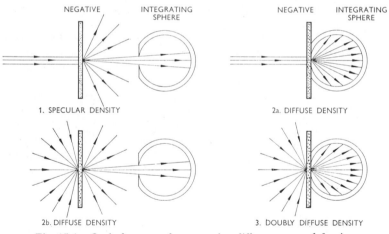

Fig. 15.1 – Optical systems for measuring different types of density

(1) *Specular density*

This is determined by using *parallel* illumination and measuring only *normal* emergence.

(2) *Diffuse density*

This is sometimes termed *totally diffuse* density. It may be determined in either of two ways:

(a) By using *parallel* illumination and measuring *total* emergence (whether normal or scattered), or

(b) By using *diffuse* illumination and measuring only *normal* emergence.

The numerical value of diffuse density is the same whichever method of measurement is employed.

(3) *Doubly diffuse density*

This is determined by using *diffuse* illumination and measuring *total* emergence.

Practical measurements of any of these types of density are based on the ratio of a photometer reading when the sample is not in place (taken as I_i), to the reading on the same photometer when the sample is in place (I_t).

The difference between diffuse density and doubly diffuse density is usually quite small, but specular density is always greater than either.

Callier coefficient

The ratio of specular density to diffuse density is termed the *Callier coefficient*, or *Callier Q factor*. The Callier coefficient, which is never less than 1, varies with both the grain size and the density of the deposit. As far as grain is concerned, the finer the grain – and therefore the lower the turbidity – the nearer to unity is the Callier coefficient.

The variation with density is more complex. The coefficient is 1 for clear film (density = 0). It then increases rapidly to a maximum value of about 1·5 at a density of about 0·3, and then gradually falls to a value of about 1·4 as density increases. One result of the variation of the Callier coefficient with density, is that the tone distribution in the shadows of a print produced with a condenser enlarger may be different from that in a print produced in a diffuser enlarger (page 376).

Density in practice

The types of density encountered in photographic practice are mainly as follows:

Type of work	*Effective density*
Contact printing	
(a) In a box, with diffused source	Doubly diffuse

(b) In a frame, using clear bulb	Diffuse (parallel illumination, total emergence)
Type of work	*Effective density*
Enlarging	
(a) Condenser enlarger (point source, no diffuser)	Specular
(b) Diffuser enlarger	Diffuse (diffuse illumination, normal emergence)

Some kinds of work represent a mixture of different types of density, as, for example, when an opal bulb or a diffusing screen is used in a condenser enlarger.

It will be noted that apart from the true condenser enlarger, the effective density in all the examples quoted is either diffuse or doubly diffuse. As already stated, the difference between the latter two forms of density is slight. For normal photographic purposes, therefore, densities of negatives are expressed as diffuse densities.

If the image in a negative or print is not neutral in tone, its measured density will depend not only on the optics employed to measure it, but also on the *colour* of the light employed and the response to colour of the device employed to measure it. According to these last two factors we may consider density as being of four main kinds, as follows:

(1) *Density at any wavelength*
Determined by illuminating the specimen with monochromatic radiation.

(2) *Visual density*
Determined by illuminating the specimen with tungsten light and measuring it with a receiver having a spectral response similar to that of the normal photopic eye.

(3) *Printing density*
Determined by illuminating the specimen with tungsten light and employing a receiver with a spectral response similar to that of photographic papers.

(4) *Photo-electric density*
Determined by illuminating the specimen with tungsten light and employing an unfiltered commercial photo-electric cell as the receiver.

This classification applies equally to all three main types of density: specular, diffuse and doubly diffuse. For most photographic purposes *diffuse visual density* is employed.

The characteristic curve

If we plot density as ordinate against exposure as abscissa, we obtain a response curve for a film or plate of the general shape shown in Figure 15.2.

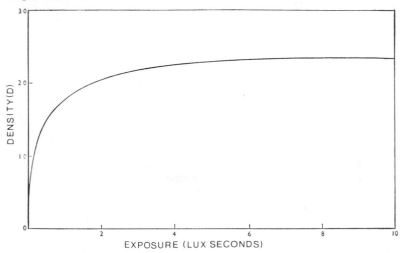

Fig. 15.2 – Response curve of an emulsion obtained by plotting density against exposure

Although a curve of this type is occasionally of value, a far more useful curve for most purposes is obtained by plotting density against *log* exposure. A curve of the shape shown in Figure 15.3 is then obtained. This is the type of response curve employed in ordinary photography. It is referred to as a *characteristic curve, D log E curve* or *H and D curve* – the latter after Hurter and Driffield, who were the first to publish curves of this type. The characteristic curve is simply a diagram which shows the effect on the emulsion of every degree of exposure from under-exposure to over-exposure – for any one development time and any particular developer.

The use of log E instead of E as the unit for the horizontal axis of the response curve of a photographic material offers several advantages:

(1) In practice, we consider changes in camera exposure in terms of the factor by which it is altered; i.e., the natural progression of exposure is geometrical, not arithmetical. (When increasing an exposure time from 1/60th to 1/30th second, for example, we speak of doubling the exposure, not of increasing it by 1/60th second.) A

logarithmic curve therefore gives the most reasonable representation of the way in which density increases when exposure is changed.

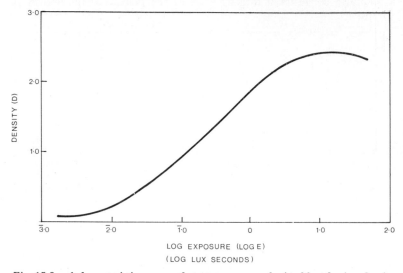

LOG EXPOSURE (LOG E)
(LOG LUX SECONDS)

Fig. 15.3 – A characteristic curve – the response curve obtained by plotting density against log exposure

(2) A D log E curve shows on a far larger scale than a density-exposure curve, the portion of the curve corresponding with just perceptible blackening, i.e., with small values of exposure. As the speed of a film is usually judged in terms of the exposure needed to produce quite small values of density (Chapter 19), the increased clarity in this region of the curve is very valuable (see page 552).

(3) The use of a logarithmic unit on both horizontal and vertical axes, enables values of negative density to be transferred readily to the exposure axis of the characteristic curve of the print. This facilitates the overall task of relating the brightnesses of the original scene, the transmission densities of the negative and the reflection densities of the print.

Main regions of the negative characteristic curve
For convenience, the characteristic curve of a negative material may be divided into four main regions: the toe, the straight-line portion, the shoulder and the region of solarization, as shown in Figure 15.4.

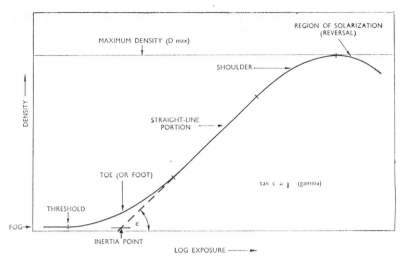

Fig. 15.4 – The *"geography"* of the characteristic curve of a negative material

It is only on the straight-line portion of the curve that density differences in the negative correspond proportionally to differences in the original scene. For this reason, the straight line is sometimes referred to as the region of correct exposure, the toe as the region of under-exposure and the shoulder as the region of over-exposure. As we shall see later, however, such descriptions are apt to be misleading (see, e.g., page 240). The value of density reached at the top of the shoulder of the curve is referred to as the D_{max}, the maximum density obtainable under the given conditions of exposure and development.

The numerical value of the tangent of the angle, c, which the straight-line portion of the curve makes with the log E axis is termed *gamma*, γ. A gamma of 1 is obtained when the angle has a value of 45°.

Gamma may also be defined in terms of the values of density and log exposure corresponding to any two points lying on the straight-line portion of the curve. Referring to Figure 15.5:

$$\gamma = \tan c = \frac{BC}{AC} = \frac{D_2 - D_1}{\log E_2 - \log E_1}$$

It is thus seen that gamma serves to measure *contrast* – i.e., the rate at which density grows as exposure increases – in the straight-line portion of the curve. It should be noted, however, that gamma gives information about only the straight-line portion of the curve; it tells us nothing about the other portions. Further, as will be seen later, the contrast of a negative is not determined by gamma alone – other factors play an important part.

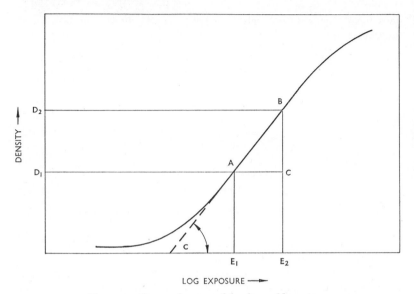

Fig. 15.5 – Gamma in terms of density and log exposure

The region of solarization, or reversal, although not employed in ordinary photography, is of interest in that here an increase in exposure actually results in a *decrease* in density. The exposure necessary to produce solarization is commonly of the order of one-thousand times greater than normal exposures and is usually reached only by such subjects as naked filaments or lightning. However, it should be noted that materials vary widely in the degree of solarization which they show.

Beyond the toe, the curve becomes parallel to the log *E* axis, a little way above the axis. The value of density in this region, usually quite small, is termed *fog*. Fog results from the development of unexposed grains (page 387). The point on the curve corresponding to the first perceptible density above fog is called the *threshold*.

The intersection of the extrapolated straight-line portion of the curve with the log *E* axis (density above fog being plotted) is referred to as the *inertia point*, and the value of exposure at this point as the *inertia*.

On published characteristic curves the exposure axis is usually marked "Relative log exposure", or "Rel. log E". Use of a relative instead of an absolute scale of exposures does not affect the shape of the curve in any way, and occasions little loss to the user, although it does mean that absolute values of speed cannot be determined from the curve.

Variation of the characteristic curve with the material

The characteristic curves of individual materials differ from one another in their shapes and in their positions relative to the log E axis. The *position* of the curve in relation to the log E axis depends upon the *speed* of the material. The faster the material, the further to the left of the scale is the curve situated. Film speed is dealt with in detail in Chapter 19. The main variations in the *shape* of the curve are:

(1) Slope of straight line (gamma).

(2) Length of straight line.

The length of the straight line is usually expressed in terms of the density at which the toe merges with the straight line, and the density at which the straight line merges with the shoulder.

Photographic materials differ both in the maximum slope that can be reached and in the rate at which a given slope is achieved. Modern negative materials are usually made to yield a gamma of 0·7 to 0·8 at normal development times. They commonly have a long toe, which may extend up to a density of as high as 0·7, and the straight line may be quite short. Some modern ultra-fast materials have a so-called "bent-leg" curve, which has in effect two straight-line portions. The lower part of the curve is fairly steep, but at a density of about 1·2 the slope changes to a much lower value. A curve of this shape may have certain advantages in the photography of subjects which contain very bright highlights, e.g., night scenes.

Materials intended for copying are usually designed to have a short toe (i.e., one which merges into the straight line at a low density), and a long straight line, the slope of which will be governed by the nature of the work for which the material is intended. Materials for copying are available capable of yielding gammas ranging from below 1 up to 10 or more.

Characteristic curves for specific materials are published by film manufacturers.

Variation of the characteristic curve with development

A characteristic curve is not a unique function of an emulsion, but alters in shape with the conditions of exposure (e.g., the colour (page 240) and intensity (page 262) of the light source) and with the conditions of processing; in particular, the curve is markedly affected by the degree of development (Chapter 23).

On varying development time, and keeping other conditions constant, a series of characteristic curves is obtained, which, in the absence of soluble bromide (or other anti-foggant) in the emulsion or developer, is of the type shown in Figure 15.6.

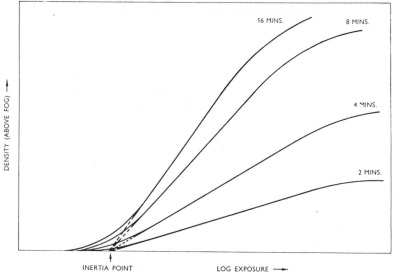

Fig. 15.6 – Effect of development time on characteristic curve of older sensitive materials

It will be seen from this figure that, whereas a single characteristic curve tells us a certain amount about the behaviour of a material, a "family" of curves made with increasing development time gives a much more complete picture. The most obvious change in the curve with increasing development is the increase in the slope of the straight-line portion, i.e., gamma. For any given emulsion, then, gamma is a measure of the degree of development, and is for this reason sometimes termed the *development factor*. Another point that may be noted is that the straight-line portions of all the four curves shown in the figure meet, when produced, at a point on the log E axis; i.e., the curves have a common inertia point.

In the early days of sensitometry, a series of characteristic curves of the type shown in Figure 15.6 could fairly readily be obtained with the sensitive materials of the time by using a bromide-free developer. This Figure, however, is not typical of materials used today. These commonly contain anti-foggants and most modern developers now contain soluble bromide, and the curves obtained are usually of the general pattern shown in Figure 15.7.

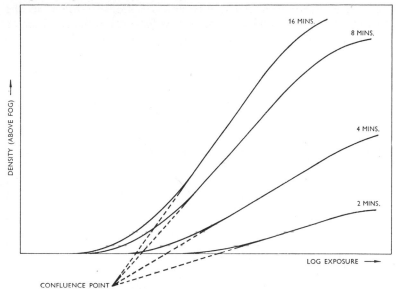

Fig. 15.7 – Effect of development time on characteristic curve of current sensitive materials

The straight lines are seen still to meet at a point (although this is not invariably the case), but this point is depressed, i.e., is now below the log E axis. As a result, not only does the slope increase but the curve as a whole moves to the left as development time is increased, the inertia shifting towards a limiting value. This shift is termed *regression of the inertia*. This corresponds to an increase in speed with increased development (page 411).

Gamma-time curve

By plotting gamma as ordinate against development time as abscissa we obtain a curve, the general shape of which is illustrated in Figure 15.8.

Gamma is seen to increase very rapidly as development begins, and then to increase at a more gradual rate until, finally, a point is reached where increased development produces no further increase in gamma. The value of gamma at this point is termed *gamma infinity* ($\gamma\infty$). Gamma infinity varies from emulsion to emulsion and depends to some extent on the developing solution used. A material capable of yielding a high gamma infinity is said to be of *high contrast*. With most materials it is rarely desirable to develop to gamma infinity, since

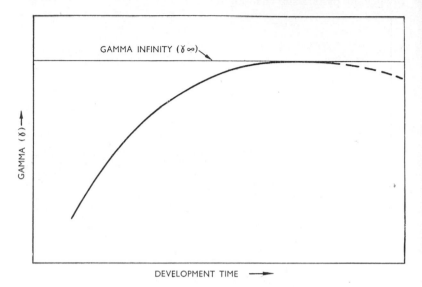

Fig. 15.8 – Gamma-time curve

prolonged development is accompanied by an increase in fog and graininess, either or both of which may reach an objectionable level before gamma infinity is attained. Owing to fog, gamma will actually fall off on very prolonged development, as the effect of the additional density due to fog is greater on low densities than on high. This fall-off is illustrated by the broken portion of the curve shown in Figure 15.8.

A gamma-time curve shows at a glance the gamma infinity obtainable with a given material and developer. It also shows the development time required to reach this or any lower value of gamma. We have seen that it is rarely desirable to employ the very top part of the gamma-time curve owing to the growth of fog and graininess. It is also usually unwise to employ the very bottom part – where a small increase in development time gives a big increase in gamma – because in this region any slight inequalities in the degree of development across the film will be accentuated, with the likelihood of uneven density, or mottle.

Figure 15.9 contains gamma-time curves for a film in two differing developer formulae. Curve *A* was produced in an M.Q. developer of normal composition; curve *B* in an M.Q. borax developer. Comparison of such curves assists in the choice of a suitable developer when

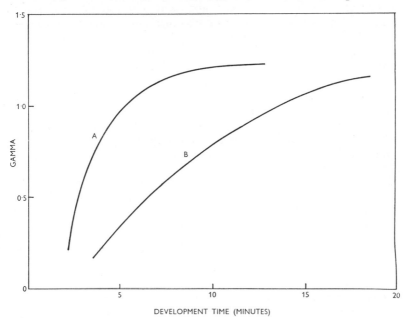

Fig. 15.9 – Gamma-time curves for the same material in two different developers

the desired gamma is known. For example, if a gamma of 0·5 is desired, the M.Q. borax developer would normally be preferable to the M.Q. developer, since, with the latter, contrast is changing too rapidly with development time at the gamma required. On the other hand, to achieve a gamma of 1·1 the M.Q. developer would be the most suitable, the M.Q. borax developer requiring an excessively long development time to reach this value.

Gamma-time curves for individual materials under stated conditions of development are published by film manufacturers. Such curves give a good indication of the general behaviour of a material, and can be of considerable assistance in the selection of a material and developer for a given task. However, because working conditions may vary from those specified and because of variations in materials in manufacture and during storage, to be of greatest value gamma-time curves for any given material should be determined by the user under his own working conditions.

Variation of gamma with wavelength

Besides being dependent on development, gamma also depends to some extent on the colour of the light used. The variation within the visible spectrum is not great, but it becomes considerable in the ultra-violet region. The general tendency is for gamma to become less as wavelength decreases. This variation of gamma can be ignored in ordinary photography, but must be taken into account in three-colour work and, most important, in spectrography (page 274).

In the visual region the gamma of an emulsion can be controlled in manufacture by the addition of suitable dyes. It has therefore been possible for three-colour work to make available special emulsions in which the gammas achieved in the three main regions of the spectrum – blue, green and red – are very nearly equal.

Placing of the subject on the characteristic curve

As we have already noted, a characteristic curve shows the response of a material under a wide range of exposures. Only a part of this curve is used by any single negative. The *extent* of the portion used depends on the subject luminance range;* its *position* depends on the actual luminances in the scene and on the exposure time and lens aperture employed.

We have already stated that the characteristic curves of most modern negative materials are characterised by a long toe. The part of the curve used by a "normally exposed" negative includes the upper part of this toe and the lower part of the straight-line portion. This is illustrated in Figure 15.10.

Average gradient ($\overline{G}$)

It follows from the fact that a negative usually occupies part of the toe of the curve as well as part of the straight line, that gamma alone gives an incomplete picture of the contrast of an emulsion. Frequently, a better measure of contrast is obtained by taking the slope of the line joining the two limiting points of the portion of the characteristic curve employed (Figure 15.11). This is referred to as the *average gradient*, or $\overline{G}$ ("gee bar"). It is always lower than gamma.

Effect of variation in development on the negative

Let us assume that the negative represented by the curve in Figure

---

* Strictly, it is the illumination range of the image on the film with which we are concerned here, and, if flare is present, this will be less than the subject luminance range (page 73). However, in the present context we shall assume that flare is absent.

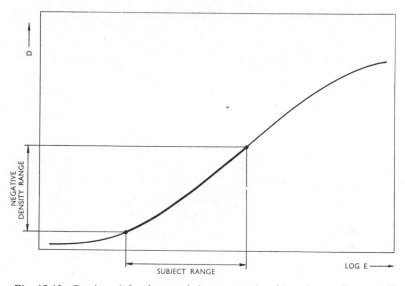

Fig. 15.10 – Portion of the characteristic curve employed by a "normally exposed" negative

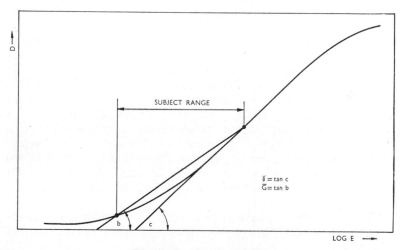

Fig. 15.11 – Average gradient

15.10 was given "normal" development. If we make two other identical exposures of the same subject, and give more development to one and less development to the other, we shall obtain two further curves such as those which are shown, together with the "normally developed"

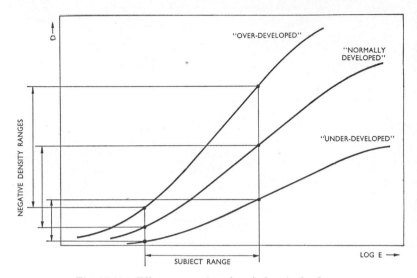

Fig. 15.12 – Effect on negative of variations in development

curve, in Figure 15.12. Because the camera exposure is the same in all three cases, the limiting points of the parts of the curves used, measured against the log E axis, are the same for all three curves.

A study of these curves shows that over-development increases the density of the negative in the shadows to a small extent and in the highlights to a large extent. As a result, the negative as a whole is denser and, more important, its *density range* – the difference between the maximum and minimum densities – is increased. Under-development does just the reverse. It decreases density in both shadows and highlights – in the highlights to a far greater extent than in the shadows – and thus the negative as a whole is thinner and its density range is reduced.

The *major* effect of variation in the degree of development is on the density range – sometimes termed the *overall contrast* of the negative.

Effect of variation in exposure on the negative

Let us suppose that we are photographing the cube shown in Figure 15.13 and that S_1 is the darkest shadow area in the subject, S_2 the next darkest, H_1 the highest highlight and H_2 the next highest. Then on a "normally-exposed, normally-developed" negative the exposures and

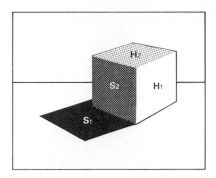

Fig. 15.13 – Subject tones

densities corresponding to these areas will be approximately as shown in Figure 15.14.

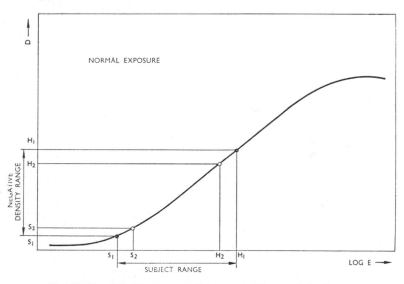

Fig. 15.14 – Densities on normal exposure and normal development

In an *under-exposed* negative of the same subject, given the same development, the location of these points will be as shown in Figure 15.15.

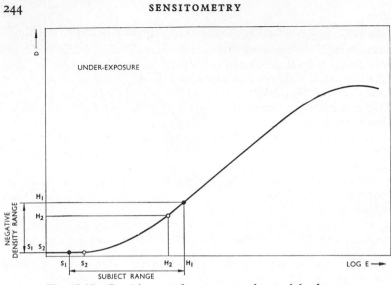

Fig. 15.15 – Densities on under-exposure and normal development

Compared with the normally exposed negative, the density range of the under-exposed negative is greatly compressed. More important,

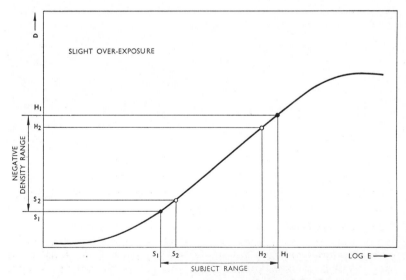

Fig. 15.16 – Densities on over exposure and normal development

the two shadow areas S_1 and S_2, although having different luminances and thus yielding different exposures on the film, yield the same density on the negative; they are thus no longer separated. Some shadow detail is therefore completely lost, and the shadow detail that remains will be degraded. This is a case of *considerable* under-exposure. *Slight* under-exposure would result in shadow detail being degraded, but not completely lost.

In a *slightly over-exposed* negative, given the same development, the four selected areas of the subject will be placed on the curve as shown in Figure 15.16.

The average density of the negative is now greater than that of the normally exposed negative, and the density range is expanded. Tone separation in the shadows, in particular, is increased.

In the case, however, of a *heavily over-exposed* negative, the shoulder of the curve may be reached (Figure 15.17). In these circumstances,

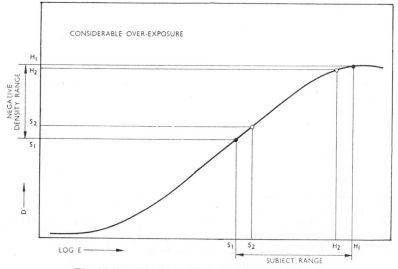

Fig. 15.17 – Densities on heavily over-exposed negative

the density range of the negative will be compressed and highlight detail degraded, if not completely lost.

Exposure latitude

We define *latitude* as the factor by which the minimum camera exposure required to give a negative with adequate shadow detail may be multiplied without loss of highlight detail. Latitude is illustrated in Figure 15.18.

We may call the distance along the log E axis between the lowest and highest usable points on the curve the *useful exposure range*.

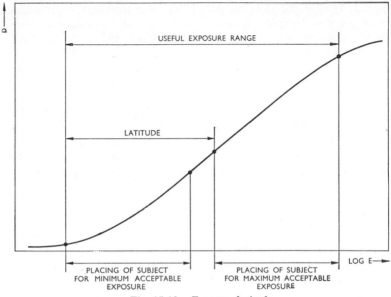

Fig. 15.18 – Exposure latitude

Useful exposure range depends principally upon the emulsion and the degree of development. These two factors also govern latitude, but in addition the latter is dependent upon the subject contrast, i.e., the subject luminance range. This is illustrated in Figure 15.19.

In practice, loss of highlight detail – which sets the upper limit to exposure – often results from loss of resolution due to graininess and irradiation, *before the shoulder of the curve is reached*. As the required level of resolution usually depends upon the negative size employed and the consequent degree of enlargement necessary in making the final print, we may add "size of negative" to the factors given above as governing useful exposure range and latitude. Thus, in general, there is less exposure latitude with a miniature camera than with a large-format camera.

The luminance range of the average subject is less than the useful exposure range of the film, and there is usually considerable latitude in exposure. If, however, we have a subject with luminance range equal to the useful exposure range of the film there is no latitude –

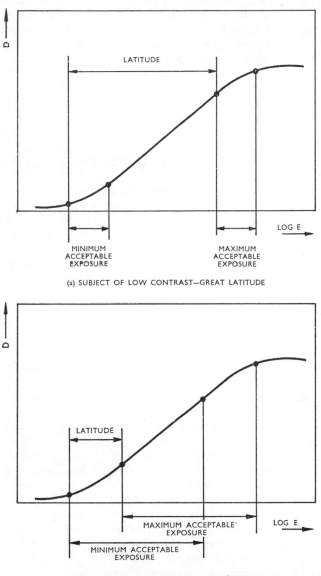

(a) SUBJECT OF LOW CONTRAST—GREAT LATITUDE

(b) SUBJECT OF HIGH CONTRAST—LITTLE LATITUDE

Fig. 15.19 —Effect of subject contrast (luminance range) on latitude

only one exposure is permissible. With the exceptional subject having a luminance range *greater* than the useful exposure range of the film, no exposure will yield a perfect result; we must either lose shadow detail or highlight detail or both. All that we can do is to decide which end of the tone range we can best sacrifice.

If the subject range is below average we have more latitude than usual. In practice, however, this is limited on the under-exposure side by the fact that an exposure too near the minimum will be located entirely on the toe and may result in an unprintably soft negative. It is usually preferable to locate the subject on the characteristic curve in such a position that part at least of it is on the straight-line portion. In this way, better negative contrast is achieved.

The response curve of a photographic paper

The characteristic curve of a paper is obtained in the same way as that of a film or plate, by plotting density against log exposure. Density in this case is *reflection density* (not transmission density) and is defined by the equation:

$$D = \log \frac{1}{R}$$

where R, the *reflection factor*, is the ratio of the light reflected by the image to the ratio of the light reflected by the base. This definition of reflection density is analogous to that of transmission density (page 227).

Figure 15.20 illustrates the general shape of the characteristic curve of a paper. This curve, like that of a negative material, can be divided into four main regions: toe, straight line, shoulder and region of solarization.

The main differences between the curve of a paper and that of a film or plate are:

(1) The shoulder is reached at a relatively low density and turns over sharply, the curve becoming parallel to the log E axis at a D_{max} which rarely exceeds a value of 2·0.

(2) The toe extends to a fairly high density, i.e., is long.

(3) The straight-line portion is short – in some papers, non-existent, the toe running into the shoulder.

(4) The slope of the straight line is generally quite steep compared with the same emulsion on film or glass.

(5) Fog – with normal development – is absent.

Differences (2) and (4) arise from the fact that when a silver image on an opaque base is viewed by reflected (as opposed to transmitted) light its effective density is increased, because light must pass twice through the image.

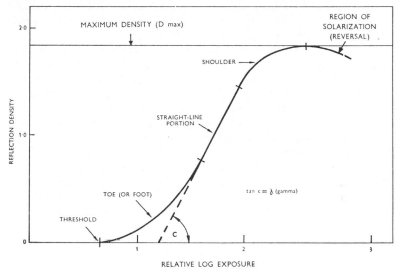

Fig. 15.20 – The "geography" of the characteristic curve of a paper

Maximum black

The practical consequence of (1) above is that the maximum density obtainable on any paper is limited, however long the exposure or the development. The highest value of density which can be obtained for a particular paper with full exposure and development is called the *maximum black* of the paper.

The maximum density obtainable on any given paper depends principally on its surface. It can be seen from Figure 15.21 that light striking the surface of a print undergoes three types of reflection:

(1) Part is reflected by the surface of the gelatin layer in which the silver grains are embedded.

(2) Part is reflected by the silver grains themselves.

(3) The remainder is reflected by the surface of the paper base itself (or the baryta coating on the base).

It is the sum of these three reflections that determines the reflection factor and hence the density of the print.

By increasing the exposure received by a paper, and thus the amount of silver in the image, we can eliminate entirely the reflection from the paper base, but reflections from the gelatin surface of the emulsion and from the individual grains themselves cannot be reduced in this way. It is these reflections, therefore, that set a limit to the maximum black available.

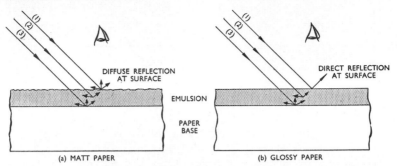

Fig. 15.21 – Diagrammatic representation of the reflection of light striking two papers of differing surface characteristics

The value of the reflection from the surface of the emulsion depends upon the nature of this surface. A print will normally be viewed in such a way that direct reflection from its surface does not enter the eye. We are, therefore, concerned only with the diffuse reflection. Now, the reflection from the surface of a glossy paper is almost entirely direct, so that the amount of light reflected from the surface of such a paper which enters the eye when viewing a print is very small indeed. In these circumstances, the limit to the maximum density of the print is governed principally by the light reflected by the silver image itself. This is usually a little over 1 per cent., corresponding to a maximum black of just under 2·0.

The reflection from the surface of a matt paper, on the other hand, is almost completely diffuse, so that an appreciable amount of light (e.g., 4 per cent.) from the surface of the paper reaches the eye, in addition to the light from the silver image. (There may also be present light reflected from starch which is usually included in the emulsion of matt papers.) The maximum black of matt papers is therefore relatively low. Semi-matt and stipple papers have maximum blacks intermediate between matt and glossy papers. The following figures are typical of the values of maximum black obtainable on papers of the three main types of surface.

Surface	Reflection density
Glossy – glazed	1·85
Glossy – unglazed	1·80
Semi-matt	1·65
Matt	1·30

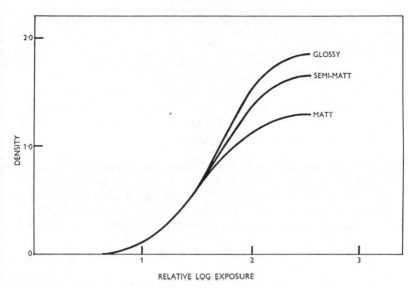

Fig. 15.22 – *Typical characteristic curves of glossy, semi-matt and matt papers*

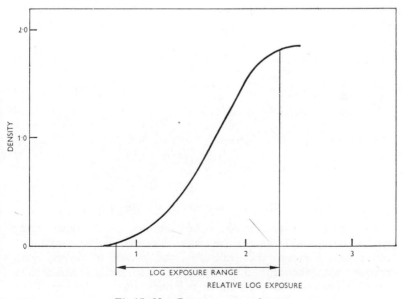

Fig.15 .23 – *Exposure range of a paper*

The effect of variation in maximum black on the characteristic curve is confined largely to the shoulder of the curve, as shown in Figure 15.22.

Exposure range of a paper
The ratio of the exposures corresponding to the highest and lowest points on the curve employed in a normal print is termed the *exposure range* of the paper (Figure 15.23). This may be expressed either in exposure units or in log exposure units.

Variation of the print curve with the type of emulsion
Photographic papers are of three main types: contact (chloride) papers, chlorobromide papers and bromide papers. (See Chapter 21.) The characteristic curves of these papers differ somewhat in shape. To illustrate these differences, characteristic curves of two widely differing papers are shown in Figure 15.24.

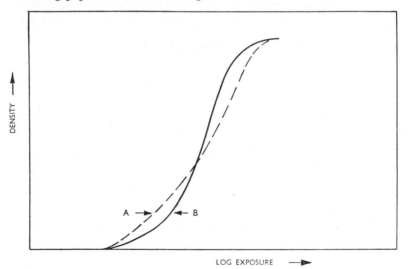

Fig. 15.24 – Characteristic curves of two different papers

It will be seen that although in the examples selected both papers give the same range of tones, i.e., have the same density range, and both have the same exposure range, the growth of density with exposure is not the same in the two cases. With paper A the density grows evenly with the increase in exposure, but with paper B the growth in density is at first slow, then grows more and more rapidly and finally grows less and less rapidly. In practice, paper A would be expected to give better tone separation in the shadows and highlights than paper B. Curve A is typical of chloride papers and curve B of bromide papers; a chlorobromide paper curve would be intermediate between the two.

Variation of the print curve with development

With papers, as with negative materials, the characteristic curve varies with development. Figure 15.25 illustrates the effect of variation in development on the curve of a contact (chloride) paper. The normally recommended development time for this paper, in the developer employed, is 45 to 60 seconds at 20°C.

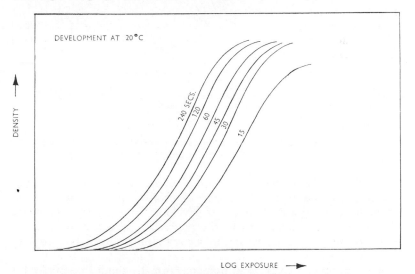

Fig. 15.25 – *Characteristic curves of a typical contact paper for different development times*

Figure 15.26 shows a similar family of curves for a bromide paper. The normally recommended development time for this paper, in the developer employed, is $1\frac{1}{2}$ to 2 minutes at 20°C.

It will be seen that at very short development times the slope of the curve of both contact and bromide papers is less steep than at the recommended time, and no amount of exposure yields maximum black. (In addition, image colour may be unsatisfactory and development uneven). At development times above 30 seconds, the chloride paper curve moves bodily to the left, but no increase in the slope of the curve or decrease in the exposure range is obtained. In other words,

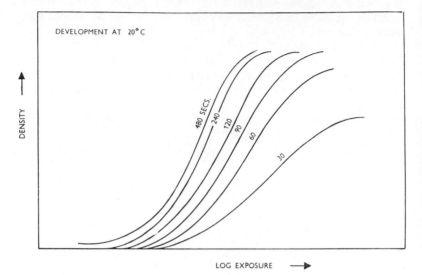

Fig. 15.26 – Characteristic curves of a typical bromide paper for different development times

on prolonged development the speed of the paper increases – and hence the exposure time required in printing is reduced – but no increase in contrast is obtained. If development is greatly prolonged, fog will become excessive and the paper may also become stained. Chlorobromide papers behave in a very similar manner to contact papers.

With bromide papers, development normally requires a minimum of about $1\frac{1}{2}$ minutes. At longer development times the curve moves bodily to the left, but, unlike the curve of a chloride paper, the slope increases slightly. In other words, both speed and contrast of a bromide paper increase on prolonged development. The increase in contrast is not great, but it is sufficient to be of practical value. The *major* effect of variation of development time on papers of all types is, however, on the speed of the paper, i.e., for a given exposure, on the density of the print.

With papers of all types, there is *development latitude* between the two extremes of under- and over-development. With the bromide paper shown in Figure 15.26, this extends from about $1\frac{1}{2}$ minutes to

4 minutes. The ratio of the exposure times required at the shortest and longest acceptable times of development is referred to as the *printing exposure latitude*. It will be apparent that development latitude and exposure latitude are interrelated; both cannot be used at the same time. Thus, when once an exposure has been made there is only one development time that will give a print of the desired density.

Requirements in a print

It is normally desirable in printing that:

(a) All the negative tones should appear in the print.

(b) The print should show the full range of tones between black and white that is capable of being produced on the paper used. (Even in high-key and low-key photographs it is usually desirable that the print should show *some* white and *some* black, however small these areas may be.)

In printing, the exposure of the paper is governed by the densities of the negative; the greater the density of any negative area, the less the exposure, and vice versa. In order, then, to meet both requirements (a) and (b) above, the exposure through the highlight areas of the negative must correspond with the toe of the curve of the printing paper, and the exposure through the shadow areas of the negative must correspond with the shoulder of this curve. Expressed sensitometrically this means that the log exposure range of the paper must equal the density range of the negative.

Now, not all negatives have the same density range; this varies with the luminance range of the subject, the emulsion used, the exposure and the degree of development. Obviously, therefore, no single paper will suit all negatives, because, as we have seen, the exposure range of a paper is a more-or-less fixed characteristic, affected only slightly, if at all, by development. A single paper with a sufficiently long exposure range would enable requirement (a) to be met in all cases, but not requirement (b). Printing papers are therefore produced in a series of *contrast grades*, or *gradations*, each of the papers in the series having a different exposure range.

Paper contrast grades

In Figure 15.27 are shown the characteristic curves of a series of bromide papers. These papers all have the same surface and differ only in their contrast grades, which are described as soft, normal and hard respectively. All three papers have been developed for the same time. It will be noted that the three curves show the same maximum black, but the steepness of the curve *increases* and the exposure range *decreases* as we proceed from the soft grade to the hard. From this we see that the descriptions "soft", "normal" and "hard" apply to the in-

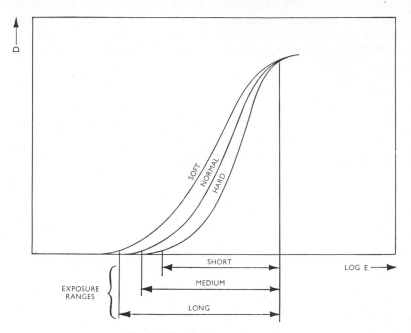

Fig. 15.27 - Paper contrast grades

herent contrasts of the papers themselves, and not to the negatives with which they are to be used. The soft paper – with long exposure range – is, in fact, intended for use with *hard* negatives, with high density range. Conversely, the hard paper – with short exposure range – is intended for use with *soft* negatives, with low density range.

If negatives of the same subject, differing only in contrast, are each printed on papers of the appropriate exposure range, the prints will be practically identical. If, however, an attempt is made to print a negative on a paper with too short an exposure range (i.e., too hard a paper), and exposure is adjusted to give correct density in, say, the highlights, then the shadows will be over-exposed and the result will appear too hard. If, on the other hand, a paper of too long an exposure range is used (i.e., too soft a grade) and exposure is again adjusted for the highlights, the shadow areas of the print will be under-exposed and the result will appear flat.

The softer the grade of paper, i.e., the longer its exposure range, the greater is the exposure latitude (as defined earlier) in printing. It is, however, generally unwise to aim at producing negatives suited to the very softest paper because one then has no grade to fall back upon if for some reason a negative proves to be exceptionally hard. It is, therefore, generally best to aim at negatives suitable for printing on a middle grade of paper.

A simple, if only approximate, check on the exposure range of a paper can be made by giving to a strip of it a series of progressively increasing exposures. The exposure range is the ratio of the exposure required to yield the deepest black that the paper will give, to the time required to produce a just perceptible density. (See also page 271.)

The problem of the subject of high contrast

Meeting the "formal" requirements (a) and (b) on page 255 does not necessarily imply that the resulting print will be technically pleasing. In practice, the print will usually be satisfactory if the subject luminance range is not high, but with a subject of high contrast the result will often appear flat, even though both the formal requirements have been met. This is because the luminance range of a high contrast subject is greater than the maximum range that can be obtained on a paper.

Two remedies are possible. The simplest is to print the negative on a harder grade of paper and to sacrifice detail at either the shadow or the highlight end of the scale. This, in effect, means abandoning requirement (a). A preferred remedy is to use a harder grade of paper but to isolate the various tone-bands within the picture, and treat them individually by "printing-in" or by use of masks. In this way we can obtain the contrast we desire within the various tone-bands of the picture without sacrificing detail at either end of the scale.

Tone reproduction

The relation of the reflection factors of the various areas of a print – or luminances when the print is suitably illuminated – to the corresponding luminances of the subject is referred to as *tone reproduction*. Our object in photography is normally to obtain an accurate reproduction of the various luminances of the original scene, thus keeping each tone in its same relative position in the tone scale. We cannot always do this, but the very least we should strive for is to retain *tone separation* throughout the whole range of tones.

Theoretical perfection aims at obtaining *proportionality* between print luminances and subject luminances throughout the whole range of the subject; *equality* can rarely be hoped for, because the range of luminances possible on a paper is less than the luminance range of the average subject.

The work of Hurter and Driffield

Hurter and Driffield were the first to study the problem of tone reproduction from the sensitometric point of view. Their work extended over the period 1874–1915, their classic paper being published in 1890. At this time, the popular negative materials and printing materials all yielded characteristic curves with a long straight line. Hurter and Driffield took the view that perfect tone rendering in the print could only be achieved by first obtaining a *negative* in which all the opacities were proportional to the luminances of the subject. They stated that, for correct reproduction, exposure should be judged so that all the tones of the subject are recorded on the straight-line portion of the characteristic curve, and the negative should be developed to a gamma of 1·0. This state of affairs is illustrated in Figure 15.28, where it is apparent that if the log exposure differences, A_1, A_2 and A_3 are all equal, then the corresponding density differences B_1, B_2 and B_3 will also be equal to one another and to A_1, A_2 and A_3.

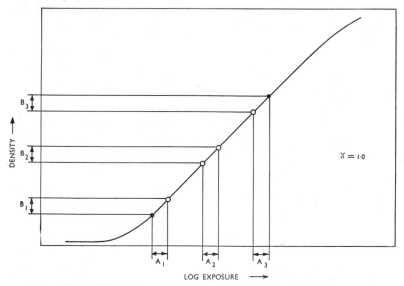

Fig. 15.28 – Using straight-line portion of characteristic curve

From their "correct" negative, Hurter and Driffield made prints on carbon, platinum or gold-toned P.O.P., using only the straight-line portion of the paper curve. All these papers had characteristic curves with a short toe and short shoulder, so that, assuming the papers to be capable of yielding a gamma of 1·0, it was quite a simple matter to obtain technically correct reproduction of many types of subjects. If the gamma of the paper selected was not 1·0 (it was usually greater), correct reproduction could be obtained by developing the negative to a gamma equal to the reciprocal of the print gamma, so that the product of the gammas of negative and positive remained unity. Hurter and Driffield's approach, although not generally applicable to modern materials, is the basis of the methods still used for the preparation of duplicate negatives.

Tone reproduction with modern materials

The introduction of chloride and bromide papers early in the present century altered the situation described above, because these papers have no very long straight-line portion, but a long toe. It is quite impracticable when printing on these materials to use only the straight-line portion of the curve, and, therefore, with such papers, a negative made to Hurter and Driffield's specification does not give correct tone reproduction. Some distortion is in fact inevitable at the printing operation; our aim must be to introduce an equal and opposite distortion in the negative to counteract this.

Now, fast modern negative materials also have a long toe, use of which does in fact introduce some distortion in the right direction. If, therefore, as is usual, we place our shadow tones on the toe of the curve of such a negative material and the highlights on the straight line (page 240), the contrast in the shadows of the negative is lower than in the highlights. In printing, however, the contrast of the paper curve in the shadows – located on the upper half of the curve – is greater than the contrast in the highlights, which are on the toe. The overall effect, therefore, in the final print, is to yield roughly proportional contrast through the whole tone range. This is illustrated in Figure 15.29.

The quadrant diagram

It has been found valuable to employ graphical methods to study the problems of tone reproduction, one very useful method being the so-called *quadrant diagram* originated by L. A. Jones. This enables practical problems in tone reproduction to be studied from a scientific point of view. The simplest form of quadrant diagram is illustrated in Figure 15.30. This employs four quadrants, representing the negative, the print and the overall reproduction, the remaining quadrant being merely a transfer quadrant. For a more complete solution of the problem, other quadrants may be added as desired, to illustrate the effects of flare, viewing conditions, intensification or reduction, etc.

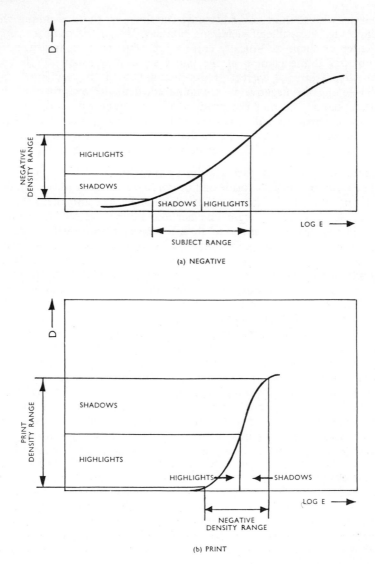

Fig. 15.29 – Obtaining proportional contrast in print

In quadrant 1 of Figure 15.30, the densities of the negative have been plotted against the log luminances of the original scene. If the camera

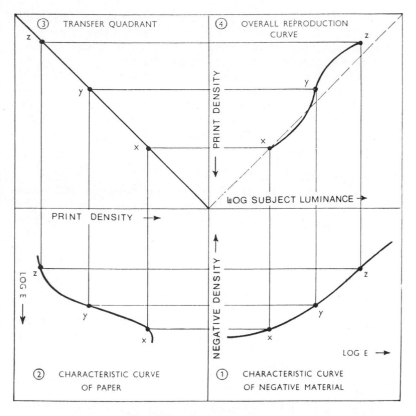

Fig. 15.30 – A quadrant diagram

is free from flare, this curve will be identical with the characteristic curve of the material, in which density is plotted against the exposure received by the film. In quadrant 2 is shown the characteristic curve of the printing paper. This is turned through 90° in a clockwise direction from its normal position to enable density values on the negative to be transferred directly to the exposure scale of the positive, since it is the negative densities which modulate the exposure on the print.

To relate print densities and scene luminances we draw lines parallel to the axes to link corresponding points on the negative and positive curves, turning the lines proceeding from the positive curve through 90° in the transfer quadrant to intersect the lines from the negative curve in quadrant 4. By linking corresponding points, such as x, y and z, for every part of the negative and positive curves we obtain an *overall reproduction curve* as shown. For exact reproduction this curve should take the form of a straight line at 45° to the axes. In practice, it is always more-or-less S-shaped, owing to the negative and positive characteristics. Flattening at the bottom of the reproduction curve indicates tone compression in the shadows, arising from the toe of the negative characteristic. Flattening at the top of the curve indicates tone compression in the highlights arising from the toe of the print characteristic.

Reciprocity failure

The reciprocity law, enunciated by Bunsen and Roscoe in 1862, states that the photographic effect is dependent simply upon the total light energy employed, i.e., upon the product of the exposure time, t, and the illumination on the film, I, time being a reciprocal of illumination, and vice versa. Assuming that the reciprocity law holds, then if either illumination or time is varied to suit practical conditions, the same density will be obtained, provided that the other factor is varied in such a way as to keep the product E (in the equation $E = I.t$, page 225) constant.

Abney first drew attention to the fact that the photographic effect depends on the actual values of I and t, and not solely on their product. This failure of the reciprocity law is termed *reciprocity failure*. Reciprocity failure arises because the effect of exposure on a photographic material depends on the rate at which the energy is supplied.

All emulsions exhibit reciprocity failure to some extent, but it is usually serious only at very high or very low levels of illumination, and for much ordinary photography the reciprocity law can be considered to hold. For this reason, we have assumed that it holds in this book so far. In the sensitometric laboratory, however, the effects of reciprocity failure cannot be ignored, nor can they in certain practical applications of photography.

Practical effects of reciprocity failure

Reciprocity failure is encountered in practice as a falling off in speed at extremely high and extremely low levels of illumination, as a falling off in contrast at high levels of illumination, and as an increase in contrast at low levels of illumination. The degree of the falling off in speed and the region at which maximum speed is obtained varies from material to material. The effects of reciprocity failure are illustrated in Figures 15.31–15.33.

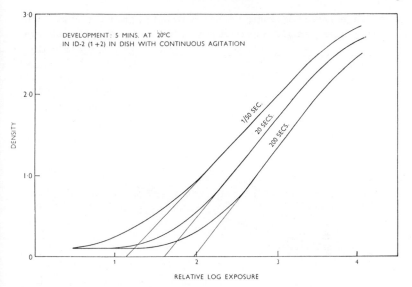

Fig. 15.31 – *Characteristic curves of a press plate for different exposure times*

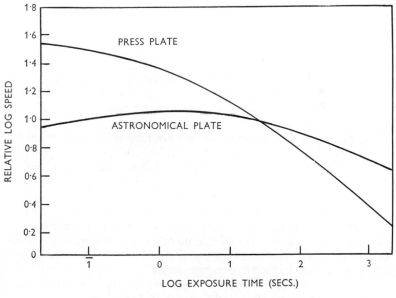

Fig. 15.32 – *Reciprocity failure – effect on speed*

It will be noted in Figure 15.32 that the variation in speed with exposure time – and therefore illumination level – is quite different

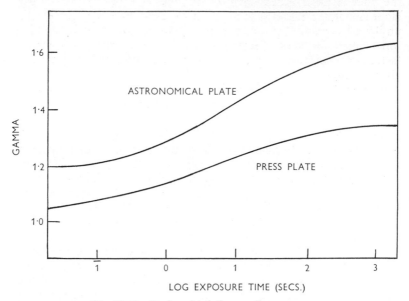

Fig. 15.33 – Reciprocity failure – effect on contrast

for the two types of emulsion shown. In manufacture, emulsions are designed so that the optimum intensity is close to the intensity normally employed. Thus, the fast press plate illustrated is intended for use at high intensities, with exposures of a fraction of a second, and the astronomical plate for use at low intensities, with exposures running into minutes or hours.

The fall-off in contrast at short exposure times assumes practical importance with high-voltage electronic flash lamps, which give exposures of the order of 1/5000th second or less. Then, the fall-off in contrast is such that it is normally desirable to increase development times by about 50 per cent. to compensate for it.

As the result of reciprocity failure, a series of graded exposures made on a time scale (page 268) yields a result different from an intensity scale of exposures. Consequently, in sensitometry, a scale appropriate to the conditions in use must be chosen if the resulting curves are to bear a true relation to practice.

For the same reason, filter factors (page 293) depend to a very marked degree on whether the increase in exposure of the filtered negative is obtained by increasing the intensity of exposure (e.g., by varying the camera stop), or by prolonging the exposure time. In the former case the filter factor is independent of the time of exposure, but in the latter case it depends largely upon the exposure time required by the unfiltered negative. Two types of filter factor are therefore quoted for some types of work: "intensity-scale" factors and "time-scale" factors. (An explanation of the terms intensity-scale and time-scale is given on page 268.)

Because of reciprocity failure, exposure times for the making of "giant" enlargements are sometimes unexpectedly long (page 382).

Intermittency effect

An exposure given in a series of instalments does not necessarily lead to the same result as a continuous exposure of the same total duration. This variation is known as the *intermittency effect*. It is associated with reciprocity failure, and its magnitude therefore varies with the material.

In practical photography, the intermittency effect is not of importance. In sensitometry, however, the effect cannot be ignored and many sensitometers give intermittent exposures. It is found, however, that a continuous exposure and an intermittent exposure of the same *average* intensity produce similar effects when the frequency of the flash exceeds a certain critical value, which varies with the intensity level. It is normally important, therefore, that intermittent exposures given in a sensitometer should be made at a rate above the critical frequency.

Sensitometric practice

It would be possible to construct the characteristic curve of an emulsion – or at least part of the curve – from a picture negative, by measuring the luminances of the various parts of the subject and plotting against them the densities of the corresponding areas of the negative. This is illustrated in Figure 15.34.

This would, however, be an exceedingly laborious method if many curves were required, and it is not normally adopted. Usually, a standard "negative" is produced by giving a known range of exposures to the material under test. The production of characteristic curves by this method involves:

(1) Exposure of a strip of the material in a graded series of exposures; this is carried out in a *sensitometer*.

(2) Processing of the exposed material under controlled conditions.

(3) Measurement of the densities obtained; this is carried out in a *densitometer*.

(4) Plotting of the results.

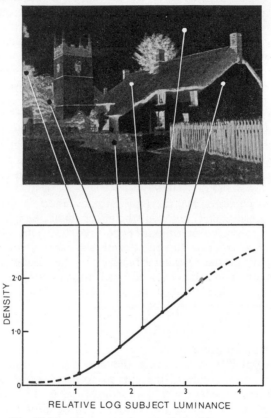

Fig. 15.34 – Characteristic curve derived from a negative

Sensitometry requires careful work and – to be of fullest value – the use of special apparatus. In manufacturers' laboratories, where the production of characteristic curves is a routine, elaborate apparatus, usually designed by the manufacturer's own research staff, is employed.

Sensitometers

A *sensitometer* is an instrument for exposing a photographic material in a graded series of steps, the values of which are accurately known. The essentials of a sensitometer are:

(1) *A light source of standard intensity and colour quality.* Many sources have been proposed and used at various times. The International Congress of Photography held at Dresden in 1931 ratified the proposals put forward at an earlier congress to adopt the vacuum tungsten lamp operating at a colour temperature of 2360K* screened with a Davis-Gibson filter as daylight standard for negative materials. This quality of light is very near to that of mean noon sunlight at Washington. When sources of higher power are required, gas-filled lamps operating at colour temperatures between 2360K and 2850K, suitably filtered, may be employed.

(a) SECTOR WHEEL   (b) FALLING PLATE

Fig. 15.35 – Two types of time-scale sensitometer shutter

(2) *A means of modulating the light intensity.* To produce the graded series of exposures, it is possible to alter either the intensity of illumination or the time for which the exposure lasts. As already stated, because of reciprocity failure the two methods will not necessarily give the same results, and, to obtain sensitometric data which will correctly indicate the behaviour of the material under the

---

* The choice of 2360K appears to have followed from the fact that this was supposed to be the colour temperature of the acetylene lamp – an earlier standard.

conditions of use, the exposure times and intensities should be comparable with those which the material is designed to receive in practice.

A series of exposures in which the scale is obtained by varying the intensity – referred to as an *intensity scale* – can conveniently be achieved by use of a neutral step wedge (page 299). A series of exposures in which the scale is obtained by varying the time – referred to as a *time scale* – may be achieved by use of a rotating sector wheel (Figure 15.35a), a falling plate (Figure 15.35b), or, as in the Eastman Type IIb Sensitometer, a sectored cylindrical drum.

Whichever system of modulation is chosen, a sensitometer is designed so that the exposures increase logarithmically along the length of the strip. The steps selected are usually $\times 2$, $\times \sqrt{2}$ or $\times \sqrt[3]{2}$, i.e., the log exposure steps are 0·3, 0·15 or 0·1. If, for any reason, it is desired to interrupt the exposure, this must be done in such a way that the intermittency effect (page 265) does not affect the results. Figure 15.36 shows a typical sensitometric strip. This particular example was produced in an intensity-scale sensitometer, being exposed behind a step wedge.

Fig. 15.36 – A sensitometric strip

As the state of affairs obtaining in the camera is best represented by an intensity scale of exposures, sensitometers used for process control are preferably of the intensity-scale type. Early commercial sensitometers were usually time-scale instruments, because the design problems with such a means of exposure modulation are easier, but this was not a serious drawback. On occasion, however, it did cause confusion, and modern commercial sensitometers are nearly always intensity-scale instruments.

Densitometers

The name *densitometer* is given to special forms of photometer designed to measure photographic densities. Instruments designed to measure the densities of films and plates are described as *transmission densitometers*, while those designed to measure papers are termed *reflection densitometers*. Some densitometers are designed to enable both transmission and reflection densities to be measured on the one instrument.

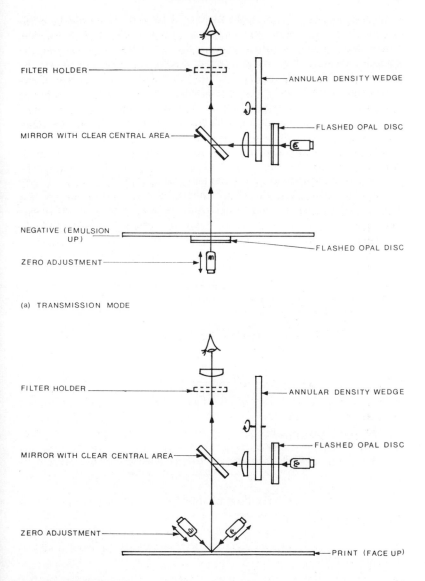

FILTER HOLDER

ANNULAR DENSITY WEDGE

FLASHED OPAL DISC

MIRROR WITH CLEAR CENTRAL AREA

NEGATIVE (EMULSION UP)

FLASHED OPAL DISC

ZERO ADJUSTMENT

(a) TRANSMISSION MODE

FILTER HOLDER

ANNULAR DENSITY WEDGE

FLASHED OPAL DISC

MIRROR WITH CLEAR CENTRAL AREA

ZERO ADJUSTMENT

PRINT (FACE UP)

(b) REFLECTION MODE

Fig. 15.37 – Arrangement of the Kodak RT Colour Densitometer

Densitometers can be broadly classified into two types; visual densitometers and photo-electric densitometers. The earliest densitometers were visual instruments and, although density measurements in quantity are nowadays invariably carried out on photo-electric instruments, visual instruments are still of value when only a few readings are required, and eye-strain is unlikely to be a problem. They have the advantages of simplicity and relative inexpensiveness. The Kodak RT Colour Densitometer is a widely used visual instrument designed to enable both transmission and reflection densities to be measured. The principle of this instrument is shown diagrammatically in Figure 15.37.

Photo-electric densitometers, sometimes termed physical, or electronic, densitometers are of many different types, ranging from simple direct-reading instruments to instruments with highly sophisticated circuits employing a null system, with, in some instances, automatic plotting of the results.

The essentials of a direct-reading instrument are a light source and a photo-electric cell in a well-defined geometrical arrangement to each other and to the specimen, the photo-electric cell being connected to an indicating or recording device either directly, or, more usually, via an amplifier (Figure 15.38).

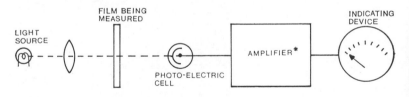

* May be omitted if photo-electric cell
  is of photo-voltaic type

*Fig. 15.38 Schematic arrangement of direct-reading
photo-electric transmission densitometer*

Widely used direct-reading photo-electric densitometers include the EEL Densitometer, employing a selenium photo-electric cell, and the Baldwin Densitometer employing a vacuum photo-electric cell. Both make provision for the measurement of transmission and reflection densities.

Elementary sensitometry
An elementary form of sensitometry, which, although not of a high degree of precision, can be of real practical value in testing the per-

formance of sensitised materials or photographic solutions, can be carried out with nothing more elaborate than a step wedge and a simple visual densitometer. If a commercial step wedge is not available, a suitable wedge can be made by giving a stepped series of exposures to an ordinary film or plate. Useful step increases in a wedge used for this purpose are density values of 0·15 for the testing of films and plates and 0·1 for testing papers.

A strip of the material under test is exposed behind the wedge by contact, or the wedge may be illuminated from the rear and photographed with a camera. If the latter procedure is adopted, care must be taken to eliminate possible causes of flare. The densities obtained on the strip are then plotted against the densities of the wedge – which govern the exposure. The wedge densities are plotted to increase from right to left, this corresponding with an exposure of the strip increasing from left to right in the usual way.

Simple sensitometry of this type may be used for various purposes, e.g.:

(1) To study the effect of increasing development on the speed and contrast of an emulsion.

(2) To compare the emulsion speeds and contrasts yielded by two developers.

(3) To compare the speeds of two emulsions.

(4) To compare the contrasts of two emulsions.

(5) To determine filter factors.

(6) To measure the exposure range of a printing paper.

The candle-power, distance, etc., of the lamp used are needed only if we wish to find the *absolute* speed of a material. All the characteristics listed above can be studied without this information.

CHAPTER 16

Spectral Sensitivity
of Photographic Materials

THE inherent sensitivity to light of the silver halides is confined to a limited range of wavelengths. This range includes the blue-violet region of the visible spectrum, the ultra-violet region and shorter wavelengths extending to the limit of the known spectrum – including x-rays and gamma-rays (see Figure 2.1). This applies, in general terms, to all types of emulsion – chloride, bromide, iodobromide, etc. – although the position of the long-wave cut-off of sensitivity varies slightly with the type of emulsion, as shown in Figure 16.1.

Response of photographic materials to shorter than visible radiation

Despite the fact that the silver halides have an inherent sensitivity to all radiation of shorter wavelengths than the visible, the recording of such radiation involves special problems. In the first place, the emulsion itself (the *grains*, not the gelatin) starts to absorb radiation shorter than about 400nm. The result is that images produced by ultra-violet radiation lie near the surface of the emulsion, since the radiation is unable to penetrate very far. Then, at wavelengths shorter than about 330nm, the radiation is absorbed by glass. To record beyond this region, quartz optics have to be employed.

At about 230nm, absorption of radiation by the *gelatin* of the emulsion becomes serious. To record beyond this region, Schumann emulsions or Ilford Q emulsions are employed. Schumann emulsions have an extremely low gelatin content, and in Q emulsions, by the adoption of a particular manufacturing technique, the concentration of the silver halide grains is made much higher at the surface than in the depths of the emulsion layer. Particular care must be taken that the surface of both types of emulsion is not abraded, or stress marks will result. As an alternative to the use of such special emulsions, fluorescence can be employed to obtain records in this region. Ordinary photographic plates are employed, and the emulsion is coated with

Vaseline, or other mineral oil, which fluoresces during the exposure to form a visible image to which the plate is sensitive. The Vaseline is removed before processing, by bathing the plate in a suitable solvent.

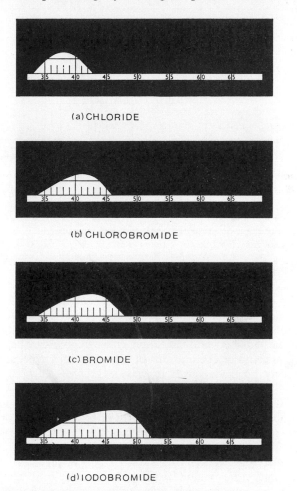

(a) CHLORIDE

(b) CHLOROBROMIDE

(c) BROMIDE

(d) IODOBROMIDE

Fig. 16.1 –Wedge spectrograms of unsensitised chloride, chlorobromide, bromide and iodobromide emulsions (to tungsten light at 2850K)

The region 230 to 360nm, sometimes referred to as the "quartz U.V. region", is of particular importance in spectrography because many elements display characteristic lines here. By a fortunate coincidence, the gamma of many emulsions which, in general, varies considerably with wavelength, is comparatively constant throughout this region. This is illustrated in Figure 16.2.

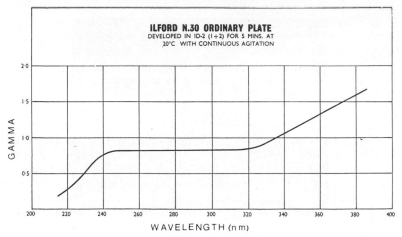

Fig. 16.2 – Relationship between gamma and wavelength in the ultra-violet for Ilford N. 30 Ordinary Plate

Beyond about 180nm, radiation is absorbed by air, and recording has to be carried out in a vacuum. At about the same wavelength, absorption of radiation by quartz becomes serious, and fluorite optics or reflection gratings have to be employed. Beyond 120nm, fluorite absorbs the radiation and reflection gratings only can be employed. Using Schumann or Q emulsions in vacuum with a reflection grating, records may be made down to wavelengths of a few nanometres, where the ultra-violet region merges with the soft x-ray (Grenz ray) region. This technique is known as *vacuum spectrography*.

No problem of absorption by gelatin or by the equipment arises in the x-ray or gamma-ray regions. In fact, the problem here is that the radiation is absorbed very little by anything – including the emulsion – and it is therefore necessary to employ a very thick emulsion layer to obtain an image. For manufacturing reasons, this is normally applied in two layers – one on each side of the film base. Another way of getting round the difficulty which arises from the transparency of emulsions to x-rays is to make use of fluorescent salt intensifying screens. Such screens, placed in contact with the x-ray film – one on either side – emit under x-ray excitation blue or green light to which the film is very sensitive. For very short-wave x-rays and gamma-rays such as are used in industrial radiography, metal screens can similarly be used. When exposed to x-rays or gamma-rays these screens eject electrons which are absorbed by the photographic material. The metal employed for such screens is usually lead.

Although invisible to the eye, ultra-violet radiation is present in daylight, and – to a much lesser extent – in tungsten light. Ultra-violet radiation from about 330 to 400 nm, sometimes referred to as the "near U.V. region", therefore affects the results obtained in ordinary photographs (see page 305). Shorter wavelengths than about 330 nm are absorbed by the lens.

Response of photographic materials to visible radiation

Photographic materials which rely on the unmodified sensitivity of the silver halides are referred to variously as *blue-sensitive, non-colour-sensitive, ordinary* or *colour-blind* materials. The materials used by the early photographers were of this type. Because such materials lack sensitivity to the green and red regions of the spectrum, they are incapable of recording colours correctly; in particular, reds and greens appear too dark – even black – and blues too light, the effect being most marked with saturated colours (see Chapter 17).

For some types of work this is of no consequence. Thus, blue-sensitive materials are still in general use today for printing papers, and for negative materials used with black-and-white subjects. Even coloured subjects such as landscapes, architectural subjects and portraits can be recorded with a fair degree of success on blue-sensitive materials – witness the many acceptable photographs which have survived from the days when these were the only materials available. One of the reasons for success in these cases is that the colours of most natural objects are not saturated, but are in fact whites and greys which are merely tinged with one colour or group of colours (page 284). Photographs on blue-sensitive materials are thus records of the blue content of the colours, and, since the blue content is often not very far from being proportional to the total luminosity of the various parts of the objects, a reasonably good picture is obtained.

Nevertheless, when the colours are not subdued or diluted, blue-sensitive materials show their deficiencies very markedly, and photographs in which many objects appear far darker than the observer sees them cannot be regarded as entirely satisfactory.* It is, therefore,

---

* That such photographs were regarded as satisfactory for so long was because photographers were so accustomed to an incorrect rendering that a sort of photographic convention was set up in their minds. They regarded the reproduction of blue sky as white and bright red as black as normal.

desirable to find some means of conferring on emulsions a sensitivity to the green and red regions of the spectrum while leaving the blue sensitivity substantially unchanged.

Colour sensitising

It was discovered by Vogel in 1873 that a silver halide emulsion can be rendered sensitive to green light as well as to blue by adding a suitable dye to the emulsion. Later, dyes capable of extending the sensitivity into the red and even the infra-red region of the spectrum were discovered. This use of dyes is termed *dye sensitising, colour sensitising* or *spectral sensitising*. The dyes, termed *colour sensitisers,* may be added to the emulsion at the time of manufacture, or the coated film may be bathed in a solution of the dye. In all commercial emulsions today the former procedure is adopted, although when *colour-sensitive materials* were first introduced it was not uncommon for the user to bathe his own materials. The amount of dye required is extremely small, sufficient only to provide a layer 1 molecule thick over the surface of the crystals of the emulsion.

The sensitivity conferred by dyes is always additional to the sensitivity of the undyed emulsion, and is always added on the long wavelength side. The extent to which an emulsion has been dye-sensitised necessarily makes a very considerable difference to the amount and quality of light which is permissible during manufacture and in processing (page 300).

For practical purposes, colour-sensitive materials may be divided into three main classes. These are:

(1) Orthochromatic.
(2) Panchromatic.
(3) Infra-red-sensitive.

Orthochromatic materials

In the first colour-sensitive materials, the sensitivity was extended from the blue region of the spectrum into the green. The sensitivity of the resulting materials thus included ultra-violet, violet, blue and green. In the first commercial plates of this type, introduced in 1882, the dye eosin was used and the plates were described as *isochromatic,* denoting equal response to all colours. This claim was of course exaggerated, since the plates were not sensitive to red at all, and the response to the remaining colours was by no means equal.

In 1884, dry plates employing erythrosin as the sensitising dye were introduced. In these, the relation in the rendering of blue and green was improved and the plates were termed *orthochromatic =* "correct colour". Again, the description was an exaggeration. The term orthochromatic is now applied generally to all green-sensitive materials. Most modern green-sensitive materials have the improved type of sensitising of which erythrosin was the first example. They are sometimes said to be *highly*, or *fully*, orthochromatic, materials of the original isochromatic type being described as *medium* orthochromatic. Although orthochromatic materials do not give correct colour-rendering, they give results which are acceptable for many purposes, provided that the dominant colours of the subject do not contain much red.

Panchromatic materials

Materials sensitised to the red region of the spectrum as well as to green, and thus sensitive to the whole of the visible spectrum, are termed *panchromatic*, i.e., sensitive to "all colours". Although red sensitising dyes were discovered within a few years of Vogel's original discovery, the sensitivity conferred by the red sensitising dyes at first available was quite small, and it was not until 1906 that the first commercial panchromatic plates were marketed.

There are many different types of panchromatic sensitising, but the differences between some of them are quite slight. The main variations lie in the position of the long-wave cut-off of the red sensitivity, and in the ratio of the red sensitivity to the total sensitivity. Usually, the red sensitivity is made to extend up to 660 to 670nm. The sensitivity of the human eye is extremely low beyond 670nm and an emusion with considerable sensitivity beyond this region gives an infra-red effect.

Panchromatic materials have two main advantages over earlier types of materials. In the first place, they yield improved rendering of coloured objects, skies, etc., without the use of filters. In the second place, they make possible the control of the rendering of colours by means of filters (Chapter 18). Where the production of a negative is concerned, and the aim is the production of a correct representation in monochrome of a coloured subject, panchromatic emulsions must be used. Again, when it is necessary to modify the tone relationships between differently coloured parts of the subject, fullest control can be obtained only by the use of panchromatic materials in conjunction with filters.

Infra-red materials

The classes of colour-sensitised materials so far described meet all the requirements of ordinary photography. For special purposes, however, emulsions sensitive to yet longer wavelengths can be made;

these are termed *infra-red materials*. Infra-red sensitising dyes were discovered early in this century, but infra-red materials were not widely used until the nineteen-thirties. As the result of successive discoveries, the sensitivity given by infra-red sensitising dyes has been extended in stages to the region of 1200nm. The absorption of radiation around 1400nm by water would make recording at longer wavelengths difficult, even if dyes sensitising in the region were available. Infra-red materials are invariably used with a filter over the camera lens or light source, to prevent any visible or ultra-violet radiation from entering the camera.

Infra-red materials find use in aerial photography for the penetration of haze, in medicine for the penetration of tissue, in scientific and technical photography for the differentiation of inks, fabrics etc. which appear identical to the eye, and in general photography for the pictorial effects they produce. The first of these applications – the penetration of haze – depends upon the reduced scattering exhibited by radiation of long wavelength (see page 305). The other applications depend upon the different reflecting powers and transparencies of objects to infra-red and visible radiation.

Lenses are not usually corrected for infra-red, so that when focusing with infra-red emulsions it is necessary to increase the camera extension (i.e., to rack out) very slightly. This is because the focal length of an ordinary lens for infra-red is greater than the focal length for visible radiation.* Some modern cameras have a special infra-red focusing setting for this purpose. With others, the increase necessary must be found by trial. It will usually be of the order of 0·3 to 0·4 per cent. of the focal length.

Other uses of dye sensitisation

Sensitising dyes have other uses besides the improvement of the colour response of an emulsion. In particular, when a material is to be exposed to a light source which is rich in green or red and deficient in blue, its speed may be increased by colour sensitising. Thus, some photographic papers are colour-sensitised to obtain increased speed

---

* This applies even when an achromatic or an apochromatic lens is used. In an achromat the foci for green and blue-violet (usually) are made to coincide, and the other rays in the visible spectrum then come to a focus very near to the common focus of green and blue-violet (page 113). Similar considerations apply to an apochromatic lens, Infra-red rays, however, are of appreciably longer wavelength than any part of the visible spectrum and do not come to the same focus as the visible rays. Lenses can be especially corrected for infra-red but such lenses are not generally available.

without affecting other characteristics of the material such as grain size.

Determination of the colour sensitivity of a material

The colour sensitivity of a material can be most readily determined in the studio by photographing a colour chart consisting of coloured patches with a reference scale of greys. In one such chart it has been arranged that the different steps of the neutral half have the same luminosities as the corresponding parts of the coloured half, when viewed in daylight. If a photograph is taken of the chart, the colour sensitivity of the emulsion being tested, relative to that of the eye, is readily determined by comparing the densities of the image of the coloured half with the densities of the image of the neutral half. The value of the test is increased if a second exposure be made on a material of known colour sensitivity, to serve as a basis for comparison.

A more precise, yet still quite practical, method of measuring the colour sensitivity of a material is to determine the exposure factors of a selection of filters (page 293). With panchromatic materials, three filters – tricolour blue, green and red – are preferably used. With orthochromatic materials, measurement of the minus blue filter factor alone provides all the information that is usually required.

In the laboratory, the colour sensitivity of a material is usually expressed in terms of filter factors or illustrated by means of a wedge spectrogram.

Wedge spectrograms

The spectral response of a photographic material is most completely illustrated by means of a curve known as a *wedge spectrogram*, and manufacturers usually supply such curves for their various materials. A wedge spectrogram, which indicates the relative sensitivity of an emulsion at different wavelengths through the spectrum, is obtained by exposing the material behind a photographic wedge (page 299) in an instrument known as a *wedge spectrograph*. The spectrograph produces an image in the form of a spectrum on the material, the wedge being placed between the light source and the emulsion. A typical optical arrangement is shown in Figure 16.3.

Examples of the results obtained in a wedge spectrograph are shown in Figure 16.4, which comprises wedge spectrograms of typical materials of each of the principal classes of colour sensitivity. We have already seen other examples of wedge spectrograms in Figure 16.1. The outline of a wedge spectrogram forms a curve showing the colour sensitivity of the material at any wavelength. Sensitivity is indicated on a logarithmic scale, the magnitude of which depends upon the

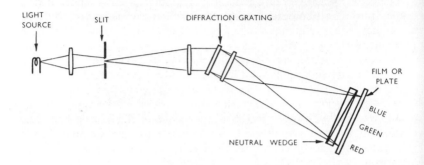

Fig. 16.3 – Optical arrangement of wedge spectrograph

gradient of the wedge employed. All the spectrograms illustrated here were made using a continuous wedge, but step wedges are sometimes used.

The shapes of the curves in Figure 16.4 are of interest. In the first place, the short wave cut-off at the left of each curve is characteristic, not of the material, but of the apparatus in which the spectrograms were produced, and arises because of the ultra-violet absorption by glass, to which reference was made earlier. Secondly, the curves of the colour-sensitised materials are seen to consist of a number of peaks; these correspond approximately with the absorption bands of the dyes employed.

It will also be apparent that the shape of each curve is dependent not only on the sensitivity of the material but on the quality of the light employed. All the curves shown in Figure 16.4 were made to a tungsten light source, with a colour temperature of approximately 2850K. Wedge spectrograms of the same materials, made to daylight, would show higher peaks in the blue region and lower peaks in the red.

The wedge spectrogram of the infra-red material in Figure 16.4 shows a gap in the green region of the spectrum. This permits the handling of the material by a green safelight (page 300). It should be noted, however, that infra-red-sensitive materials do not necessarily have this "green gap".

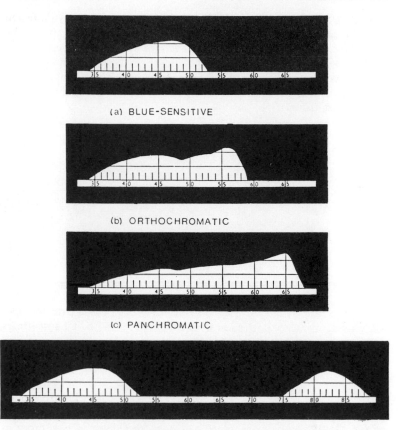

(a) BLUE-SENSITIVE

(b) ORTHOCHROMATIC

(c) PANCHROMATIC

(d) INFRA-RED

Fig. 16.4 – Wedge spectrograms of typical materials of each of the principal classes of colour sensitivity (to tungsten light at 2850K)

Uses of wedge spectrograms

Although they are not suitable for accurate measurements, wedge spectrograms do provide a ready way of presenting information. They are commonly used:

(1) *To show the way in which the response of an emulsion is distributed through the spectrum.*

(2) *To compare different emulsions.* In this case, the same light source must be used for the two exposures. It is normal practice to employ as a source a filtered tungsten lamp giving light equivalent in

quality to daylight (approx. 5400K) or an unfiltered tungsten lamp operating at 2850K, whichever is the more appropriate.

(3) *To compare the quality of light emitted by different sources.* For this type of test, all exposures must be made on the same emulsion.

(4) *To determine the spectral absorption of colour filters* (Chapter 18). For this, all exposures must be made to the same light source and on the same emulsion.

CHAPTER 17

The Reproduction of Colours
in Black-and-white

IN black-and-white photography, all objects of whatever colour are reproduced as shades of grey varying from black to white, i.e., in monochrome. The eye will accept a black-and-white picture as a true representation of coloured objects provided that the greys in which the colours are reproduced are related to the brightnesses of the original colours. To understand how this is achieved we need to know something about the response to different colours of the eye and of the principal types of photographic materials.

Colours in the spectrum
We saw in Chapter 4 that white light can be separated by means of a prism into light of different colours – notably violet, blue, green, yellow, orange and red. We also saw that these colours correspond to different wavelengths. White light is thus seen to be a *mixture* of light of different wavelengths. Light consisting of a *single* wavelength, or narrow band of wavelengths, is invariably strongly coloured, colours of this type being referred to as *spectral*, or *spectrum, colours*.

Colours of natural objects
The pure colours of the spectrum are rarely to be found in the objects which we see around us; instead we see many colours not to be found in the spectrum. This does not mean that light of a different nature is emitted by these objects, but simply arises from their power of selective absorption or subtraction. Objects are visible because of the light which they pass on to our eyes, most objects deriving this light from some outside source of illumination. Coloured objects appear so because they absorb some wavelengths and reflect others.

Let us illustrate this with an example. Suppose that we have a lamp giving out white light, and that under its illumination we examine a number of pieces of coloured paper. Now, although we can discern six or more colours in the spectrum of white light, for many purposes we may consider it as a mixture of three main colours – blue (properly blue-violet), green and red (see page 12). Suppose the first piece of paper reflects only the blue part of the light falling on it, the green and red portions being absorbed. Then, when illuminated by white light, it will look blue, and we say that it is a "blue" piece of paper. Similarly a "green" paper will reflect green and absorb blue and red, and a red paper will reflect red and absorb blue and green. Sometimes, an object reflects more than one of the three groups. For example, one of the papers may reflect green and red, absorbing only the blue; this paper will look yellow. In the same way, a paper reflecting blue and red will look magenta, while a paper reflecting blue and green will have the blue-green colour which we call "cyan". In general, any common object assumes a colour which is a mixture of the spectral colours present in the illuminant and not absorbed by the object.

The colours described in the above example were all produced as a result of the complete absorption of one or more of the main colour groupings of white light. Such colours are termed *pure*, or *saturated*, colours. The pigments of most commonly occurring objects, however, absorb generally and reflect generally – no part of the spectrum being reflected completely and no part absorbed completely. The colours of natural objects – sometimes referred to as *pigmentary* colours – therefore contain all wavelengths to some extent, with certain wavelengths predominating. They are of much lower purity (saturation) than the colours of the papers supposed in our example. Thus, a red rose, for example, appears red not because it reflects red light only, but because it reflects red light better than it reflects blue and green.

Colours occurring in natural objects	Degree of reflection in indicated region of spectrum		
	Blue-violet	Green	Red
Red	Badly (5%)	Badly (5%)	Very well (45%)
Orange	Badly (6%)	Fairly well (15%)	Very well (50%)
Yellow	Badly (7%)	Very well (50%)	Extremely well (70%)
Brown	Very badly (4%)	Badly (8%)	Less badly (12%)
Flesh	Well (25%)	Well (30%)	Very well (40%)
Blue	Well (30%)	Rather badly (15%)	Badly (5%)
Green	Badly (6%)	Rather badly (10%)	Badly (7%)

Table 17.1 – Typical reflectances of natural objects in the three main regions of the spectrum

Table 17.1 shows the degree of reflection in the three principal regions of the spectrum, of some of the main colours in the world around us. It will be seen that the general rules connecting the kind of absorption with the resulting impression are the same as with the pure colours of the papers considered in the example above. The figures quoted in the table, which are approximate only, are percentages of the amount of incident light in the region concerned, not of the total incident light.

Effect of light source on appearance of colours

We noted above that the colour assumed by an object depends both upon the object itself and on the illuminant. This is strikingly illustrated by a red bus, which by the light of sodium street lamps appears brown. We are accustomed to viewing most objects by daylight, and therefore take this as our reference. Thus, although, by the light of sodium lamps, the bus appears brown, we still regard it as a red bus.

The change from daylight to light from a sodium lamp represents an extreme change in the quality of the illuminant, viz., from a continuous to a line spectrum. The change from daylight to tungsten light – i.e., from one continuous source to another of different energy distribution – has much less effect on the visual appearance of colours. In fact, over a wide range of energy distributions the change in colour is not perceived by the eye. This is because of its property of *chromatic adaptation*, as a result of which the eye continues to visualise the objects as though they were in daylight.

If we are to obtain a faithful record of the appearance of coloured objects, our aim in photography must be to reproduce them as the eye sees them in daylight. Unlike the eye, however, photographic materials do not adapt themselves to changes in the light source, but faithfully record the effects of any such changes. If, therefore, a photograph is not being taken by daylight, the difference in colour quality between daylight and the source employed must be taken into account if technically correct colour rendering is to be obtained. Colour filters find application in this connection. (See Chapter 18.)

In practice, a technically correct rendering is rarely required in black-and-white photography, and changes in the colour quality of the illuminant can for much work be ignored. In colour photography, however, very small changes in the colour quality of the illuminant may produce significant changes in the result, and accurate control of the quality of the lighting is therefore required, if good results are to be obtained.

Response of the eye to colours

Our sensation of colour is due to a mechanism of vision which is complicated, and which operates in a different way at high and low levels of illumination. In considering the reproduction of colours in a photograph we are concerned with the normal mechanism, i.e., the one operating at fairly high light-levels. For the purposes of photographic theory, it is convenient to consider this as consisting of three receptors. A consideration of the way in which these receptors work is known as the *trichromatic theory of colour vision*.

This theory, usually associated with the names of Young and Helmholtz, postulates receptors which differ in their sensitivity and in the regions of the spectrum to which they respond. The first set of receptors is considered to respond to light in the region of 400 to 500nm, the second to light in the region of 450 to 630nm and the third to light in the region of 500 to 700nm. The behaviour of the eye, considered on this basis, is probably best grasped from a study of curves in which the response of the receptors is plotted against wavelength, as in Figure 17.1. From this figure it is seen that the three sets

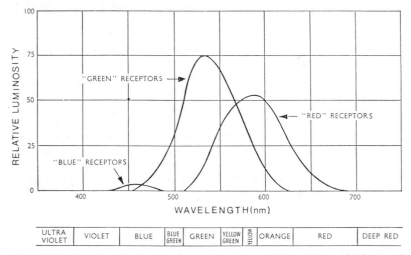

Fig. 17.1 – The three fundamental sensation curves of the trichromatic theory of colour vision

of receptors overlap in sensitivity and that the green set of receptors is far more sensitive than the other two.

The validity of the three-colour theory was for a long time a subject of controversy, but it is now supported by a firm basis of experimental evidence. The justification of the use of the theory for our purposes is that a person with normal colour vision can match almost any given colour by mixing appropriate amounts of blue-violet, green and red light.

By adding together the ordinates of the three curves shown in Figure 17.1, we obtain a curve showing the sensitivity to different wavelengths of the eye as a whole. Such a curve is shown in Figure 17.2. This *visual luminosity curve* shows the relative luminous efficiency of radiant energy.

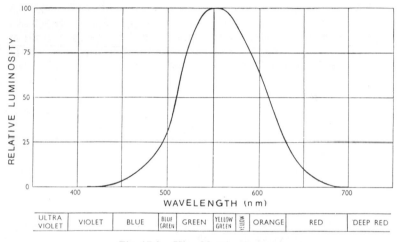

Fig. 17.2 – Visual luminosity curve

It is a commonly recognised fact that the normal human eye does not see all colours equally brightly. Most blues, for example, when compared with medium shades of orange or green appear dark, while yellows, including even the deepest shades, are light. The visual luminosity curve illustrates this diagrammatically. It shows exactly how the human eye responds to the series of spectral colours obtained by splitting up a beam of pure white light – sometimes referred to as an *equal energy spectrum* – to which sunlight approximates roughly. It is important to notice how many times the luminosity of the brightest colour, yellow-green, exceeds that of colours nearer the ends of the spectrum.

Primary and secondary colours
When any one of the three sets of receptors of the eye is stimulated by itself the eye sees blue-violet, green, or red light respectively. These

three colours are known to the photographer as the *primary colours*. If the blue-violet and green receptors are stimulated together the eye sees the blue-green colour known as cyan; if the green and red receptors are stimulated together the eye sees yellow; and if the blue-violet and red receptors are stimulated together the eye sees magenta. These three colours – cyan, yellow and magenta, – are referred to by photographers as the *secondary colours*, since they are obtained when two sets of receptors are stimulated. If all three sets of receptors are stimulated in suitable proportion the eye sees white.

Some care is needed when speaking of primary and secondary colours because a painter is accustomed to refer to the photographer's secondary colours as blue, yellow and red and to call them primary colours, since by mixing *pigments* of these three colours he can, if he wishes, obtain almost all the colours he needs.

Complementary colours

Any two colours (i.e., coloured lights, not pigments), which when added together produce white, are said to be *complementary*. Thus, the secondary colours are complementary to the primary colours. These secondary colours, cyan, yellow and magenta – sometimes given the names minus red, minus blue, and minus green – are known as the *complementary colours*.

Low light-levels

At low light-levels, when the eye becomes *dark-adapted* a different mechanism of vision operates. The dark-adapted, or *scotopic,* eye has a sensitivity differing from the normal, or *photopic,* eye. The maximum sensitivity, which, in the normal eye, is in the yellow-green at about 555nm, moves to about 515nm – near the blue-green region. This change in sensitivity is referred to as the *Purkinje shift* (Figure 17.3). It is because of this shift that the most efficient dark-green safe-light for panchromatic materials has a peak transmission at about 515nm rather than at 555nm (page 300).

Response of photographic materials to colours

As already stated, a photographic emulsion reproduces colours in monochrome, and is considered to do so faithfully when the relative luminosities of the greys produced are in agreement with those of the colours as seen by the eye. So far as a response to light and shade is concerned – and this, of course, has a very large part to play in the photographic rendering of the form and structure of a subject – it is clear that any type of light-sensitive material will answer the purpose.

If, however, our photograph is to reproduce at the same time the colours of the subject in a scale of tones corresponding with their true

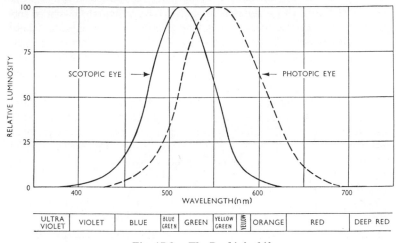

Fig. 17.3 – The Purkinje shift

luminosities, then it is essential that the film employed shall have a spectral response corresponding closely to that of the human eye.

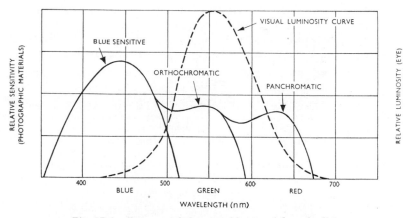

Fig. 17.4 - Response of photographic materials to daylight

We saw in Chapter 16, that, although the ordinary silver halide emulsion is sensitive only to ultra-violet and blue, it is possible by dye-sensitising to render an emulsion sensitive to all colours of the visible spectrum. To assist us in evaluating the performance of the various materials in common use, there are reproduced in Figure 17.4 curves showing the sensitivity of the eye and the sensitivity to daylight of typical examples of the three main classes of photographic materials. Figure 17.5 contains curves for the same materials when exposed to tungsten light, the visual response curve being repeated.

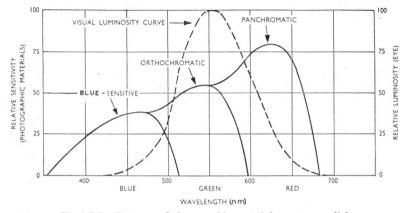

Fig. 17.5 – Response of photographic materials to tungsten light

Table 17.2, which lists the primary and secondary colours and indicates how each is recorded in monochrome by the three main classes of emulsion, illustrates the practical effects of the differences shown between the visual luminosity curve and the emulsion spectral

Colours	Blue-sensitive Daylight	Ortho-chromatic Daylight	Panchromatic	
			Daylight	Tungsten
Primaries				
Blue-violet	Very light	Light	Rather light	Correct
Green	Dark	Rather dark	Slightly dark	Slightly dark
Red	Very dark	Very dark	Slightly light	Light
Secondaries				
Yellow	Very dark	Slightly dark	Correct	Rather light
Cyan	Light	Very light	Slightly light	Slightly dark
Magenta	Slightly light	Correct	Rather light	Rather light

Table 17.2 – Recording of the primary and secondary colours by the main types of photographic emulsion

sensitivity curves in the foregoing figures. The descriptions given in the table are relative to the visual appearance of the colours.

Less saturated colours than the primaries and secondaries follow the general pattern shown in the table but to a lesser extent. Thus, brown can be regarded as a degraded yellow, and pink as a desaturated magenta.

It is clear from the curves in Figures 17.4 and 17.5 and from Table 17.2 that:

(1) No class of material has exactly the same sensitivity as the human eye, either to daylight or to tungsten light. In the first place, the characteristic peak of visibility in the yellow-green coincides with a region of comparatively low photographic response – even with panchromatic materials. On the other hand, the relative sensitivity of panchromatic materials to violet, blue and red greatly exceeds that of the human eye.

(2) The closest approximation to the eye is given by panchromatic materials.

(3) Of the three groups of light-sensitive materials listed, only panchromatic materials can be employed with complete success for the photography of multi-coloured objects, since they are the only ones which respond to the whole of the visible spectrum.

(4) Even with panchromatic materials, control of the reproduction of colours may be needed when a faithful rendering is required, since no type of panchromatic material responds to the different colours of the emulsion in *exactly* the same manner as the eye. Control of colour rendering is also sometimes needed to achieve special effects.

The control referred to under (4) above, is achieved by means of *colour filters*. These are sheets of coloured material having the power to absorb certain colours either partially or completely, while transmitting others freely. By the correct choice of a filter, it becomes possible to reduce the intensity of colours to which the response of the emulsion is too strong. The use of colour filters is considered in detail in Chapter 18.

CHAPTER 18

Optical Filters

THREE main types of optical filter are employed in photography. These are: colour filters, neutral density filters and polarizing filters.

Colour filters

A *colour filter* consists of a transparent flat sheet of coloured material which is placed over the lens of the camera (usually) so that the exposure takes place through it. A colour filter acts by selective absorption of part of the light incident upon it, as shown in Figure 18.1.

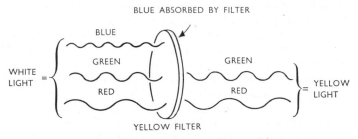

Fig. 18.1 – How a colour filter works

From this figure it will be seen that just as a yellow sheet of paper – an *opaque* object – *reflects* green and red light and absorbs blue, so a yellow *transparent* object *transmits* green and red light and absorbs blue. Other colour filters behave in a similar manner, transmitting the light which, in the case of an opaque object of the same colour, would be reflected.

Colour filters are of value only with colour-sensitive – i.e., orthochromatic or panchromatic – materials. Since blue-sensitive materials are sensitive only to the blue region of the visible spectrum, control of colour rendering by filters is not possible with such materials. Even with orthochromatic materials, only partial control of colour rendering can be achieved, and only yellow filters can usefully be employed. For the fullest control of colour rendering, panchromatic materials must be used; these permit the use of filters of a wide range of colours.

Absorption curves

The transmission characteristics of a filter are expressed most fully by means of a curve in which transmission throughout the spectrum is plotted against wavelength. Such curves are commonly plotted with transmission decreasing as we go up the vertical axis, and are referred to as *absorption curves*. Absorption curves for each of the filters referred to in this Chapter are given on pages 309-15.

Filter factors

To obtain a properly exposed negative when using a filter, a somewhat greater camera exposure than usual must be given, to compensate for the absorption of light by the filter. The increase in exposure may be obtained either by increasing the exposure time or by using a larger aperture. The absorption by a filter is partly wanted and partly unwanted. For example, we employ a yellow filter to absorb blue light and transmit green and red. In practice, however, a yellow filter will absorb not only blue but a little green and red as well. An efficient filter has a minimum of unwanted absorption.

The ratio of the filtered exposure to the corresponding unfiltered exposure is termed the *exposure factor*, or *filter factor*. The value of the filter factor for any given filter depends upon the colour sensitivity of the photographic material used and upon the quality of the light illuminating the object to be photographed. Filter factors are also affected by reciprocity failure (see below).

We sometimes find a filter described as a "2X yellow" or a "4X orange". Although this terminology is really incorrect – in that it implies that the filter factor is 2 or 4, etc., irrespective of the particular sensitive material and light source employed – such numbers do give a useful indication of the exposure factor likely to be required on panchromatic materials – at least in the case of pale filters with relatively low filter factors. In the examples quoted, the actual filter factors will probably range from $1\frac{1}{2}$ to $2\frac{1}{2}$ and from 3 to 5, depending upon the particular sensitive material and light source employed, but the latitude of the material will normally hide any variation from the quoted figure.

Determination of filter factors

To determine the exposure factor of a filter, a neutral subject, e.g., a black-and-white print, should be photographed first without the filter and then with the filter, under the same conditions of illumination.

The films or plates should then be developed for the same time. Several exposures should be made with the filter, the exposure being increased until a filtered negative is obtained which matches the unfiltered one. The ratio of the exposure required through the filter to that required without the filter gives the filter factor.

Filter factors may be influenced by reciprocity failure, and in work requiring the highest accuracy in exposure – as in the making of colour separation negatives – it is necessary to take this into account (see page 264).

Filters for black-and-white photography

In black-and-white photography, colour filters are employed primarily as a means of controlling the reproduction of colours. The filters used for this purpose are of many colours and intensities. In terms of the purpose for which they are used they can be divided into two main types: *correction filters*, and *contrast filters*. In general, correction filters tend to be pale in colour and contrast filters deep, although a given filter may serve as a contrast filter on one occasion and as a correction filter on another.

Correction filters

Correction filters are employed with the aim of recording the colours of the subject in their true luminosities. Filters giving full correction usually require a considerable increase in exposure, and consequently only partial correction is sometimes permissible.

Although technically "correct", the result obtained using a correction filter – especially one giving full correction – is often disappointing from the pictorial point of view, being dull and flat. A more effective interpretation of the subject is frequently obtained by retaining the colour contrasts existing in the original and modifying them as necessary to produce the desired effect in each case. Filters employed for this latter purpose are properly termed contrast filters, and are described in a later section of this Chapter. (See also under (2) below.)

Correction filters include a long series of yellow and yellow-green filters. They can conveniently be subdivided into four main types, as follows:

(1) *To obtain partial correction in daylight.* In unfiltered photographs taken in daylight, blues tend to be too light and greens too dark. Blues – the sky in particular – can be improved by pale filters which do not seriously increase the exposure needed. Pale yellow filters, such as the Ilford Alpha and Iso filters, are employed to obtain this partial correction. These filters may be used with both orthochromatic

and panchromatic materials, although, with orthochromatic materials, reds are still much too dark.

One of the most important uses of yellow filters is to improve the rendering of the sky. Blue sky and white clouds often form a very beautiful part of a landscape. To be shown to advantage in the picture, white clouds should stand out against a grey background representing the blue sky. The result obtained with blue-sensitive materials is frequently disappointing, the sky being recorded almost as brightly as the clouds, so that the two together form an uninteresting white area. By using orthochromatic materials, the green content of the light from the clouds may be utilized to render these a little more brightly than before, and by using panchromatic materials we can add to this the red content of the light. By placing a yellow, i.e., a blue-absorbing filter over the camera lens, we subdue (darken) the rendering of the blue sky, and so in the picture the contrast between sky and clouds is still further increased.

(2) *To obtain full correction in daylight*, we must lighten green in addition to darkening blue. This can be done by using a panchromatic material with a filter which partly absorbs all except green light. We have seen that, in practice, such a filter will inevitably absorb some green as well and will thus have a fairly high filter factor. The filters used for the purpose are yellow-green in colour. The Ilford Gamma filter is a filter of this type. Where the filter factor of the Gamma filter is too high, almost complete correction can be obtained by using the Ilford Beta filter, which is pale yellow-green and necessitates a smaller increase in exposure.

When it is desired to obtain a rendering in which yellows and reds appear bright, yellow filters of varying degrees of absorption are usually employed, instead of yellow-green filters. Although it might perhaps appear that these would be better described as contrast filters rather than correction filters, it can be argued that, since yellows and reds do, for psychological reasons, stand out even more than their luminosities warrant, the aim in using yellow filters is still one of obtaining a true impression of the original, i.e., one of correction.

(3) *To obtain partial correction in tungsten light.* Tungsten light contains more red and less blue than daylight. Since daylight is taken by the eye as its reference for correct colour rendering (page 285), the filters required for correction are not the same in tungsten light and in daylight. We require, in fact, filters which will correct colours to the level at which the eye sees them in daylight. It is probably in portraiture that errors in colour rendering in tungsten light are most

noticeable, as, for example, when lips are recorded too light and eyes too dark. Partial correction in tungsten light – sufficient to correct the most noticeable errors – can be obtained by use of a pale greenish-blue filter. The Ilford HS filter is of this type. It gives adequate correction for portraiture without necessitating a great increase in exposure.

(4) *For full correction in tungsten light*, a bluish-green filter which transmits more blue but less red than the Gamma filter is required. The Ilford HW filter is of this type. As with the Gamma filter, its filter factor is appreciable.

Contrast filters

We noted in Chapter 1 that differences in colour and differences in luminance in the subject are both represented in the print as differences in tone. Contrast filters are used to control the tone contrast in the print which arises from colour contrast in the subject. They may be employed to make a colour appear lighter, to make it appear darker, or simultaneously to make one colour darker and another lighter.

As an example of the use of contrast filters let us consider an original with areas of green and orange. These have considerable colour contrast, but they may have little difference in luminance, and when photographed may both be recorded as equal shades of grey with no tone contrast between them at all. Here is a case where the technically "correct" rendering fails, and a contrast filter is required to produce the tone separation that is essential if the photograph is to be an objective reproduction.

The basic rules for the selection of contrast filters are:

(1) *To lighten a colour*, use a filter which favours that part of the spectrum which the colour reflects well. (This commonly means using a filter of the same colour as the object being photographed.) To obtain the maximum effect, use a filter which transmits only that part of the spectrum which the colour reflects best.

(2) *To darken a colour*, use a filter which favours that part of the spectrum which the colour reflects badly. (This commonly means using a filter of colour complementary to that of the object being photographed.) To obtain the maximum effect, use a filter which transmits only that part of the spectrum which the colour reflects worst.

From a study of Table 17.1 (page 284), which shows the reflectances of natural objects in the three main regions of the spectrum, it will be seen that although it is usually possible to exercise *some* degree of control over most colours, it is by no means always possible to render a colour completely black or completely white (i.e., to eliminate it) at will. Reds and yellows can usually be controlled to any desired extent, but greens and browns, in particular, often prove intractable because these colours are rarely highly saturated, i.e., they always contain a fairly large proportion of white light.

The most important contrast filters for ordinary photography are as follows:

(1) *The standard tricolour set*, i.e., tricolour blue, tricolour green, and tricolour red. Of these, only the red filter is used to any great extent in ordinary black-and-white photography.

(2) *The narrow-cut tricolour set*, i.e., narrow-cut tricolour blue, narrow-cut tricolour green and narrow-cut tricolour red. Again, the red filter is the most used in black-and-white photography.

(3) *The complementary filters*, i.e., minus blue (yellow), minus green (magenta) and minus red (cyan). Of these, the minus blue filter is the most frequently useful.

(4) *An orange filter*, with short-wave cut-off at about the middle of the green region, i.e., at approximately 550nm. The Ilford Micro 5 filter is of this type.

Detail filters

Contrast filters of the same (or "narrower") colour as the object being photographed are sometimes referred to as *detail filters*. Their purpose is to lower the contrast between an object and its surroundings so that contrast in the object itself can be increased by photographic means. The chief use of detail filters is in photomicrography, but they are also of value in ordinary photography when it is desired to bring out the texture of a self-coloured object. With such subjects, a detail filter serves to reduce the effect of direct (specular) reflection from the surface of the subject.

Furniture filters

The orange contrast filter referred to under (4) above is sometimes termed a "furniture red" filter, because it is frequently used to bring out the grain of furniture – especially of the darker kinds. Its action can be considered to result from three effects:

(1) It acts as a detail filter to lighten the tone of the furniture as a whole – which would otherwise appear very dark – in relation to its surroundings, and thus lessens the overall contrast of the photograph.

(2) It reduces the effect of minor surface reflections, e.g., finger-marks, etc., by lessening the effect of the white light directly reflected

from the surface, without seriously reducing the light diffusely reflected from the wood itself – which light is coloured.

(3) It increases the contrast between the light (coloured) areas of the wood and the dark (almost black) areas of the grain.

Special filters

In addition to correction and contrast filters, many other filters are employed for special purposes. Some examples are described below.

Ultra-violet absorbing filters

Although the eye is not sensitive to ultra-violet radiation, photographic materials are. Now, ultra-violet radiation is strongly scattered by haze (page 305). Consequently, for photographs of distant landscapes, snow scenes or scenes at high altitudes, where the effect of ultra-violet radiation is pronounced, it is sometimes desirable to employ a filter – such as the Ilford Q filter – which, while passing visible light, cuts out ultra-violet radiation. This eliminates the effect of excessive haze otherwise obtained.

Ultra-violet transmitting filters

Most sources of ultra-violet radiation produce also visible radiation. In ultra-violet photography it is frequently desirable to filter out the latter radiation, and a special ultra-violet transmitting filter is available for this purpose. It is a very dark filter, almost black, and is invariably supplied as a dyed-in-the-mass glass filter, i.e., it is not available in gelatin.

Infra-red filters

Special filters are employed with infra-red sensitive materials. These are usually dark red filters which are almost opaque to visible light but transmit freely in the infra-red region. Their purpose is to cut out the ultra-violet and blue sensitivity of infra-red materials, which, unless filtered out, would completely obscure the effects due to the infra-red sensitivity.

Photometric filters

Photometric filters are filters employed to alter the colour temperature of light sources. They find their main use when light sources of different colour temperatures are compared visually by means of a photometer, the filters being used to lessen the difference between the sources. Photometric filters employed to lower colour temperature are pinky-yellow in colour; filters employed to raise colour temperature are bluish. A photometric filter may conveniently be allotted a *mired shift value*, which indicates the change in colour quality which the filter will effect (see page 19).

Neutral density filters

Neutral density filters are filters which absorb all wavelengths almost equally, and thus appear grey in colour. In ordinary photography they are used chiefly for the control of exposure time, e.g.:

(1) When conditions are so bright that over-exposure would otherwise be obtained even with the lens fully stopped down. This arises mainly in cinematography with cameras having a fixed shutter angle, and thus no means of reducing the exposure time. It can also sometimes arise in still photography when ultra-fast films are employed.

(2) To lengthen exposures of street scenes when it is desired to obtain the appearance of an empty street. In this case, a neutral density with a large filter factor is employed to give an exposure so long that people and passing vehicles are not recorded.

Neutral density filters are also sometimes used as viewing filters, to reduce glare. (See Viewing filters, below.)

Two main types of neutral filter are employed in photography: (1) scattering (silver), and (2) non-scattering (carbon). A filter for use over a lens must be of the non-scattering type. Filters of the scattering (silver) type are intended for use where it is desired to simulate a photographic negative, e.g., for experimental purposes. Since a neutral density filter has no selective absorption its filter factor is independent of the light source and the emulsion.

Photographic wedges

Photographic wedges are a special form of neutral density filter employed for sensitometric purposes. Wedges are of two types: continuous wedges and step wedges (step tablets). The density of a continuous wedge increases linearly from zero to a maximum which may be of almost any desired value. As its name indicates, the density of a step wedge increases stepwise, in a regular order.

The most valuable characteristic of a wedge for many purposes is that it enables a series of exactly specified exposures to be given to a material in one operation. Continuous wedges are also very suitable for the continuous control of illumination in optical instruments.

Wedges are usually rectangular in shape, although continuous wedges of annular pattern can be obtained for use in instruments in which it is more convenient to traverse the wedge by rotation.

Viewing filters

Viewing filters are intended for observation purposes only – not for use over the camera lens. Three main types are employed:

(1) *Neutral density filters.* Neutral density filters (see above) can be useful as an aid to viewing because they lower the general brightness

of the scene, thus reducing glare and making viewing more comfortable. Viewing filters of this type are commonly used in photomicrography, the filter being removed while the exposure is made.

(2) *Monochromatic vision filter*. The Ilford Monochromatic Vision (MV) filter is a dark yellow filter transmitting a narrow band between 555 and 630nm. It acts by "killing" all colour differences in the scene, leaving only differences in brightness. Filters of this type are sometimes used by technicians arranging the lighting of cine studio sets.

(3) *Photographic vision (panchromatic) filter*. This Ilford filter, which is purple in colour, converts the sensitivity of the eye to that of a panchromatic emulsion. It may be used for judging the effect of filters, particularly contrast filters. For this purpose, the scene is viewed through the "PV Pan" filter together with the filter to be used on the camera lens.

Darkroom safelights
Darkroom safelights are a special application of colour filters. Their function is to filter the light from a tungsten or other lamp so as to pass light of a restricted range of wavelengths. With blue-sensitive and orthochromatic materials, this range is chosen to fall outside the range of wavelengths to which the material is sensitive. Thus, orange or brown safelights are used with blue-sensitive materials, and red safelights with orthochromatic materials (Figures 18.2a and 18.2b). With panchromatic materials the problem is different, because these materials are sensitive to light of all colours. The solution is either to process in total darkness or to employ a very low level of blue-green illumination (Figure 18.2c), this being the colour to which the eye is most sensitive at low levels of illumination (page 288). Infra-red materials are commonly produced without green sensitivity so that they may be handled by a special dark green safelight passing only wavelengths lying within the "green gap" (Figure 18.2d).

The Ilford range of darkroom safelights, and the materials with which they are designed to be used, are listed in Table 18.1. Absorption curves of these safelights are given in Figure 18.17.

Commercial forms of colour filters
When a filter is required, it is important to employ one specially intended for photographic use. It is not sufficient merely to use any piece of coloured glass or film which is of the correct colour. In the first place, the absorbing properties of such a substitute may be quite

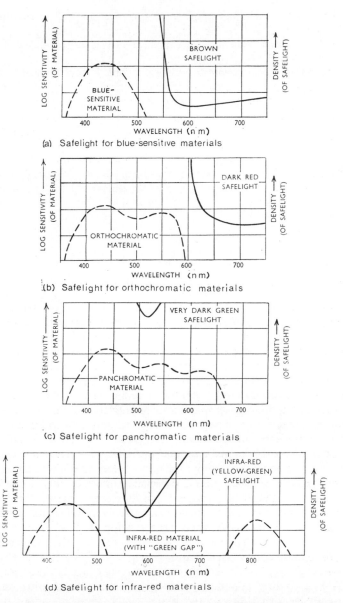

(a) Safelight for blue-sensitive materials

(b) Safelight for orthochromatic materials

(c) Safelight for panchromatic materials

(d) Safelight for infra-red materials

Fig. 18.2–Absorption curves of the principal types of safelight shown in relation to the spectral sensitivity curves of the materials with which they are employed

For use with:	Symbol	Safelight Number	Colour
Blue-sensitive materials:			
Very slow	VS2	910	Orange
Slow	S	902	Light brown
Fast	F	904	Dark brown
Orthochromatic materials:			
Very slow	BR	900	Bright red
All others	Iso	906	Dark red
Panchromatic materials:			
Very slow	G	907	Dark green
All others	GB	908	Very dark green
Infra-red materials	Infra-red	903	Yellow-green; absorbs infra-red completely
Desensitised panchromatic materials	Bright Green	909	Green
X-ray materials	NX	914	Sepia

Table 18.1 – Ilford darkroom safelights

different from a properly designed filter. Not only may the transmission be poor in the regions where maximum transmission is desired, but the filter may pass light where complete absorption is required. Secondly, and possibly more important, the definition of the resulting photograph may suffer appreciably. Filters produced for photographic use are designed to have suitable absorption characteristics and suitable optical quality.

Commercial filters are supplied in various forms. The most convenient and most permanent form is a sheet of coloured glass, and many general-purpose filters, especially those supplied for amateur use, are of this kind. They are sometimes referred to as "dyed-in-the-mass" filters. Coloured glass filters are widely used for pictorial photography, but are available only in a restricted range of colours.

Where filters of special transmission characteristics are required – as, for example, in technical and scientific work – filters in which the absorbing layer is dyed gelatin are usually employed. These filters are made by mixing organic dyes in gelatin and coating this on glass. After it has dried, the coated film – which measures about 0·1 mm thick – is stripped from the glass.

Gelatin filters are of excellent optical quality – exceeding that of the best quality glass filters – and do not affect definition, cause lateral movement of the image or change of focus. They require, however, very careful handling, and are somewhat difficult to keep in the desired state of cleanliness. For regular and constant use, therefore, it is generally desirable to have the gelatin cemented between suitable pieces of glass. Three qualities of glass are employed for this purpose, the choice of glass depending on the work for which the filter is to be used. The three types of cemented filter supplied by Ilford Limited are as follows:

(1) *Instrument filters* – *cemented between glass of ordinary quality* (formerly known as A quality filters)
These are suitable for use with visual optical instruments, such as colorimeters, but are not suitable for photographic use.

(2) *Camera filters* – *cemented between optically-worked glass* (formerly known as B quality filters)
These are suitable for all general photographic work with the highest classes of lens, except in cases where the utmost precision is required.

(3) *Optical flats*
These are filters cemented between glass worked to optical flatness; they are suitable for the highest quality photomechanical work and wherever the utmost precision is required.

Safelight screens for use in darkroom lamps consist (usually) of dyed gelatin coated on glass and bound with a cover glass for protection.

It is sometimes desired to place colour filters before a light source, and "lamp filters" for this purpose are supplied in the same form as safelights, i.e., coated on glass. These filters must not be confused with cemented filters. Their optical quality (and cost) is much lower, and they are not suitable for use in an image-forming part of an optical system.

Care in handling
It cannot be over-emphasized that a filter must not be allowed to affect the definition of the image produced by the camera lens. This means that filters must be handled with care and kept clean.

Gelatin filters require especial care in handling, since contact with the fingers inevitably produces permanent marks on them. Hence, if gelatin filters are to be rapidly interchanged, it is advisable to mount them in some kind of support, which may be made of cardboard and can be fixed in front of the lens. Sometimes it may be convenient when using a gelatin filter to mount it permanently inside the camera, or between the components of the lens. When not in use, gelatin filters should be kept in a cool, dry place.

Glass filters are usually held in special mounts which slip over or screw onto the front of the lens barrel. Great care must be taken to avoid undue pressure on cemented filters; the least distortion by pressure may completely destroy definition. For this reason, special fixing devices are used on many types of filter mount so that there is no risk of straining a filter when fitting it into its mount.

With safelights and lamp filters, care must be taken that the lamp and bulb used are such that the filter does not become overheated, or the gelatin layer may be damaged. Care must also be taken that safelight screens are not allowed to become damp or contaminated by processing solutions.

Focusing when using filters

Gelatin filters have no appreciable effect on focusing. This is true whether they are placed before or behind the lens, or between its components. Glass filters, on the other hand, whether dyed-in-the-mass or cemented, have a definite though small effect on the image-forming rays, the extent of this depending on the thickness of the filter and its position with respect to the lens. For general photographic purposes, however, the alteration of focus is negligible when the filter is placed in *front* of the lens, and for this reason, together with the greater accessibility which it affords, this is the position in which glass filters are normally employed. When a thick filter is placed *behind* the lens, the image is focused at a point slightly farther from the lens than normally, and focusing must then be carried out with the filter in position, or else due allowance must be made for it. (The displacement of the image is about one-third of the thickness of the filter.) In work at or near same-size, allowance must be made for the filter even if it is placed in front of the lens. The best procedure, in this case, is to focus visually with the filter in position over the lens.

General notes on use of colour filters

It is usually bad practice to use a panchromatic emulsion with a filter if the same result can be obtained with an orthochromatic or blue-sensitive material without a filter. For example, a panchromatic film with a cyan filter merely produces the same result as an orthochromatic film, while a panchromatic (or orthochromatic) film with a tricolour blue filter produces very much the same result as a blue-sensitive film.

With orthochromatic materials, only yellow filters should be employed. It may be considered that green filters could also be used. A study of the absorption curves, however, will show that with an orthochromatic material, an Ilford Delta filter, for example, will do all that a Tricolour Green filter will do, with the advantage of a much smaller filter factor. (Transmissions at 550nm. Tricolour Green 49 per cent., Delta 89 per cent.)

Haze in photographs

Distant objects frequently exhibit low contrast because the light reaching the observer has been scattered by molecules of the gases composing the air, and by suspended droplets of water condensed on combustion or sea salt nuclei. The scattering produced by particles small compared with the wavelength of light, which includes molecules of gases and combustion nuclei with little condensed water, is not equally strong for all colours. It is at a maximum for ultra-violet radiation, and decreases steadily as we pass through the visible spectrum from blue to red, reaching a minimum in the infra-red. Thus, the direct light tends to have a relatively higher red content than the original radiation, while the scattered light has a correspondingly higher blue content. This fact is readily apparent when a row of street lamps is viewed on a misty night: the more distant the lamps, the redder does their light appear to be.

In photography, we sometimes wish to retain the effect of haze and sometimes wish to eliminate it. In pictorial work, we normally wish to retain the effect, since much of the artistic appeal of a landscape and the sense of perspective depends upon the increasing mistiness of the receding planes. Now, all types of photographic materials are sensitive to blue, violet and ultra-violet light, the very groups of radiations for which the scattering effect of haze is most pronounced. They are, in fact, more sensitive than the eye to these radiations. As a result, panchromatic materials used without a filter give an impression of slightly more haze than the eye, orthochromatic materials much more haze and blue-sensitive materials very much more haze.

If we wish to prevent the strongly scattered radiation from recording, and so reduce the impression of haze, we can do so by employing colour filters in conjunction with colour-sensitive materials. All that is necessary is to select a filter which absorbs heavily at the blue end of the spectrum while transmitting freely at the red end. Thus, a panchromatic material with a pale yellow filter (e.g., the Ilford Alpha filter), gives an effect very close to that obtained by the eye. For greater penetration of haze, an orange or red filter may be employed – again with a panchromatic material. For maximum penetration of haze, infra-red materials may be used (page 277).

It should, however, be noted that while the use of infra-red materials will assist in the penetration of haze consisting of combustion nuclei with little condensed water, it will not assist in the penetration of haze consisting of large droplets – such as fog or sea mist – since scattering by such particles is almost independent of wavelength.

To absorb ultra-violet radiation only, without affecting the visible spectrum, an ultra-violet absorbing filter may be used (page 298). A filter of this type is especially valuable in colour photography. It requires no increase in exposure.

Interference filters
Ordinary colour filters depend upon the selective absorption of light by coloured glass or gelatin. *Interference filters* make use of the principle of light "interference" to give a selective transmission of any colour in the visible spectrum within narrow limits of wavelength. They consist of glass discs on which are deposited, by evaporation in a high vacuum, a series of very thin dielectric or metal and dielectric layers.

Interference filters are supplied for use in a number of scientific applications. Compared with ordinary types of filter they give a much higher light transmission for the same colour value, or, alternatively, a more selective colour value for the same light transmission; i.e., they have a higher efficiency.

Polarizing filters
As we saw in Chapter 2, light can be considered as a transverse wave motion or vibration, with vibrations normally occurring in all possible directions at right angles to a ray of light. Thus, looking down a ray, the vibrations can be represented by arrows, as in Figure 18.3a.

Under certain conditions, however, light vibrates in one particular plane only (Figure 18.3b). This is known as the plane of polarization, and the light is said to be *plane polarized* or, simply, *polarized*. Such light can be controlled by means of a special type of filter termed a *polarizing filter*.

A polarizing filter comprises a large number of very small needle-shaped crystals (e.g., herapathite), all arranged pointing in one

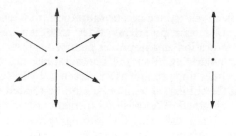

(a) ORDINARY LIGHT   (b) POLARIZED LIGHT

Fig. 18.3 – Vibration of ordinary and polarized light

direction in a plastic sheet sandwiched between two pieces of glass. The crystals have the peculiar optical property of passing light polarized in one direction, but almost totally rejecting light polarized at right angles to this direction – light vibrating in planes between these angles being partially transmitted and partially rejected. A polarizing filter may therefore be used to select light if some of it is polarized.

The main applications of polarizing filters are:

(1) *To control the rendering of the sky*. Light from a clear, blue sky at a right-angle to the sun is partially polarized. The sky in this region can thus be made darker by placing a polarizing filter over the camera lens. When used for this purpose, a polarizing filter has the advantage over a normal filter that it does not distort colour rendering and may therefore be used in colour photography.

(2) *To reduce unwanted reflections*. Light which is directly reflected from the surface of a non-metal at a certain angle (about 55° from the normal for many substances*) is almost totally polarized, and light reflected from a reasonably wide range of angles about this angle is partially polarized. Polarizing filters may, therefore, be used for the control of reflections from, for example, glass, wood, paint, oil, french polish, varnish, paper and any wet surface. Their practical applications include the photography of swimming pools and the interiors of rooms – where glare spots on painted walls, wood panelling and furniture, and reflections from glass-fronted furniture may be objectionable.

(3) *To increase colour saturation in colour photography*. In colour

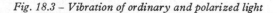

* More precisely, the angle of incidence whose tangent is equal to the refractive index of the material.

photograghy, reflections reduce colour saturation, thus degrading the picture quality. Use of a polarizing filter to eliminate reflections increases colour saturation and improves picture quality.

When using a polarizing filter the photographer can observe the effect produced, either upon the focusing screen or by looking through the filter itself at the subject. The filter should be rotated slowly until the best effect is obtained. The position of marks on the edge of the filter should then be noted, and the photograph taken with these marks in the same position as when viewing.

For subjects which show reflection at only one surface or group of similarly placed surfaces, it is usually possible to select a camera position from which the polarizing filter will subdue the reflection to any desired extent. On the other hand, when the reflections come from very different angles it is not possible, merely by placing a polarizing filter over the lens, to suppress them all at once.

A polarizing filter on the lens offers little control of reflections in copying, because the unwanted light is not usually reflected at the appropriate angle. Only in the case of oil paintings – when individual brush marks may cause reflections at the appropriate angle – is any control achieved, and this is very limited. Control of reflections in copying can be obtained, however, by using filters both over the lens and over the lamps. When this method is employed, the diffusely reflected light is depolarized and forms the required image, whereas the unwanted directly reflected light is still polarized, and can be cut out by the filter over the lens. In the same way, reflections from metal objects can be controlled to some extent by placing polarizing filters over the light sources as well as over the camera lens. The use of filters on both lamps and lens is not, however, without difficulties, unless special lamps are available. In particular especial care must be taken that a polarizing filter placed in front of a light source does not become overheated.

The ideal polarizing filter works equally well for all wavelengths, and therefore has no effect on colour. In practice, polarizing filters are not always neutral in their effect, particularly if old, and care should be taken in selecting a filter for colour photography. A perfect polarizing filter would stop one-half of the light passing through it and have an exposure factor of $\times 2$. In practice, some light is absorbed by the bonding material between the crystals, and a factor of nearer $\times 4$ should be used, although the filter factor appears to vary somewhat from one individual filter to another. The filter factor of a polarizing filter, unlike that of a colour filter, is independent of the sensitive material and light source employed.

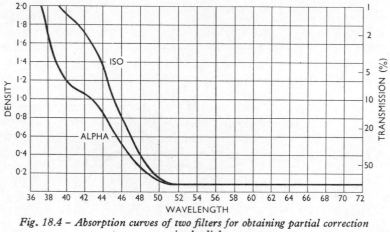

Fig. 18.4 – Absorption curves of two filters for obtaining partial correction in daylight

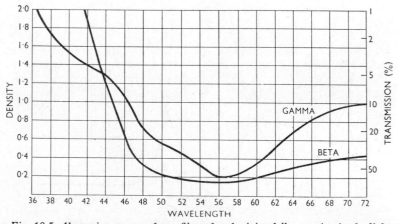

Fig. 18.5–Absorption curves of two filters for obtaining full correction in daylight

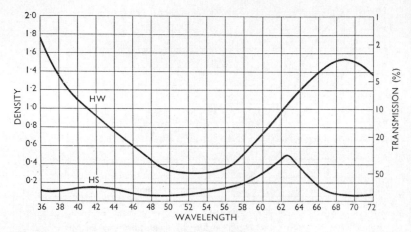

Fig. 18.6 –Absorption curves of two filters for obtaining correction in tungsten light

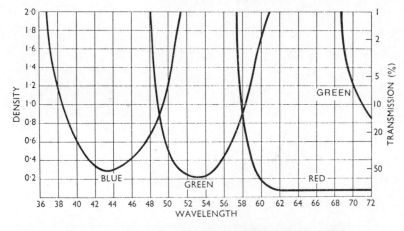

Fig. 18.7 – Absorption curves of the standard tricolour filters

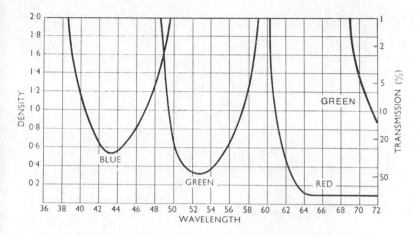

Fig. 18.8 - *Absorption curves of the narrow-cut tricolour filters*

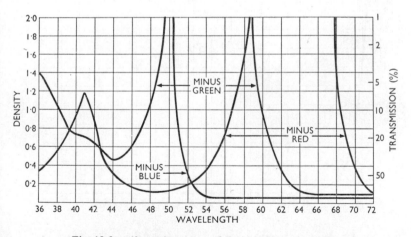

Fig. 18.9 - *Absorption curves of the complementary filters*

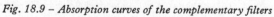

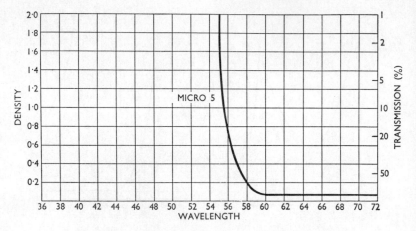

Fig. 18.10 – Absorption curve of an orange contrast filter

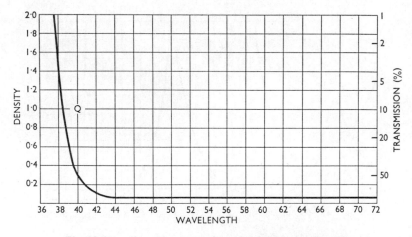

Fig. 18.11 – Absorption curve of an ultra-violet absorbing filter

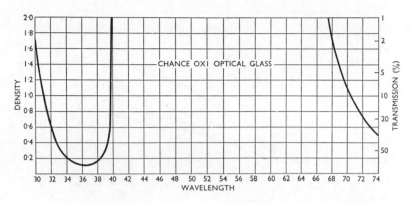

Fig. 18.12 – *Absorption curve of an ultra-violet transmitting filter*

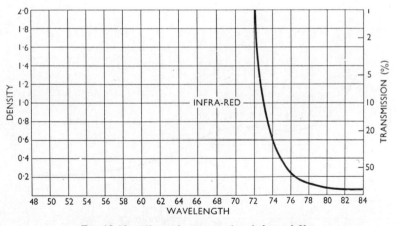

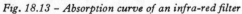

Fig. 18.13 – *Absorption curve of an infra-red filter*

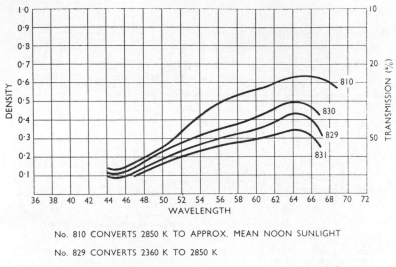

No. 810 CONVERTS 2850 K TO APPROX. MEAN NOON SUNLIGHT

No. 829 CONVERTS 2360 K TO 2850 K

No. 830 CONVERTS 3400 K TO APPROX. MEAN NOON SUNLIGHT

No. 831 CONVERTS 2850 K TO 3400 K

Fig. 18.14 – Absorption curves of four photometric filters (for raising colour temperature)

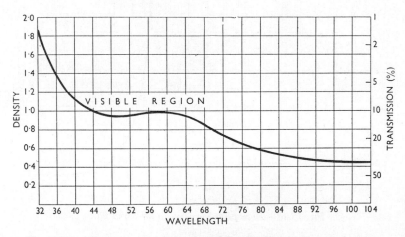

Fig. 18.15 – Absorption curve of a neutral density filter (non-scattering type, density 1·0)

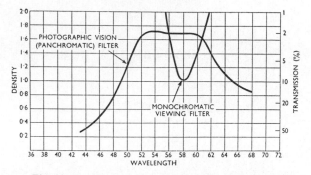

Fig. 18.16 – Absorption curves of two viewing filters

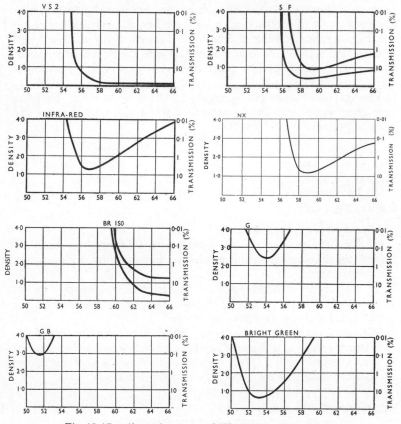

Fig. 18.17 – Absorption curves of Ilford darkroom safelights

CHAPTER 19

Film Speed

Two films are said to differ in *speed* if the exposure required to produce a negative on one differs from the exposure required to produce a negative of similar quality on the other, the material requiring the lesser exposure being said to have the higher speed. The speed of a material is thus seen to vary inversely with the exposure required, and we can therefore express speed numerically by selecting a number related to exposure.

The response of the photographic emulsion is, however, complex and speed varies with many factors, of which the following are the most important:

(1) *Exposure*

(a) The colour of the exposing light, e.g., whether daylight or tungsten light. This is dealt with later in this Chapter.

(b) The intensity of the exposing light. This is because of reciprocity failure (page 262).

(2) *Development* (see Chapter 23)

(a) The composition of the developing solution – especially as regards the developing agent used and the amount of bromide or other restrainer present.

(b) The degree of development – e.g., as measured by the contrast achieved. This depends principally upon the development time, the temperature and the degree of agitation.

We must, therefore, disabuse our minds once and for all of the idea that the speed of a material can be completely expressed by any one number. Nevertheless, a speed number can provide a useful guide to the performance that may be expected from a material.

Methods of expressing speed
The problem of expressing the speed of a material numerically is one

that exercised the minds of photographers and scientists almost from the beginnings of photography, but only comparatively recently has there been produced a *speed system* which has gained anything approaching universal approval. From some points of view, the problem of allotting a speed number appears simple. It would seem, for instance, that if we wish to compare the speeds of two materials, all we have to do is to make exposures on each to yield comparable negatives, and the ratio of the exposures will give us the ratio of the speeds. It is true that we can usefully *compare* speeds in this way, but the comparison may not be typical of the relation of the two materials under other conditions, and in any case will tell us nothing about the *absolute* speed of the materials. It is in trying to obtain absolute speed numbers of general application that difficulties arise.

The problem of allotting speed numbers arose first in connection with the use of black-and-white negative materials and it is with such materials that we shall be principally concerned in this Chapter. The evolution of speed systems for colour materials followed on similar lines.

One of the first problems in allotting speed numbers is connected with the variation in the speed of photographic materials with the conditions of use. This problem is generally overcome by agreeing upon standard conditions of exposure and processing for the speed determination. A further problem is concerned with the *criterion* of exposure to be used as the basis for the measurement of speed, i.e., the particular conception of speed which is to be adopted. This problem arises from the fact that a negative consists not of a single density but of a range of densities. Consequently, it is not immediately apparent which density or other negative quality should be adopted as the basis for comparison. The characteristic curve is a help here, and several different points related to this curve have from time to time been suggested as speed criteria. Most of these points are related to the toe of the curve, i.e., to the shadow areas of the negative.

These criteria can be divided into five main types, as follows:
(1) Threshold.
(2) Fixed density.
(3) Inertia.
(4) Minimum useful gradient.
(5) Fractional gradient.

The underlying principles of these various criteria are outlined below. Later in the Chapter, specific speed systems which are or have been in general use – employing one or other of these criteria – are described in detail.

Threshold systems

The threshold is the point on the characteristic curve corresponding to just perceptible density above fog – i.e., the point where the toe

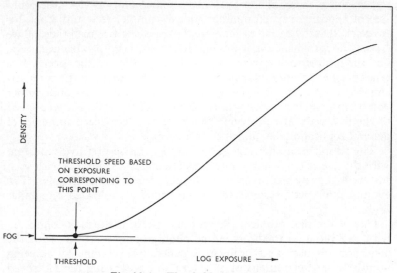

Fig. 19.1 – Threshold criterion of speed

begins (page 234). Under the heading "threshold systems", we group those systems in which speed is based on the exposure needed to give such a density (Figure 19.1).

The earliest method of expressing the speed of a silver bromide-gelatin emulsion was a threshold system evolved by Warnerke. Warnerke exposed plates behind a sensitometric tablet, i.e., a step wedge, the steps being numbered with opaque figures. A candle or phosphorescent tablet was used as light source, and the last number which could be read on the developed plate was taken as indicating the speed of that plate. The Scheiner system, described later, was another threshold system.

The disadvantages of the threshold as a criterion of speed are that it is difficult to locate exactly and that it is not closely related to the part of the characteristic curve used in practice.

Fixed density

Another method of comparing film speeds is in terms of the exposure required to produce a given density above fog. For general-purpose films, a (diffuse visual) density of 0·1 or 0·2 is frequently selected, to correspond roughly with the density in the shadows of an average negative. With high-contrast materials in which a dense background

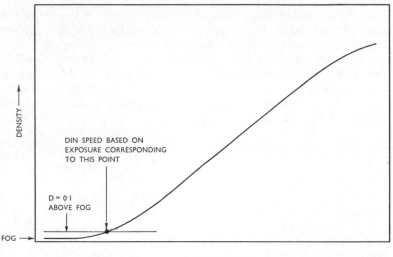

Fig. 19.2 – DIN speed criterion (fixed density)

is required, a density of from 1 to 2 is a more useful basis for speed determination, while for materials used in astronomy, a density of 0·6 has been suggested. It will be apparent that the exposure corresponding to a specified density can be more precisely located than the threshold.

A fixed density criterion (of $D = 0·1 + \text{fog}$) was adopted in the first National Standard speed system, the DIN system, in 1934 (page 324), and is now employed in American, British and German Standard speed systems (page 326).

Inertia

The inertia point was the basis selected by Hurter and Driffield for their pioneer work. Under certain conditions prevalent in Hurter and Driffield's day (page 236), inertia is independent of development and so offers a fixed point of reference. Further, the inertia point is related to the straight-line portion of the characteristic curve, i.e., the part of the curve in which correct reproduction in the negative is obtained. With short-toe materials, as used by Hurter and Driffield, this would appear to be an advantage. With modern long-toe materials, the straight-line portion of the curve assumes less importance (page 259).

Minimum useful gradient

Threshold speed systems work at the very bottom of the toe of the characteristic curve, while systems based on inertia ignore the toe completely. Neither system approximates very closely to actual practice today, where a part – but only a part – of the toe is used. It was at one time suggested that a criterion more closely related to practice could be obtained from that point on the toe of the characteristic curve at which a certain minimum gradient is reached. A value for tan a in Fig. 19.3 of 0·2 was proposed.

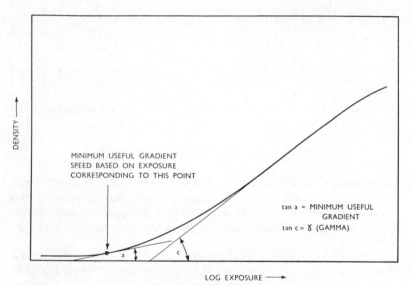

Fig. 19.3 – Minimum useful gradient criterion

The *minimum useful gradient criterion* was based on the idea that loss of tone separation in the shadows (shadow detail) is the first sign of under-exposure, and that this in turn is due to unacceptably low contrast in the portion of the characteristic curve occupied by the shadows. The minimum useful gradient criterion did not come into general use, but is of interest because it led to the more fundamental fractional gradient criterion.

Fractional gradient

Consideration of the minimum useful gradient criterion reveals that the minimum value of contrast acceptable in the shadows is not a constant, but depends upon the contrast grade of the paper on which the negative is to be printed. If the overall contrast of the negative is such that it needs a hard paper, the contrast of the negative in the shadows can be lower than with a negative requiring a soft paper. In other words, the minimum contrast acceptable in the toe depends upon the contrast of the negative as a whole. Realization of this fact led to the conception of the *fractional gradient criterion*.

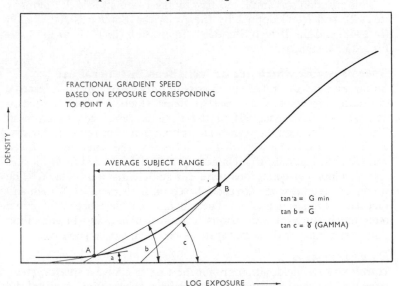

Fig. 19.4 – Fractional gradient criterion

The point chosen for this criterion is the point A in Figure 19.4, where the slope of the tangent to the curve at A equals a given fraction of the slope of AB, the line joining the points marking the ends of the portion of the curve employed. This is usually expressed by the equation:

$$G_{min} = K \times \overline{G}$$

where $G_{min} = \tan a$
$\overline{G} \quad = \tan b$

and K is a constant to be determined empirically.

Practical tests by L. A. Jones showed that a value for K of 0·3 gave results corresponding very well with the minimum exposure required to give a negative from which an "excellent" (as opposed to a merely "acceptable") print could be made. In Jones's work, the *fractional gradient point A* was located by the equation:

$$G_{min} = 0.3 \times \overline{G}(1.5)$$

where $\overline{G}(1.5)$ means the average gradient over a log exposure range of 1.5, a value which has been shown to be fairly typical for exterior scenes in daylight. When located in this way, point A is sometimes referred to as the "Jones point".

This criterion was employed first by the Eastman Kodak Company in 1939, and later adopted by the American Standards Association (in 1943) and the British Standards Institution (in 1947) as the basis for national standards.

Speed systems which are or have been in general use

So far we have described speed *criteria* only. We shall now describe the more important of the speed *systems* which are or have been in general use. The essentials of the systems described are given in Table 19.1 Through the years many systems have been evolved and discarded in turn. Some were discarded because the criterion employed was felt to be insufficiently related to practice; others because exposure and development conditions were not sufficiently well defined. The preferred systems today are those based on the American, British and German national standards. These standards have been laid down after much study of the various factors involved, and in compiling them experience with earlier systems has been put to good use.

H and D numbers

Hurter and Driffield, although not the first to evolve a speed system, were the first to obtain speed numbers from the response curve of the material and thus put the subject on a really sound basis. In fact, the whole of their work was inspired by the desire to obtain useful speed numbers.

Hurter and Driffield based their speed system on the inertia point. They did this because, as already stated, under certain conditions inertia is a fixed characteristic, independent of development time, and because inertia represents the minimum exposure that can be tolerated if all the densities of the negative are to fall on or near the straight-line portion of the curve. This part of the curve – the only part on which correct reproduction in the negative is obtained – was considered by Hurter and Driffield to be the region of correct exposure.

Hurter and Driffield published details of their speed system in 1890, a year after they had described their exposure calculator, the

System	Date of intro- duction	Type of unit	Speed criterion	Development
H and D	1890	Arithmetical	Inertia	Developer to be bromide free; development time not important.
Scheiner	1894	Logarith- mic	Threshold	Not specified.
DIN	1934	Logarith- mic	Fixed density $(0\cdot1+\text{fog})$	To be continued until maximum speed is obtained (optimal development).
BS	1941	Logarith- mic	Fixed density $(0\cdot1+\text{fog})$	To be under carefully controlled conditions giving a degree of development comparable with average photofinishing.
ASA	1943	Arithmetical	Fractional gradient	To be under carefully controlled conditions giving a degree of development comparable with average photofinishing.
BS and ASA	1947	Arithmetical and logarithmic	Fractional gradient	To be under carefully controlled conditions giving a degree of development comparable with average photofinishing.
DIN	1957	Logarith- mic	Fixed density $(0\cdot1+\text{fog})$	To be under carefully controlled conditions giving a degree of development comparable with average photofinishing.
ASA DIN BS	1960 1961 1962	Arithmetical Logarithmic Arithmetical ⎫⎬⎭	Fixed density $(0\cdot1+\text{fog})$	To be under carefully controlled conditions giving a degree of development comparable with average photofinishing (see Fig. 19.5 and accompanying text).

Table 19.1 – The principal methods of expressing film speed

Actinograph. To obtain speed numbers suitable for use with this calculator they used the formula:

$$\text{Actinograph speed (i.e., H and D Speed No.)} = \frac{34}{i}$$

where i (inertia) is the exposure in lux seconds at the inertia point. The progression of H and D speed numbers was therefore arithmetical, i.e., a doubling of film speed was represented by a doubling of the speed number. (The odd value 34 for the constant into which i was divided to yield speed numbers suitable for the actinograph, resulted from the fact that the actinograph was already scaled for an earlier system of speed numbers.)

Hurter and Driffield used a standard wax candle as light source for the determination of inertia. When the candle was replaced by an artificial light source approximately equivalent to daylight (a tungsten lamp with a blue filter) the increased actinic value of the light was compensated by replacing the number 34 by 10, the same speed numbers being then obtained for blue-sensitive materials.

Scheiner

In 1894, Professor J. Scheiner published details of a system for measuring the speeds of the plates used by him for astronomical photography. In the Scheiner system, emulsion speeds were determined by ascertaining the minimum exposure necessary to produce a visible image on the developed plate, this being examined visually while being held against white paper. The exposures were made by means of a sector wheel, and the source of light was the Hefner amylacetate lamp at a distance of 1 metre. The steps of the sector wheel were arranged to increase exposure by the cube root of 2 at each step, the Schener speed number being derived from the last step which was visible above fog. The progression of speed numbers was therefore logarithmic (page 328).

Because exposure and development conditions were not sufficiently regulated, it was possible to obtain fictitiously high H and D and Scheiner numbers for a film. Owing to the commercial and advertising value of speed numbers, some manufacturers yielded to the temptation to publish the highest numbers possible. As a result, both H and D numbers and Scheiner numbers came to be discredited. The situation was aggravated by the fact that with modern materials speed is considerably influenced by the degree of development. Efforts were therefore made to establish new speed systems with safeguards to avoid a repetition of this "inflation". This led to the present-day national Standards. The first such system to appear was worked out in Germany in 1931 and published in 1934 by the German Standards Association as DIN 4512*.

DIN

In the original DIN system (which has since been modified) the light source was a 40-watt lamp, filtered so that it approximated closely to the colour quality of daylight, and the range of exposures was given

---

* DIN = Deutsche Industrie Norm (German Industrial Standard).

through an optical wedge of thirty steps, the exposure time being constant and equal to one-twentieth of a second. Development was continued to give maximum speed ("optimal development"), and after processing the material was examined to determine the highest wedge density which had produced a density of 0·1 above fog. The speed number allotted depended upon the density of this step. DIN speed numbers, which are logarithmic, were originally specified in fractional form (e.g., 14/10°) to distinguish them from Scheiner numbers.

Development to give maximum speed is open to the objection that such development is nearly always greater than is employed in practice, and that materials which go on gaining speed after a desirable degree of contrast is reached are given undue credit for speed in relation to other materials. This form of development was adopted because it was claimed by the Germans that precise and reproducible results could not be ensured with limited times of development without the use of elaborate apparatus for the control of temperature and agitation of the solution.

In a revision of the DIN Standard published in 1957, "optimal development" was replaced by "time-temperature" development, as in the BS and ASA methods, and the fractional form of the numbers was abandoned. Further revision in 1960–2 resulted in the DIN, BS and ASA methods all being brought into line (see below).

BS and ASA

The British and American Standard speed systems have been developed upon parallel, but not identical, lines. The original British Standard (published in 1941) employed the same fixed density speed criterion as the DIN system; the original American Standard (1943) employed the fractional gradient criterion. In 1947, the use of a fixed density criterion in the British Standard was abandoned, in the interests of international standardisation, in favour of the fractional gradient criterion.

The original British Standard specified logarithmic speed numbers, following the example of the Scheiner and DIN systems, and a formula for deriving speed was adopted which gave numbers that were interchangeable for practical purposes with Scheiner ratings. The original American Standard specified arithmetical speed numbers, to give ratings suitable for use with existing American exposure meters (Weston and GE). Following a joint revision of the two Standards in 1947, both for a number of years specified two types of rating, logarithmic and arithmetical, although the logarithmic ratings were not intended to be used in America. In the current versions of the two standards, logarithmic (to base 10) ratings have been discontinued.

The British and American Standards are designed to yield speed ratings suitable for "snapshot" work in daylight. Exposure and processing conditions, which are closely laid down, are therefore related to pictorial photography with roll films developed by the average photofinishing establishment. An intensity scale of exposures is given. The Standards both incorporate a very simple method of "time-temperature" development – devised by S.O. Rawling – for which the necessary apparatus consists only of a vacuum flask and a thermometer.

In 1960–2, the American, British and German Standard speed systems were brought into line in all respects except for the type of speed rating employed, the American and British Standards specifying arithmetical numbers and the German Standard logarithmic ones. This agreement was made possible by work which showed that good correlation exists between speeds based on a fixed density of $0 \cdot 1$ above fog and the fractional gradient criterion, for a wide variety of materials when developed to normal contrast. Speed in all three systems is therefore now determined with reference to the exptosure required to produce a density of $0 \cdot 1$ above fog density, this criterion being much simpler to use in practice than the fractional gradien criterion.

The common method adopted for determining speed in the three Standards is illustrated in Figure 19.5 In this, the characteristic curve of a photographic material is plotted for specified developing conditions. Two points are shown on the curve at M and N. Point N lies $1 \cdot 3$ log exposure units from point M in the direction of increasing exposure. The developing time of the negative material is so chosen that point N has a density $0 \cdot 80 \pm 0 \cdot 05$ greater than the density at point M. When this condition is satisfied, the exposure corresponding to point M represents the criterion from which speed is calculated. It is for the degree of development thus obtained that the correlation between the fixed density criterion and the fractional gradient criterion referred to above holds good.

In the American and British Standards, speed (arithmetical) is computed by use of the formula:

$$\text{Speed} = \frac{0 \cdot 8}{E_M}$$

where E_M is the exposure in lux seconds corresponding to the point M.

In the German Standard, speed (logarithmic) is computed by use of the formula:

$$\text{Speed} = 10\log \frac{1}{E_M}$$

where E_M is the exposure in lux seconds corresponding to the point M.

The additive system of photographic exposure (APEX)
When a camera exposure is made, the illumination at the surface of the sensitive material is dependent primarily on the luminance of the subject and the relative aperture of the lens (Chapter 16). The effect of the exposure can, therefore, be predicted from a knowledge of these

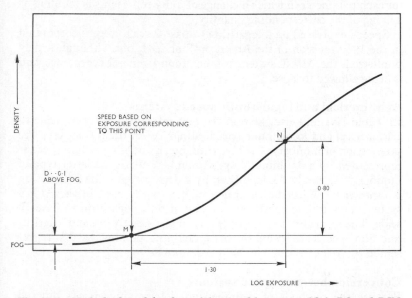

Fig. 19.5 – Method adopted for determining speed in current ASA, BS and DIN systems

two variables, the exposure time and the speed of the sensitive material. This can be stated in the form of a camera exposure equation which takes the basic form:

$$\frac{\text{Subject}}{\text{luminance}} \times \frac{\text{Lens}}{\text{aperture}} \times \frac{\text{Exposure}}{\text{time}} \times \frac{\text{Film}}{\text{speed}} = \text{Constant}$$

The *additive system of photographic exposure (APEX)*, is a simplified method of expressing the camera exposure equation. In this system, each of the parameters is expressed in terms of the logarithm to base 2 of that parameter. The values are assigned in such a way that the form of the equation becomes:

$$E_v = A_v + T_v = L_v + S_v$$

where E_v = exposure value
        A_v = lens aperture value
        T_v = exposure time value
        L_v = subject luminance value
        S_v = film speed (logarithmic, to base 2)

The advantage claimed for this system is that the relationships between the various parameters are expressed in a way in which they can be handled by simple addition, a set of numbers being obtained for each parameter in which a change of unity represents a doubling or halving of the corresponding quantity.

Speeds expressed on a logarithm to base 2 scale were incorporated in the 1960 revision of the American Standard, but, although widely publicized, the APEX system has not found general acceptance and is being allowed to lapse.

Arithmetical and logarithmic speed systems

In Table 19.1 and elsewhere in the text reference has been made to arithmetical and logarithmic speed ratings. With the former type the progression of numbers is *arithmetical,* i.e., a doubling of film speed is represented by a doubling of speed number. With the latter type of numbers – formerly distinguished by a degree sign – the progression is *logarithmic*. With the exception of the speeds used in the APEX system, logarithmic speeds are expressed on a logarithm to base 10 scale. The logarithm to base 10 of 2 is almost exactly 0·3 and logarithmic film speeds are scaled so that a doubling of film speed is represented by an increase of 3 in the speed number.

Conversion between speed systems

Because the methods of defining and determining speeds differed there was not necessarily any parallelism between the results obtained using the early speed systems, and any conversions between the various systems could therefore only be approximate.

Now, however, that a common basis is adopted in the determination of America, British and German standard film speeds direct conversion between the systems is possible as indicated in Table 19.2.

Speed ratings in tungsten light

Because the quality of tungsten light differs from that of daylight, different speed ratings may have to be used when an exposure meter is employed in tungsten light. As compared with daylight, artificial light is marked by an increase in red content and an approximately equal

Relative speed	American standard speed (arithmetical) (ASA speed)	British standard arithmetical speed	British standard logarithmic speed (obsolescent)	DIN speed
2048	3200	3200	46°	36
	2500	2500	45°	35
	2000	2000	44°	34
1024	1600	1600	43°	33
	1250	1250	42°	32
	1000	1000	41°	31
512	800	800	40°	30
	650	650	39°	29
	500	500	38°	28
256	400	400	37°	27
	320	320	36°	26
	250	250	35°	25
128	200	200	34°	24
	160	160	33°	23
	125	125	32°	22
64	100	100	31°	21
	80	80	30°	20
	64	64	29°	19
32	50	50	28°	18
	40	40	27°	17
	32	32	26°	16
16	25	25	25°	15
	20	20	24°	14
	16	16	23°	13
8	12	12	22°	12
	10	10	21°	11
	8	8	20°	10
4	6	6	19°	9
	5	5	18°	8
	4	4	17°	7
2	3	3	16°	6
	2·5	2·5	15°	5
	2·0	2·0	14°	4
1	1·6	1·6	13°	3
	1·2	1·2	12°	2
	1·0	1·0	11°	1

Table 19.2 – Conversion table between speed systems

decrease in blue content. As all photographic materials derive a large proportion of their speed from their sensitivity to blue light (Chapter 16), some drop in speed is to be expected in tungsten light. With fully colour-sensitive (panchromatic) materials this drop in speed is quite small, and may normally be ignored, but with orthochromatic materials – and even more with blue-sensitive materials – the loss is considerable. Speed ratings for use in tungsten light, for all except panchromatic materials, are therefore lower than daylight ratings. The ratios between the daylight and tungsten speeds are usually as follows:

Type of material	Speed ratio: daylight/tungsten	Difference in logarithmic ratings
Orthochromatic	× 2	3
Blue-sensitive	× 4	6

Speed ratings of Ilford films and plates
The speed ratings printed on the boxes of Ilford films and plates are daylight ratings of two types – ASA (arithmetical) and DIN (logarithmic). The ratings are determined on the basis of sensitometric tests confirmed by practical tests in the camera.

Speed ratings are not published for high-contrast Ilford materials such as those used in the graphic arts or for microcopying, nor for special materials such as astronomical plates and recording films. As we have already seen, any system for expressing the speed of a photographic material must take into account exposure and development conditions, and must be related to some particular criterion of correct exposure. The systems in general use for ordinary photographic materials cannot be applied to high-contrast or special materials since the conditions of exposure and development are quite different.

Practical value of speed numbers
The only useful speed number in practice is one which adequately represents the speed of a material under the conditions in which it is likely to be used. Published speed numbers aim at providing exposures which will secure a printable negative under a wide range of conditions. The published number for a given material cannot therefore be the best to use under *every* condition.

It follows that the serious photographer should determine for himself speed numbers for each type of material he uses, to suit his own equipment and desired image quality. Published speed numbers provide a valuable starting point for such a determination. But, when the photographer has selected the number that suits his needs, he should remember that this number is no more "correct" than the published one – except for his own conditions of working.

CHAPTER 20

Camera Exposure Determination

IN earlier Chapters we have considered the part played by the camera lens in forming an image, and have also studied the response to light of photographic materials. When we "make an exposure" we are permitting light to pass through the lens to form an image on the film, which the latter records. In any given circumstances (subject, lighting, film etc.), the densities produced upon the film – which govern the quality of the prints which are subsequently made from it, and the ease with which these are made – depend upon the intensity of the light which is permitted to pass through the lens to the film and on the time for which this light is allowed to act. These two factors are controlled by the *camera exposure*, i.e., the combination of lens aperture and shutter speed employed. Determination of a suitable camera exposure is therefore important whenever any photograph is taken.

Let us look at this in more detail. We saw in Chapter 15 that any subject comprises a range of varying luminances, so that when a photograph is taken the film actually receives a range of exposures – using the word "exposure" in the sense of illumination × time. The range of densities produced by these exposures depends firstly upon the characteristic curve of the film, which is governed by the particular film used and the development conditions employed, and secondly upon the placing of the range of exposures on this curve. This placing is determined principally by the following factors:

(1) Luminance of the different parts of the subject.
(2) Lens aperture (*f*-number).
(3) Ratio of reproduction.
(4) Filter factor (if any) under the particular working conditions.
(5) Shutter speed.

The first four of these factors together determine the illumination falling on the film;* the last factor determines the time for which this light is permitted to act.

---

* Other, usually less important, factors affecting the illumination on the film are lens transmission, flare and off-axis losses due to cos⁴ law and vignetting (Chapter 5).

The basic need in the determination of camera exposure (by any method except practical trial) is a knowledge of the luminance of the different parts of the subject. This, in turn, depends upon the illumination on the subject and its reflection characteristics. If the luminance of the subject is known we can readily make allowance for the other factors determining camera exposure (type of film, development, lens aperture, ratio of reproduction, filter factor, shutter speed), since these are known quantities.

Here, we may note that for a given camera exposure there is usually a range of combinations of lens aperture and shutter speed which may be used. Sometimes, the nature of the subject is such that achieving a suitable exposure time is the most important factor, after which the aperture is adjusted so that the correct amount of light reaches the film during the time that the shutter is open. This applies particularly with moving subjects, where it is normally desirable for the shutter speed to be sufficiently fast to freeze any movement of the subject. On other occasions the aperture may be the most important factor, e.g., to obtain suitable depth of field, and the exposure time must then be chosen to fit in with the particular aperture selected. Sometimes we are able to vary the illumination on the subject in order to obtain a suitable aperture and exposure time. This applies especially to work by artificial light.

Correct exposure

The greater part of this Chapter will be taken up with a consideration of ways by which we may obtain a knowledge of the luminance of the subject, and from this find the required camera exposure. Before proceeding to this we need to remind ourselves that whichever method of exposure determination we adopt, the criterion of the correctness of exposure rests finally upon the printing quality of the resulting negative. We may define a *correctly exposed negative* as the one which will yield an excellent print with the least difficulty. Judging negative quality requires considerable experience, since the values of density required in any given circumstances depend on the printing material to be employed and on the printing conditions; they are also to some extent influenced by personal preference. As a guide it may be said that a correctly exposed (continuous-tone) negative will generally have some – but not excessive – detail in the shadows, with highlights which just permit print to be read through them when the negative is laid on a newspaper in good light.

We saw in Chapter 15, that, provided the luminance range of the subject is not excessive, there are usually several exposures capable of giving good results, the ratio of the longest to the shortest being termed the *exposure latitude*. If we give an exposure outside the permissible latitude, negative quality will suffer. Thus, if the exposure is too short, shadow detail will be lost; we term this *under-exposure*. If the exposure is too long, highlight detail will be lost and the negative may suffer from excessive graininess and poor resolution; we term this *over-exposure*.

Although, by definition, all the exposures within the latitude of the film will yield good negatives, they will not yield identical negatives. For example, with the minimum acceptable exposure, a subject of average range will generally be located almost entirely on the toe of the characteristic curve. This negative will be of low density and of low contrast. Being thin, it will have the advantages that it will require a short printing time and will enable the printer to see clearly what he is doing when enlarging. But, being soft, it will almost certainly require a hard paper for printing, and while this may not be a disadvantage in itself it will mean that if for any reason we give insufficient development the negative may be unprintably soft. Further, if we miscalculate in exposure, we run the risk of under-exposure, with consequent loss of shadow detail.

If we give the maximum acceptable exposure, a subject of average range will generally be located almost entirely on the straight-line portion of the characteristic curve. This negative will be of high density and may be of high contrast. Being dense, it will require a long printing exposure and may prove trying to enlarge. If it is hard, it will require a soft paper for printing, and, while this may not be a disadvantage in itself, it will mean that, if for any reason we over-develop, the negative may be unprintably hard. On the other hand, if we aim at this denser type of negative we can be more sure of a picture of some sort, even if we miscalculate, than if we aim at a very short exposure – and miss.

In practice, we have to strike a mean between the minimum and maximum acceptable exposures, and, for an average subject, *an exposure of $1\frac{1}{4}$ to $2\frac{1}{2}$ times the minimum is recommended.**

Such an exposure normally places an average subject partly on the toe and partly on the straight-line portion of the characteristic curve (Figure 20.1) and corresponds closely with our earlier definition of a correctly exposed negative. Most exposure tables and meters are calibrated on the basis of an exposure of this order.

---

* The higher factor, $2\frac{1}{2}$, is especially recommended for professional work under difficult conditions, where failure must be avoided at all costs.

With a subject of exceptionally short luminance range the best placing is usually as shown in Figure 20.2. This results in the shadows

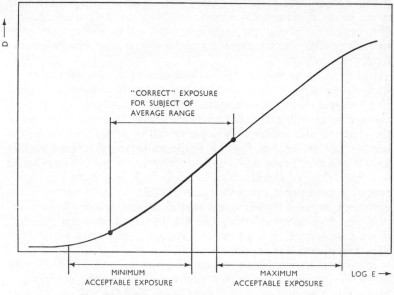

Fig. 20.1 – "Correct" exposure for an average subject

having rather more density than in the negative of the average subject, but the highlights have less density. If the negative of a short-range subject is exposed so as to produce similar shadow density to the negative of the average subject, it will be located entirely on the toe of the curve and will normally be undesirably soft.

With a subject of exceptionally long luminance range the best placing is usually as shown in Figure 20.2. This results in the shadows having less density than in the negative of the average subject, but the highlights have greater density. If the negative of a long-range subject is exposed so as to produce similar shadow density to the negative of an average subject it is likely to be too hard, and detail in the highlights may suffer.

Exposure determination

The most reliable way of determining exposure is to make a series of trial exposures, e.g., in the form of a "test strip", and then assess the results. This method has the advantage that it automatically takes into account variations in the performance of equipment, materials etc. It is of especial value for studio work, in particular for copying, but is usually impracticable for work away from the studio.

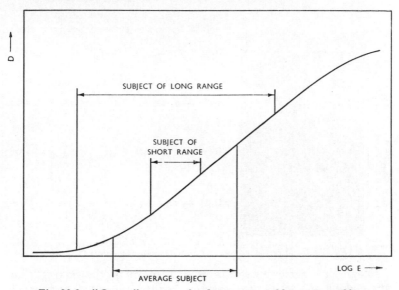

Fig. 20.2 – "Correct" exposure for short-range and long-range subjects

The principle of the "test strip" method is that the dark-slide cover is used as a shield by means of which progressively increasing exposures are given across the film. A suitable series of exposures is 2, 4, 8 and 16 seconds, or 5, 10, 20 and 40 seconds. The "2, 4, 8, 16" series is obtained by exposing the whole film for 2 seconds, then replacing the lens cap and pushing in the dark-slide cover to cover one-quarter of the film. A further 2 seconds exposure is given, the lens cap replaced, and the dark-slide cover pushed in to cover one-half of the film. A further 4 seconds exposure is given, the lens cap again replaced, the dark-slide cover moved to cover three-quarters of the film and a final 8 seconds exposure is given (Figure 20.3). Care must be taken to allow the camera to become perfectly stationary before each exposure. A "5, 10, 20, 40" series is obtained in a similar way, the four exposures in this case being 5, 5, 10 and 20 seconds.

Where the "test strip" method cannot be adopted, exposures must be determined on the basis of either:

(1) An exposure table or calculator.

(2) Experience.

(3) Measurement with an exposure meter.

Even with these aids, there will always be occasions when we are unable to be absolutely sure of the best exposure to give. If the

	1st EXPOSURE	2nd EXPOSURE	3rd EXPOSURE	4th EXPOSURE	TOTAL
	2 SECS.	—	—	—	= 2 SECS.
	2 SECS. +	2 SECS.	—	—	= 4 SECS.
	2 SECS. +	2 SECS. +	4 SECS.	—	= 8 SECS.
	2 SECS. +	2 SECS. +	4 SECS. +	8 SECS.	= 16 SECS.

(left margin, vertical: DARK-SLIDE COVER MOVED IN THIS DIRECTION BETWEEN EXPOSURES)

Fig. 20.3 – *A processed test strip for determining camera exposure*

photograph is important we must then resort to "bracketing", i.e., the making of a series of exposures. For this purpose it is generally useful to make three exposures, one at the most likely value and the other two a stop or so on either side of this.

Exposure criteria

The basic principle behind the design and use of exposure tables and exposure meters is that of measuring the luminance of part or parts of the subject and using this information to locate the subject in a suitable position on the characteristic curve.

It will be apparent from our earlier consideration of this problem, that, to locate subjects of all types in the best position on the curve, we require fundamentally to know the luminance of the darkest part of the subject in which detail is required and the luminance of the brightest part of the subject in which detail is required. A double exercise of judgement is thus required of the photographer. In the first place, he must decide on the darkest and brightest areas in which he requires detail; this choice will be governed to some extent by aesthetic considerations. Secondly, the photographer must decide where these areas can be most favourably located on the characteristic curve. This choice will be determined principally by the requirements of the printing process. In view of the many "links" in the chain, the best location of the shadows and highlights on the curve will usually be found more readily by practical trial under the photographer's own conditions, than from sensitometric considerations.

This "fundamental", or "luminance range", method of exposure determination is somewhat complicated and is not very suitable for use under everyday working conditions. Other exposure criteria which, if less exact, are simpler to apply are therefore usually adopted in ordinary photographic practice, with varying degrees of success. These criteria include:

(1) Luminance of darkest object.

(2) Luminance of brightest object.

(3) Luminance of selected object intermediate between shadows and highlights ("key" tone).

(4) Integrated effect.

(5) Incident light.

Descriptions of each of these criteria are given below. They all represent attempts to obtain a simpler method than the "fundamental" one, while still retaining a useful degree of precision, and each method has its own advantages. Because, however, these methods are necessarily compromises, it is important that when we adopt any of them we should be quite sure of (a) what we are measuring, and (b) what we must allow for.

Measurement of luminance of darkest object
In this method the darkest object in the subject is located at a fixed point on the toe of the characteristic curve. This ensures that there is a little, though not excessive, density in the shadows, and that all the other tones of the subject are recorded as progressively increasing densities. The method has the advantage that it appears simple, but it suffers from serious drawbacks. In the first place, measurement of the luminance of the darkest object in a scene is usually a difficult one to make because most measuring devices are limited in their sensitivity at low luminances. Secondly, when making the measurement it is not always easy to prevent stray light from the brighter parts of the subject from being included. Thirdly, the method tells us nothing about what happens to the highlights, and, as will be apparent from our earlier discussion, with subjects of long luminance range it may lead to loss of highlight detail and with subjects of short luminance range to too low contrast.

Measurement of luminance of brightest object
In this method the brightest object in the subject is located at a fixed

point on the characteristic curve. This enables the density in the highlights to be controlled at a suitable level, and the other tones in the subject are recorded as progressively decreasing densities. The method tells us nothing about what happens to the shadows, but by placing the highlights well up on the curve it is possible to ensure that detail is obtained in the shadows of all but the most contrasty subjects. This usually means, however, that the average subject receives more exposure than is really desirable.

Measurement of luminance of selected object intermediate between shadows and highlights ("key" tone)

In this method a selected object, or "key" tone, is placed at a fixed point on the characteristic curve. The method ensures a favourable rendering of an important tone. In much work where the method is adopted the "key" tone selected is a flesh tone. The key-tone method is of greatest application where lighting is under the control of the photographer, so that both highlights and shadows can be lit in such a way that they too are suitably recorded. The method may be employed, after suitable practical trial, in any class of work in which it is desired to record a selected tone at a given level.

Measurement of total amount of light coming from the subject ("integration" method)

This method is the one most widely used in everyday photographic practice. It consists in taking a reading by directing a meter at the subject as a whole. Despite its popularity, this method is open to serious objection on theoretical grounds, because the reading obtained bears no direct relation to the luminance of either the shadows or the highlights of the subject, or to any selected tone. With subjects having identical luminances at the two ends of the scale, but different luminance distributions, the readings obtained using the meter by the "integration" method may differ widely, although both subjects will require the same exposure. Nevertheless, the simplicity of this method makes it attractive, and, as we have stated, it is widely used. Its fair degree of success is due partly to the statistical relationship between the total amount of light reflected from a subject and the amounts reflected from the deepest shadows and highest highlights, and partly to the fact that the useful exposure range of modern negative materials is generally much greater than the luminance range of the average subject. Nevertheless, if we use this method we should be alive to its limitations, and to the fact that it is liable to let us down from time to time.

Measurement of light incident upon the subject

In the "incident-light" method, the light falling on the subject is measured, instead of the reflected light; i.e., we are measuring illumination rather than luminance. With a suitably designed meter the measurement is an easy one to make. This method results in the placing at fixed points on the characteristic curve of all surfaces in the subject which are directly illuminated by the major light source. Like measurement of the luminance of the brightest object (see above), measurement of the light incident upon the subject tells us nothing about the shadows.

Where reference is made to the incident-light method today it is implicit that the illumination measured is the maximum illumination. This method of exposure determination was first suggested by P. C. Smethurst in 1936.

Exposure tables and calculators

Under readily describable conditions of illumination and type of subject, exposure tables can be remarkably successful. Many forms of table have therefore been devised – some for daylight use, and others for artificial light exposures. In designing daylight exposure tables, the illumination is estimated at its most likely value, bearing in mind the height of the sun above the horizon (which depends on the time of day, time of year and latitude) and the state of sky. Hurter and Driffield, who produced exposure tables which were used in one form or another for over half-a-century, made a series of observations of the strength of daylight throughout the year, using a continuously-recording differential airbulb thermometer, and based their exposure tables on these observations.

From the estimated value of illumination, the luminance of the shadows is estimated by designers of tables for different types of scene. A great many measurements of scene luminances have been made by various workers to provide the necessary information in this connection. In general, it is found that the luminance of the shadow areas of a subject increases with the subject distance. This is because small shadow details which are significant in close-up pictures merge with lighter areas and are diluted by atmospheric haze in more distant scenes. The practical result of this is that a "distant" or "semi-distant" scene requires only about one-half the exposure required by a "nearby" scene receiving the same illumination, while a "close-up" requires $1\frac{1}{2}$ times the exposure of the "nearby" scene. Exposure tables make allowance for this. Exposure tables sometimes also make allowance for subjects which do not receive full illumination, such as people under trees in leaf. A properly designed exposure table places both the shadows and highlights of the subject in appropriate positions on the characteristic curve, i.e., it is based on the "fundamental" criterion of exposure.

Exposure calculators differ from exposure tables only in their layout; the basic principles on which they derive exposures are the same. The main difference between a table and a calculator is that, in the latter, provision of rotating discs or sliding members simplifies the derivation of camera exposure, and enables a great deal of information to be provided in a relatively small space.

Artificial light exposure tables and calculators
When working by artificial light, illumination can be estimated fairly accurately in terms of lamp output, distance and direction. Very many tables and calculators have been evolved for specific purposes and different types of lighting. They vary in detail, but follow the same general pattern, making allowance for type and power of lamps (depending upon wattage and efficiency), reflector efficiency, distance and direction of lamps, general tone of room and general tone of subject.

Flash exposure guide numbers
The exposure required with a flashbulb (or electronic flash tube) is conveniently expressed in the form of an *exposure guide number*, or *flash factor*. A guide number represents the product of the lens aperture (*f-number*) and the bulb-to-subject distance* required for correct exposure with a particular film and flashbulb. Given the appropriate guide number, the lens aperture required can be obtained by dividing the guide number by the bulb-to-subject distance, and vice versa.

Example. The foot guide number for a certain combination of film and flashbulb is 40. Then:

(a) If the bulb is to be used at a given distance, say 5 feet, from the subject, the *f*-number required to give correct exposure is $40/5 = f/8$. With the bulb 10 feet from the subject, the *f*-number required is $40/10 = f/4$.

(b) If it is desired to work at a given aperture, say $f/5\cdot6$, then the

---

*At the time of writing, guide numbers published in Britain are usually based on distances in feet, but Continental manufacturers commonly quote guide numbers based on distances in metres. This is likely to become common practice in Britain too with the adoption of metric units. Care must therefore be taken when using flash guide numbers to ascertain whether they are *foot guide numbers* or *metric guide numbers*.

bulb must be $40/5 \cdot 6 = 7$ feet from the subject. At $f/11$, the bulb must be $40/11 = 3\frac{1}{2}$ feet from the subject.

Guide numbers are a variant of artificial light exposure tables. Because a guide number takes into account only the power of the light source and its distance from the subject, separate allowance must be made for reflector, type of surroundings and type of subject, if these differ from the conditions under which the guide numbers were determined. Unless otherwise specified, when guide numbers are published the assumption is made that the whole of the flash will be employed. Such guide numbers are applicable to exposures by open flash and to synchronized exposures at slow shutter speeds. Guide numbers specially determined for the higher shutter speeds are lower than those quoted for slow speeds, since at high speeds only a part of the flash is employed.

Basing exposure on experience

We may regard the basing of exposure on experience as making use of a mental exposure table of the user's own compiling. The older school of photographers liked to rely entirely on experience, and commonly prided themselves on their ability to determine exposures with sufficient accuracy without any assistance from tables or measuring devices. For certain types of work this procedure serves very well, since minor errors in estimation are covered up by the latitude of the photographic material.

Exposure meters

Nowadays, photographers in general like to get as much assistance as possible in determining exposures. Measuring devices which are available to assist the photographer in the determination of correct exposure fall into two main categories:

(1) Photo-electric exposure meters

(2) Exposure photometers

Each of these types of meter is described in detail below. No meter entirely eliminates the need for personal judgement; to get the best out of any instrument it is necessary to understand what it is doing and how to make allowance for factors with which it may be unable to deal unaided.

Photo-electric exposure meters

By far the most popular type of exposure meter today is the *photo-electric exposure meter*. This consists essentially of a photo-electric cell, a device to limit the acceptance angle of the cell, a galvanometer and a calculator from which the necessary exposure can be derived from the galvanometer reading in terms of exposure time and lens aperture for a given film speed.

The photo-electric cells used are of two main types. The most widely used is the "barrier-layer" cell, which has a light-sensitive layer of copper oxide or, more usually, selenium. Photo-electric cells of this type are self-generating, i.e., when light falls on the light-sensitive surface a potential difference is set up between two layers in the cell. As a result, the needle of the galvanometer – which is connected in series with the cell – is deflected, the deflection giving an indication of the total amount of light falling on the cell. A baffle is needed to limit the acceptance angle, because the cell reacts to all the light that falls upon it, from whatever direction. For a meter which is to be used from the camera position, the acceptance angle should preferably not exceed the angle of view of the camera; otherwise, light coming from outside the area being photographed may influence the meter reading.

A drawback of the photo-electric exposure meter fitted with the usual type of cell (selenium) is that its sensitivity is limited. Increased sensitivity can be obtained by using a larger cell and/or a galvanometer which is more sensitive than those normally employed, but the instrument is then more costly and probably more delicate. Alternatively, the angle of acceptance of the meter may be increased, but then the readings of the meter are less useful – in particular, the sky will affect them. As a compromise, the baffle is sometimes made oblong in shape, i.e., wider in the horizontal direction. In the Weston meter, the angle of acceptance for normal use (high light-levels) is 50°, i.e., close to the average camera angle. When the low light-level scale is used, the angle of acceptance is increased to 70°, to assist in obtaining the desired increase in sensitivity.

The sensitivity of some meters using selenium cells may be increased by means of a special "booster" element containing an additional photo-electric cell. This is attached to the meter when it is required to take readings at very low light-levels. In one such meter, an increase in sensitivity of about four times is obtained by use of a booster.

The second type of photo-electric cell employed in exposure meters is the cadmium sulphide (CdS) cell. This is of the photo-conductive type, i.e., when light falls on the cell its electrical resistance drops. If, therefore, the cell is connected in series with a small battery and a galvanometer, the deflection of the needle will give an indication of the amount of light falling on the light-sensitive surface of the cell. The main advantage of the cadmium sulphide cell over the more usual selenium one is that the cadmium sulphide cell has a much higher sensitivity.

There are several methods by which a photo-electric exposure meter may be used. The one adopted in any given circumstances will depend upon the type of material being used, the degree of sensitivity required, or, simply, upon convenience. The following are the three most commonly used methods:

(1) *Measurement of total flux (integration method)*. This is the general method for which the scales of practically all photo-electric meters are calibrated. It consists in taking a reading, from the camera position, of the total amount of light coming from the subject, the calibration of the meter being based on an assumed average subject. As we have already stated (page 338), this method, while theoretically unsound, usually gives useful results, although it may fail on difficult subjects. When taking readings on outdoor scenes by this method the meter should preferably be held with its axis pointing slightly below the horizontal, to prevent the sky from exerting an undue effect on the readings. If the angle of acceptance of the meter is larger than the camera angle, readings should preferably be taken, not from the camera position, but from a point nearer the subject – to ensure that it fills the angle of acceptance of the meter.

A slight variant of the integration method, which aims at avoiding the most gross errors to which it is prone, is to direct the meter at the brightest and the darkest parts of the subject in turn, and base the exposure on the point lying in the middle of the swing of the needle.

(2) *Measurement of light incident upon the subject*. This measurement may be made in two different ways:

(a) By directing a suitable meter at the light source.

(b) By taking a reading of the light reflected from a white (or grey) card placed to receive the maximum incident light, and making allowance for the reflection factor of the card.

Method (a) requires the use of a special "incident-light" meter, i.e., a meter fitted with a diffusing medium over the photo-electric cell. Some ordinary meters can be converted into "incident-light" meters by means of a special diffuser which fits over the photo-electric cell. Method (b) can be adopted with an ordinary "reflected-light" meter; a piece of white blotting paper makes a very suitable white card. This method is sometimes called the "artificial highlight" method. Both methods are particularly suitable for work where the placing of the highlights is the principal factor governing exposure, as, for example, in reversal work (page 347).

(3) *Measurement of luminance of most important area of subject* ("*key*" *tone*). This method may be used where one particular tone, e.g., a flesh tone, constitutes the most important part of the subject. Where the method is used in portraiture, the procedure is to take a reading on the highlight side of the face. The key-tone method can be applied in most branches of photography by choosing the most important area and deciding on the grey in which it is to be recorded. For this method to be of maximum value, the lighting of the subject must be carefully controlled, so that both shadows and highlights are suitably recorded.

It is not usually convenient to measure the luminance of either the shadows or the highlights with a photo-electric exposure meter. To do so, the subject must be approached until the shadow or highlight area fills the angle of acceptance, and the meter is then usually so close to the subject that it obstructs the incident light. In addition, at the shadow end, the luminance of the subject is usually so low that it is difficult to obtain a significant needle deflection.

The simplest photo-electric exposure meters are calibrated for the integration method only. More elaborate meters are provided with a diffuser so that the meter may be used in addition as an incident light meter. With some meters, such as the Weston, the diffuser is supplied separately from the meter. The Weston meter is calibrated for all of the methods described above.

The first photo-electric exposure meters were completely separate from the camera. Later, as smaller meters were developed, some of these were designed to fit the accessory shoe of a camera. Today, an exposure meter is incorporated as an integral part of many cameras. In some, the meter is coupled to the lens diaphragm or shutter speed controls so that the camera exposure is set automatically (or semi-automatically) as the camera is pointed towards the subject. Notwithstanding these developments, separate exposure meters are still widely used and offer a greater flexibility in use which is of value in serious photography.

Exposure photometers

A *photometer* is an instrument which enables the luminance of an object to be measured by comparison with a surface of known luminance. With a photometer, the luminance of any area of the subject may be measured even at quite low values. A *telephotometer* is a photometer incorporating a telescope to enable readings to be taken from the camera position, however far away the subject may be. In practical photography, a telephotometer is much more useful than an ordinary photometer.

The idea of the telephotometer is not new, but for a long time the standardization of the luminance of the reference surface presented a

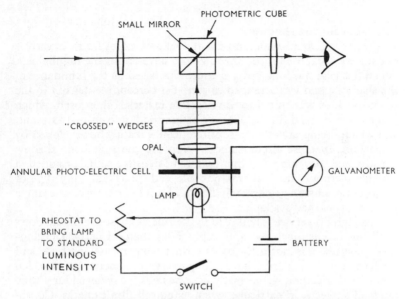

Fig. 20.4 – Simplified arrangement of the S.E.I. Exposure Photometer

difficulty. In the S.E.I. Exposure Photometer the problem has been overcome by the use of a photo-electric cell in a circuit which enables the light output of the standard lamp to be measured, and, if not at the required level, brought back to standard by a rheostat in the lamp supply circuit. The S.E.I. Exposure Photometer is illustrated diagrammatically in Figure 20.4.

Although a telephotometer can be used to measure the luminance of any part of a subject, when employed for exposure determination it is generally used to measure one of the following:

(a) Luminance of the darkest shadow.

(b) Luminance of the brightest highlight.

(c) Luminance of a selected "key" tone, e.g., a flesh tone.

The S.E.I. exposure photometer is specially calibrated for the "darkest shadow" and "brightest highlight" methods. It may also be used to measure the luminance range of a subject. The telephotometer is the only type of meter permitting exposures to be determined by the fundamental "luminance range" method (page 336).

Exposing for the shadows

In the early days of photography, the rule of exposure in negative-making was "expose for the shadows and develop for the highlights". When this rule was followed, exposure was based on the luminance of the shadows, and was arranged to give just perceptible density in the shadows. This was suited to the negative materials then used, which had a short toe and (in the absence of bromide) a fixed inertia point, and which, being non-colour-sensitive, could readily be developed by inspection. In these circumstances, exposure controlled the shadow density and development the highlight density, and, provided a suitable plate was used, it was possible with practically any type of subject to produce a negative which would print correctly on the single grade of paper then available.

Although lip-service is still paid to the rule "expose for the shadows . . ." this rule is much less applicable today than formerly. Development nowadays is normally by the time-temperature method, and modern negative materials have a long toe with an inertia point which is not fixed. Further, we normally use one negative material for a wide range of subjects, in particular when using roll film cameras. Consequently, the characteristic curve of our negative material is usually fixed before we start. Fortunately, we have today a wide range of paper grades at our disposal to cater for negatives of varying density range, but, nevertheless, for various reasons, our aim is still usually to produce negatives the majority of which will print on "normal" paper.

In many cases we can adopt the rule, "expose for the shadows and let the highlights take care of themselves". With subjects of normal luminance range this will usually lead to negatives of suitable quality. Negatives of subjects of very short range, exposed in this way, will, however, usually be on the soft side. Better contrast with such subjects is achieved by giving two to three times the exposure based on the shadows. On the other hand, with subjects of extremely high luminance range with important highlight detail, better results will usually be achieved by giving one-half to one-third of the exposure based on the shadows (see Figure 20.2).

"Expose for the shadows and develop for the highlights" is still, to some extent, applicable today when negatives are developed individually by inspection, but if this rule is adopted it must not be overlooked that with most modern materials shadow density as well as highlight density is influenced by the degree of development.

Exposure of reversal materials

In this Chapter so far we have been concerned solely with the determination of exposure for negative materials. The methods used for the determination of exposure for reversal-processed materials (page 419), whether black-and-white or colour, are generally similar to those used for negative materials, and the "fundamental" method of determining exposure, that of measuring the luminance of both shadows and highlights and placing these on the curve in the most suitable positions remains unaltered.

There is, however, one important difference between reversal and negative materials. With a transparency, the one fixed factor is the highlight end of the tone range, which is set by the clear film. When, therefore, we require a simpler method of exposure determination than the "fundamental" method, the best part of the subject on which to base exposure is the highlights. If we do this, i.e., arrange exposure so that there is just perceptible density in the highlight areas of the resulting transparency, the shadows will "take care of themselves". This procedure will produce satisfactorily exposed transparencies of most subjects. With light subjects, with no important dark areas, some improvement will usually be obtained by reducing the indicated exposure by one-half to one stop. On the other hand, when dealing with dark subjects, with no important light areas, the exposure should be increased by one-half to one stop. Subjects falling in these two classes however, will usually be few.

We have already noted that when using a photo-electric exposure meter it is not usually convenient to measure the luminance of the highlights of a subject directly. We can, however, obtain a close approximation to this by using the meter by the incident-light method. Since the highlights of most subjects are white or near-white in tone, it will be apparent that a measurement of the illumination on the subject provides in effect a measurement of the luminance of the highlights. The incident-light method of using a photo-electric exposure meter – using either an ordinary meter with an artificial highlight, or a special meter – is therefore of particular value in reversal work.

When the incident-light method of exposure determination was first suggested by P. C. Smethurst and embodied in practical form in the Avo-Smethurst High-Light Exposure Meter, the system was intended solely for work using reversal materials. The Avo-Smethurst meter used an artificial highlight consisting of a flat opal diffuser covering the photo-electric cell window.

J. F. Dunn has described a method of using an incident-light exposure meter which he claims to be the most accurate simple method for the determination of exposures with reversal colour films. This method, termed by Mr. Dunn the *Duplex method*, consists in taking two readings of incident light, one with the meter facing the camera and the other with the meter facing the main light source. The *f*-number midway between the two apertures indicated is then used. The practical effect of this method is to help to preserve detail in the shadows of subjects having side or back lighting. This necessarily involves some loss of highlight detail, but in general provides a satisfactory compromise. As with the conventional incident-light method, it is still desirable to make allowance for subjects of exceptionally light or exceptionally dark average tone.

CHAPTER 21

Photographic Papers

WE have confined our attention in this book so far largely to the preparation of negatives. The negative, although important, represents only the first stage in the preparation of a photograph. We have now to deal with the second stage – the preparation of the positive from the negative. In this Chapter we shall consider the papers used for printing, and in the next Chapter the printing operation itself.

Developing-out and printing-out papers
The sensitive papers used today for the preparation of photographic prints are almost exclusively of the *development*, or *developing-out*, type. In these, an invisible image is formed on exposure, being subsequently rendered visible by development. As far as the method of image production is concerned, developing-out papers behave in exactly the same way as negative materials.

At one time, the printing papers in general use were almost all of the *printing-out* type, in which exposure to strong daylight produces an image which is immediately visible. Developing-out papers have gradually displaced printing-out papers and are now used exclusively – with the single exception of the preparation of portrait proofs, for which printing-out papers are still sometimes used. In this Chapter we shall be concerned entirely with papers of the developing-out type.

The light-sensitive material used for developing-out papers is very similar to that used for negative materials, i.e., it is a suspension of silver halides in gelatin. It is coated on base paper which must be entirely free from substances that would have a harmful effect on the emulsion (Chapter 13).

Types of developing-out papers
Many different types of developing-out paper are made. They differ as regards the nature and contrast of the emulsion they employ, and

also in purely mechanical characteristics such as thickness and tint of the base and the nature of its surface. For convenience, we may classify the characteristics of the various types of papers under the following headings:

(1) Type of silver salt employed in the emulsion.
(2) Contrast of the emulsion.
(3) Nature of the paper surface.
(4) Tint and thickness of the paper base.

We shall consider each of these in turn.

Type of silver salt employed
Papers can be divided into three main classes in terms of the type of silver halide employed as the sensitive material. There are thus, *chloride papers, bromide papers* and *chlorobromide papers*, the sensitive material in the latter being a mixture of silver chloride and silver bromide. In all three types of emulsion, silver halides other than those specifically mentioned may be present in small quantities. Chloride papers are commonly referred to as *contact papers* (page 352).

The nature of the silver salt employed in a paper emulsion largely determines its speed, image colour and tone reproduction qualities. These three characteristics will be considered in detail.

Speed. Papers differ widely in speed, bromide papers being the fastest. These are very much faster than contact papers – usually about 50 times as fast. Chlorobromide papers are made in various speeds between the two extremes represented by contact and bromide papers. The faster chlorobromide papers are in the same speed class as bromide papers.

Whereas negative materials are colour-sensitised to enable the reproduction of colours to be controlled, printing papers are employed only to reproduce negatives, which are monochromatic, and so no question of colour rendering normally arises. Some printing papers, are, however, colour sensitised for other purposes. One reason is to utilize more of the available printing light – which is normally rich in green and red radiation and deficient in violet and ultra-violet – and thus increase the effective printing speed of the paper. This may be employed by the manufacturer in almost all kinds of paper but is most widely used in contact and chlorobromide papers, which have an inherent sensitivity limited to the ultra-violet and violet (Figure 16.1), and which tend to be slow. As a result of dye sensitising, modern contact papers are very much faster than the early "gaslight" papers which could be handled fairly freely in dim white artificial light. Modern contact papers require to be handled by a yellow or orange safelight.

Image colour. The colour of the image on a photographic paper (untoned) depends primarily upon the state of division of the developed image, i.e., upon its grain size, although it is also affected by the tint of the base. The grain size of the image depends in turn upon the nature and size of the grains in the original emulsion, on any special additions which may be made to the emulsion and on development.

The grain size of paper emulsions is very small, so that no question of visible graininess due to the paper ever arises, even with the fastest papers. In fact, with many paper emulsions, the individual grains of silver in the developed image are so small that their size is comparable with that of light waves; the image then appears no longer black but coloured. As grains become progressively smaller, the image, which with large grains is black, becomes first brown, then reddish and then yellow, finally becoming practically colourless. When a paper is developed, the grains are small at first but grow as development proceeds; it is, therefore, only on full development that the image gets its full colour. Certain papers are made to yield warm tones by making use of the effect produced by incomplete development, but to achieve some particular tone with these papers, development must go just so far and no further. The finer the original grains of the emulsion, the greater the possibility of controlling the image colour, both in manufacture, and by control during development.

Bromide papers have relatively coarse grains, and, when developed normally, yield images of a neutral-black image colour. This image colour does not readily respond to control in development. Contact (chloride) emulsions are of finer grain. Some contact papers are designed to yield blue-black images by direct development, others to yield warm-black images by direct development – the colour depending upon the treatment the emulsion has received in manufacture. In Britain a blue-black image colour is generally preferred for contact prints and an organic compound termed a *bluing agent* is therefore incorporated in the emulsions of most popular contact papers. Chlorobromide emulsions are intermediate in grain size – as in many other properties – between contact papers and bromide papers. Some chlorobromide papers are designed to give only a single warm-black image colour; others can be made to yield a range of tones – from warm-black and warm-brown to sepia.

Tone reproduction qualities. Contact, bromide and chlorobromide papers are all available in a range of *contrast grades*, or *gradations*, to suit negatives of different density ranges. We saw the need for this in Chapter 15. With any given negative, therefore, it is usually possible to make a good print on any of the three types of paper, provided that the appropriate contrast grade is chosen. There will, however, be certain differences in tone reproduction between the three prints. The differences arise because the characteristic curves of different papers vary somewhat in shape (see page 252).

So far we have been dealing with the characteristics of the three main types of paper emulsion. We will now consider their uses.

Contact papers

Papers employing silver chloride as the sensitive material are used almost exclusively for contact printing, on account of their slow speed, and as we have already noted are usually referred to not as chloride papers but as *contact papers*.

Because of their slow speed, contact papers have the advantage that they can be worked by a bright yellow or orange light. Another advantage is that development is more rapid than with other papers, usually occupying less than a minute at 20°C. The image colour of the contact papers employed in Britain is usally blue-black, although contact papers are available which yield a warm-black image colour – this being usually accentuated by use of a cream base.

Bromide papers

Bromide papers are the fastest type of development papers. Their high speed makes them very suitable for enlarging and also for the rapid production of prints by contact. Bromide papers must be handled and processed by orange or greenish-yellow light.

Bromide papers give prints of a neutral-black colour by direct development, which normally requires from 1½ to 2 minutes at 20°C. Because of the popularity of bromide papers for professional and commercial work, many processes have been worked out for subsequent toning of the finished print, so as to facilitate the production of warm-black, sepia and other toned images. Details of some of these processes are given in Chapter 25.

Chlorobromide papers

The third important group of papers comprises the chlorobromides. These papers are of many different kinds. In all of them, silver bromide and silver chloride are present in important quantities, but the proportion of the two may vary widely from paper to paper. In many respects, the properties of chlorobromide papers may be regarded as intermediate between those of chloride and bromide papers, the balance struck between the characteristics of the two depending very largely upon the proportions in which the two halides are present.

Some chlorobromide papers are in the same speed class as bromide papers; others are much slower. They may be used for both contact printing and enlarging, although the slower papers require a high-intensity light source for enlarging. Chlorobrom de papers have, in general, a characteristic curve which results in good tone separation throughout the whole range of tones, and most of the papers are designed to give warm-toned images. They also tend to have good development latitude. For these reasons chlorobromide papers are favoured for studio and exhibition work.

Some chlorobromide papers are designed to give a range of warm tones by partial development; others are meant to give only one tone.

Chlorobromide papers, like bromide papers, must be handled and processed in a darkroom with an orange or greenish-yellow safelight. Many chlorobromide papers are colour-sensitised – to increase their speed – so that especial care must be taken to use only the recommended safelights. Some safelights which are suitable for use with bromide papers may, with chlorobromide papers, cause fogging.

If a mercury vapour light source (page 377) is employed when printing with a colour-sensitised chlorobromide paper, the contrast obtained will tend to be low and a harder grade of paper than usual may be required. The speed of the paper, in relation to that of bromide paper, may also be reduced.

Paper contrast grades

We saw in Chapter 15 that the contrast of a paper, unlike that of a negative, can be varied only within narrow limits by altering development, and that to print satisfactorily from negatives of different density ranges, papers are required in a range of contrast grades, or gradations.

At one time, printing papers were manufactured in one contrast grade only, and it was standard practice to control the gradation of each negative by individual development, in order to produce a satisfactory print from the paper available. The introduction of the roll film, however, made this method of working impossible, and it was probably this, as much as anything, which made necessary the manufacture of papers in several contrasts.

All types of developing-out paper – contact papers, bromide papers and chlorobromide papers – are therefore made today in several grades. Glossy surfaced papers – the most widely used variety – are usually made in five grades, although some other surfaces are available only in two or three grades. Some special surfaces are produced in one grade only. These are usually surfaces produced for the printing of negatives produced in the portrait or commercial studio, where lighting, exposure and processing are completely under control, thus making possible the production of negatives of uniform density range.

The selection of a suitable grade of paper for a given negative is a matter for personal judgement based on experience, or for practical trial. If a trial is considered necessary, it is important that, during this, development should be standardized at the recommended time and temperature (see page 356). If the correct grade of paper has been selected, and exposure adjusted so that the middle tones of the picture have the required density, then the highest highlights in the picture will be almost white – though with just a trace of detail – and the deepest shadows black. If the highlights show appreciable greying, and the shadows are nowhere black, the paper selected is of *too soft* a contrast grade for the negative selected; a harder paper should be tried. If the highlights are completely white with no detail at all, and not only the shadows but the darker middle tones are black, the paper selected is of *too hard* a contrast grade for the negative selected; a softer paper should be tried.

In addition to the conventional printing papers so far described, special types of paper are manufactured – although not widely used in Britain – in which the effective contrast can be changed at will by varying the colour of the printing light. With such *variable-contrast papers* it is possible to produce good prints from negatives of any degree of contrast on one paper – which thus does the work of the entire range of grades in which other printing papers are supplied, and so makes it unnecessary to keep stocks in a variety of grades.

Paper surface

The surface finish of a paper depends upon two factors: (1) the texture, or mechanical finish of the paper, and (2) its sheen.

The texture of a paper is usually smooth, fine-grained or rough. The texture of a given paper depends upon the treatment that the paper base receives in manufacture. Glossy papers, for example, are calendered, to produce a very smooth surface, while fine-grained papers are usually embossed on an embossing roller. Rough papers receive their finish from the felt on the paper-making machine. Surface texture governs the amount of detail in the print. Where maximum detail is required, a smooth surface is desirable, whereas a rough surface may be employed to hide graininess or slight lack of definition. A smooth surface is desirable also for prints which are required for reproduction and have to be copied in the camera. Various textures are available for special effects.

Sheen arises largely from the thin layer of gelatin – the super-coating – which is applied over the emulsion of many papers in manufacture, to provide protection against abrasion (page 212). This layer gives added brilliance to the print, by increasing the direct (specular) reflecting power of the paper surface. Glossy papers are smooth with a high sheen; a higher maximum black is obtainable on glossy papers than on others. Matt papers are smooth but have no sheen; starch is usually included in the emulsion to subdue direct reflection.

Tint and thickness of paper base
The colour, or tint, of the base paper used for photographic papers may be white or one of a variety of shades of cream. In general, cream papers tend to give an impression of warmth and friendliness; they are very suitable for prints of warm image colour. A white base may be used to simulate coldness and delicacy; snow scenes should always be printed on a white base, as should prints with a blue-black image colour.

Two thicknesses of base are commonly available, designated *single-weight* and *double-weight* respectively. Double-weight paper, which is of about the thickness of a postcard, is sometimes referred to as *card*. Prints produced by photofinishers are nearly always on single-weight paper. Both double-weight and single-weight papers are used for enlargements; single-weight is often sufficient if the print is to be mounted on card, but in the larger sizes double-weight paper is to be preferred since there is a danger, with the thinner papers, of creasing in the wet state. A third weight of paper – *light-weight*, or *air-mail* – is sometimes used when weight or bulk of prints has to be kept to a minimum.

Exposure of papers
See Chapter 22.

Development of papers (*see also Chapter 23*)

The developers used today for paper of all types are commonly M.Q. or P.Q. formulae. For contact papers, energetic formulae containing very little bromide are generally used in Britain in order to obtain the best blue-black image colour. Amidol developer is sometimes employed with bromide paper to obtain cold black tones, and glycin formulae are sometimes used with chlorobromide papers to obtain warm tones.

Development time

The timing of the development of paper is usually done on the basis of a combination of the time-temperature and inspection methods of development. Initially, the exposure time is adjusted so that a correctly exposed print is obtained in the development time recommended by the paper manufacturer. This means that any trial exposures must be developed strictly by the time-temperature method.

We saw, however, in Chapter 15 that there is a range of development times within which a paper will yield good prints, provided that the exposure time is adjusted accordingly. The development time recommended by the manufacturer lies within this range. A print which has been given slightly more exposure than normal, may usually be removed from the developer after a little less than the recommended time, without loss of quality. Similarly, a slightly under-exposed print can usually be brought to the required density by a little longer development than recommended. This latitude between exposure time and development time, permitting slight errors in exposure to be compensated in development, on the basis of inspection of the print, is of great practical value. It must not, however, be pushed to extremes, i.e., the latitude of the paper must not be exceeded. Excessively short development times are to be avoided because no good blacks are achieved, image colour is often poor, and the degree of development may not be uniform across the print. At the other extreme, excessively long development is bad because it is accompanied by a risk of fog and staining.

The degree of latitude available varies to some extent with the type and contrast grade of the emulsion. It is, in general, greatest with chloride papers, and is also considerable with chlorobromide papers designed to give only one image colour. On the other hand, with chlorobromide papers in which the image colour varies with the degree of development, latitude is small if one particular image colour is required. With bromide papers, development latitude is limited by the fact that contrast varies to an appreciable extent with the degree of development (page 254). Development latitude is greatest with soft papers and least with hard papers. It is generally very small indeed with the hardest grades.

Development technique

The exposed print should be immersed in the developer by sliding it face upwards under the solution. Development of papers is a straightforward operation, but prints must be kept on the move and properly covered with solution. Several prints may be developed at one time in the same dish, provided that there is sufficient depth of developer and that the prints are "leafed" repeatedly. The busy printer will find it convenient to develop prints in pairs, back to back, feeding them into the solution at regular intervals, keeping the pairs in sequence and removing them in order when fully developed. The action of "leafing" the prints, i.e., withdrawing pairs sequentially from the bottom of the pile and placing them on the top, will help to dislodge any air-bells which may have formed on the prints.

When making enlargements of very large size, the provision of large dishes or trays sets a problem. Where very big enlargements are made only occasionally, the dishes need only be a few inches larger than the narrow way of the enlargement, since development can be carried out by festooning the paper, or by drawing it up and down in the same manner as when developing a roll film in a dish. In exceptional cases, development can be carried out by placing the enlargement face up on a flat surface and rapidly applying the developer all over the print with a large sponge or swab. Previous wetting with water will assist in obtaining rapid and even coverage of the print by developer. Fixing can be done in the same way. Alternatively, makeshift dishes can be made from large pieces of cardboard by turning up the edges, clipping the corners (which should overlap), and coating the insides with paraffin wax.

Fixation (*see also Chapter 24*)

Prints are fixed in much the same way as negatives. With prints, an acid fixing bath is very much to be preferred to a plain hypo bath since it reduces the danger of staining – especially objectionable on prints – to a minimum. The hypo concentration of print fixing baths is not usually made to exceed 20 per cent., compared with a concentration of up to 40 per cent. for films and plates (page 428).

A fixing time of about 10 minutes is usually recommended, although in a fresh bath 5 minutes is quite adequate. To avoid the risk of staining, prints should be moved about in the fixing bath, especially for the first few seconds after immersion. Prolonged immersion of prints in the fixing bath beyond the recommended time should be avoided as it may result in loss of detail, especially in the highlights, since the fixer will gradually attack the image. The action is most marked with chloride and chlorobromide papers, because silver chloride fixes more rapidly than the bromide. Over-fixation should be especially avoided with warm-tone prints, not only because they usually contain a proportion of silver chloride, but also because images of warm tone are of very fine grain and fix more rapidly than coarser-grained ones. The solvent action of the fixer on a warm-tone print may not only destroy highlight detail, but may also cause a change in image colour, if fixation is very prolonged.

Because the print is the consummation of all the efforts of the photographer, everything should be done to ensure its permanence, and proper fixation is therefore essential. Improper fixation may not only lead to tarnishing and fading of prints, but also to impure whites on sulphide toning. For the most effective fixation of papers, it is better practice to use a single fairly fresh bath, than to use two fixing baths in succession. With the latter method, the first bath contains a relatively high silver concentration. Silver salts are taken up by the paper base in this bath, and tend to be retained in the paper even after passing through the second, relatively fresh, bath.

Where processing temperatures are unavoidably high, as in tropical countries, a hardening-fixing bath should be employed. For the hardening of papers, potassium alum is to be preferred to chrome alum since the latter has a tendency to impart a greenish tint to prints. Several proprietary liquid hardeners are available for addition to paper fixing baths. Use of a hardener is often an advantage even in temperate climates if prints are to be hot glazed or dried by heat.

A fixing bath that has been used for negative materials may affect unfavourably the image colour of prints, if these are fixed in the same bath. The trouble is caused by silver iodide from the negative emulsion. The remedy is to use separate fixing baths for negatives and prints.

Washing (*see also Chapter 24*)

The purpose of washing prints is to remove all the soluble salts (hypo, complex silver salts) carried on and in the print from the fixing bath. Where only a few prints are being made they may be washed satisfactorily by placing them one by one in a large dish of clean water, letting them soak there for five minutes, removing them singly to a second dish of clean water, and repeating this process six or eight times in all. A method which is equally efficient and much less laborious – though requiring a larger consumption of water – consists in the use of three trays, arranged as in Figure 21.1, through which

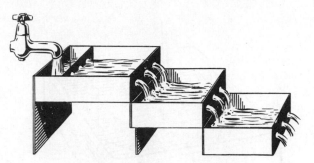

Fig. 21.1 – "Cascade" print washer

water flows from the tap. Prints are placed to wash in the bottom tray of this so-called "cascade" washer. When others are ready for washing, the first prints are transferred to the middle tray and their place taken by the new ones. When a further batch is ready, the first prints are put in the upper tray and the second batch in the middle one, leaving the bottom tray for the latest comers. In this way, prints are transferred from tray to tray against the stream of water, receiving cleaner water as they proceed. For washing large quantities of prints, this type of washer is made with fine jets for the delivery of water to each tray. These afford a more active circulation of water and dispense with the occasional attention required with the simpler pattern.

Another efficient arrangement for washing prints is shown in Figure 21.2. It consists of a stoneware sink fitted with an adjustable overflow; water is led in by a pipe which is turned at right-angles in the sink and terminates in a fine jet nozzle. The effect of this is to give a circular and also a lifting motion to the water – and equally to the prints – which overcomes the tendency of the prints to bunch together and remain in contact.

When large batches of prints have to be handled, the above arrangement can be duplicated or increased in size as desired, providing a most practical and efficient method of ensuring thorough washing.

Numerous mechanical print washers are sold which are designed to keep prints moving while water passes over them. In purchasing any print washer it is necessary to be satisfied that prints cannot clot together in a mass – in which state water cannot get at their surfaces –

nor be torn or "kinked" by projections in the washing tank. Generally, commercial print washers are suited only to prints of relatively small size.

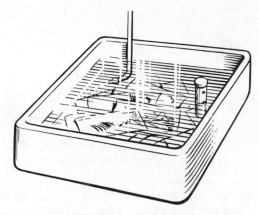

Fig. 21.2 – Washing sink

Drying (*see also Chapter 24*).
When thoroughly washed, prints intended to be dried naturally should be placed face upwards in a pile on a piece of thick glass. The excess of water should be squeezed out and the surface of each print wiped gently with a soft linen cloth or chamois leather. The prints should then be laid out on blotters or attached to a line with print clips. Alternatively, an efficient drying apparatus can be made by stretching good quality butter muslin on wooden frames, and placing the prints face downward on the muslin.

Where a large volume of work is being handled, prints are usually dried by heat, using flat-bed or rotary glazing machines (see below), or special rotary driers. For drying on a glazing machine, prints are placed facing the apron instead of towards the glazing sheet or glazing drum. Rotary drying machines are similar in construction to rotary glazing machines, except that the drum is covered with felt. It is usually an advantage when prints are to be dried by heat to use a hardening-fixing bath.

The drying of matt and semi-matt papers by heat gives a higher sheen than natural drying, because raising the temperature of the paper causes bursting of starch grains included in the emulsion to provide matting. With semi-matt papers the higher sheen may in some instances be preferred, but with matt papers it will usually be considered a disadvantage. In the latter event, natural drying should be employed.

When dry, a print will sometimes be more or less curled. If so, it may be straightened by laying it face downwards on a smooth flat surface and drawing a ruler along the back from end to end or from corner to corner, the end or corner being lifted fairly sharply but steadily as the rule is drawn back. Prints dried on heated machines do not usually require straightening.

Glazing

The appearance of prints on glossy papers is considerably enhanced by *glazing*, a process which imparts a very high gloss. Glazing is effected by squeegeeing the washed prints on to a polished surface; when dry the prints are stripped off with a gloss equal to that of the surface to which they were squeegeed.* Glass is usually considered to give the finest gloss, although some other surfaces are also suitable. Chromium-plated metal sheets and drums are widely used – as is polished stainless steel.

Before prints are squeegeed on to the glazing sheet, the surface of the sheet must first be thoroughly cleaned, and then prepared by treating it with a suitable glazing solution to facilitate stripping of the prints. The cleaning of new glazing sheets and drums is particularly important and is described later.

For the finest glaze, it is probably best to allow prints to dry naturally on glass, e.g., overnight. Where, however, a considerable volume of work is handled it is usual to employ glazing machines, on which prints are dried by heat, to speed up the operation. With these machines – which are of two types, flat-bed and rotary – glazing can be completed in a few minutes. So-called "flat-bed" glazers accommodate flexible chromium-plated sheets on to which prints are squeegeed. The glazing sheet is placed on the heated bed of the glazer and assumes a slightly cylindrical form when held in place by a cloth apron which serves to keep the prints in close contact with the glazing sheet. In rotary machines, prints are carried on a rotary heated chromium-plated (or stainless steel) drum on which they are held in place by an apron. Glazing can also be carried out on some rotary drying machines, by squeegeeing prints on to flexible glazing sheets and feeding these into the drier.

Detailed directions for cold glazing and hot glazing are given below.

* Glazing is best carried out immediately after washing, before prints are dried. If it is desired to glaze prints that have been dried, they should first be soaked in water, preferably for an hour or more.

Cold glazing

The following materials are required:

Glazing sheet. This may be a commercial glazing sheet or a sheet of glass of any convenient size. Plate glass is usually considered to give the best glaze.

Squeegee. This should preferably be of the flat type.

Glazing solution. Several proprietary brands are available; alternatively, a solution of wetting agent may be employed.

Waterproof cloth. A thin rubberized cloth is very suitable. In the absence of such a cloth, clean fluffless blotting paper may be used.

Fill a dish with glazing solution diluted according to the manufacturer's instructions and place the wet prints in it for a few minutes. Place the glazing sheet on a level surface and carefully clean the top surface to remove all traces of grease or dust. Then thoroughly wet the surface by going over it with a tuft of cotton wool dipped in the glazing bath in which the prints are soaking. When the prints have soaked for a few minutes, remove them one by one and lay them face down on the glazing sheet, taking care that they do not touch each other. When all the prints are in position, lay the waterproof sheet over them, rubber side down, and remove surplus water with the squeegee. To do this, draw the squeegee lightly across the sheet once in each direction, taking care that the prints do not slip across the glazing sheet. Hard pressure with the squeegee is to be avoided.

Finally, remove the waterproof sheet, stand the glazing sheet on edge away from draughts and allow the prints to dry. When dry, they will peel from the sheet with a perfectly glazed surface.

Notes. 1. Some workers prefer not to soak prints in glazing solution but to lift them straight from the wash water on to a glazing sheet which is wet with solution.

2. If desired, the backs of prints may be blotted with a folded towel when the waterproof sheet is removed after squeegeeing.

3. Strips of wet blotting paper laid around the edges of doubleweight prints, after squeegeeing, will help to prevent the edges coming away before glazing is complete.

Hot glazing

Hot glazing is carried out using a chromium-plated (or stainless steel) glazing sheet or glazing drum as the glazing surface. A new glazing sheet or drum should be brought into condition by washing it in turn with 1 per cent. acetic acid solution, fresh water, warm soapy water (Castille soap) and ammoniacal methylated spirit (e.g., 1 part of ammonia to 9 parts spirit). The drum or sheet should then be dusted with French chalk and polished until all the chalk is removed. A power-operated polisher is useful for this operation. Finally, the drum may be wiped over with glazing solution or a solution of wetting agent. (The use of glazing solution at this stage or subsequently is not absolutely necessary, but it helps to condition the drum more quickly and in the opinion of some workers produces a slightly better glaze.)

A drum can lose its condition by overheating, by the presence of a lime deposit arising from hard water or by chemical (hypo) contamination from badly washed prints. The remedy for this is to clean and polish the drum, using the procedure described above. In addition, prints for glazing should in future be washed more thoroughly to ensure that chemicals are not transferred to the felt and so to the drum. The felt itself should be removed from the machine and washed at regular intervals.

Prints for heat glazing should be processed in the usual way, and thoroughly washed in water as free as possible from air-bells and dirt. Use of a hardening-fixing bath may be an advantage, in particular under summer conditions when the wash water is likely to be warmer than usual.

Operation of a flat-bed glazing machine. The glazer must at first be allowed to warm up to the required temperature. The glazing sheet should then be thoroughly cleaned and a little glazing solution rubbed all over the surface. The wet prints are then placed on the sheet and squeegeed, preferably under a waterproof cloth. The glazing sheet is then placed on the glazer, face uppermost, and the apron tightened down over the prints. As prints dry, they will begin to leave the glazing sheet with a series of sharp sounds. When this "cracking" ceases, the apron may be lifted back and the glazed dry prints peeled off.

Operation of a rotary glazing machine. The glazer should first be switched on and the drum allowed to warm up to a steady temperature. Prints should then be placed face upwards on the moving felt, one after the other, the interval between taking prints out of the wash water and putting them on the felt being kept to an absolute minimum. Immediately after placing the prints on the felt they may be lightly swabbed, e.g., with a folded towel, to remove surplus water.

The speed of the machine should be adjusted in relation to the drum temperature so that prints strip off the drum on emerging from the felt. Care should be taken not to allow the drum to overheat and so lose its condition, and under no circumstances should it be so hot as to boil the water on the surface of prints, as indicated by a sizzling sound when prints first touch the drum. The pressure of the squeegee roller should be sufficient to ensure good contact of prints with the drum and to remove much of the superfluous water, but excessive pressure should be avoided. The drum surface should be cleaned as frequently as possible with a fluffless polishing cloth free from grit. As previously mentioned, the felt should be washed periodically to prevent accumulation of dirt and impurities.

Faults in hot glazing
The chief troubles liable to be encountered during hot glazing operations are as follows:

(a) *Oyster-shell markings.* These markings on the surface of the glazed prints are obtained when the rate of drying is too slow, so that prints still partially adhere to the drum when the support of the felt has been withdrawn; the trouble is more likely to occur with double-weight paper (card) than with single-weight. To overcome the defect, the machine should either be run at a slower speed, or a greater degree of heat should be applied, though this must not become excessive.

(b) *Pits.* Any dirt or grit on the surface of prints during glazing will give rise to unglazed pits. These are similar in appearance to fleck-marks (see below), but the offending grit can often be seen in the centre. The contamination may be present in the water, in which case filtration is necessary, or it may arise from the glazing solution, swabs etc.

(c) *Fleck-marks.* These small irregularly-shaped unglazed areas may occur in a variety of ways, some being due to processing technique and some being associated with the material. Serious fleck-marks can be obtained if glazing is carried out at too high a temperature, so that the surplus water boils as prints come into contact with the drum. Highly aerated water such as would be produced from a high-pressure mains supply may be a potential source of trouble, due to fine air-bells, often not visible to the naked eye, being trapped in the film of water adhering to the print surface. An anti-splash device together with a filter fitted to the tap should be of help in this connection.

Over- or under-squeegeeing is also a source of fleck-marks. The correct pressure to be applied is a matter of experience; it need only be sufficient to bring the print into good contact with the drum.

Over-hardening of the emulsion film is probably the most frequent cause of fleck-marks, and where it arises to any serious extent a non-hardening fixing bath must be used. Fleck-marking is also associated to some extent with the age of the photographic material, and if the trouble persists it may sometimes be obviated by briefly soaking prints in lukewarm water before glazing. The time of immersion and temperature of the soaking water must be found by experience.

(d) *Patchy glazing*. Areas of poor glaze are likely to occur if the glazing surface is dirty, or if the prints are not properly in contact with the drum, owing to inadequate squeegeeing. Prints which have become partly dry on the surface before placing on the felt are very liable to glaze irregularly. In this event, they must be thoroughly resoaked before glazing.

(e) *Sticking*. Prints rarely stick to the surface of the glazing drum, but if they do, the trouble is probably due to one of two causes: (i) the drum surface is dirty, or scummy owing to lime from hard water; in either case, cleaning is necessary; (ii) the glazer is running at too low a temperature for the print to come off in one cycle.

Clearing and reducing prints

Clearing or reducing of prints by chemical means is rarely required when the technique of printing has been mastered. There are, however, exceptional cases where chemical treatment improves the results and formulae for this purpose are given in Appendix 1.

Toning prints
See Chapter 25.

Stabilization papers

Papers have been introduced in recent years in which a developing agent, usually hydroquinone, is incorporated in the emulsion. They are designed for rapid processing in small processing machines. In such "two-bath" processors, the paper passes first through an activator – a strongly alkaline sulphite solution – and then through a stabilizer (page 442). The print emerges from the machine in a semi-dry state, the whole processing operation taking only about 10 seconds. The restrainer required in development may be incorporated in the activator or in the paper, so that not all stabilization papers and activators are compatible. It is therefore normally wisest to employ the chemicals recommended by the manufacturer of the paper.

Stabilization papers are available in both contact and projection speeds, and in a range of contrast grades and surfaces.

CHAPTER 22

Printing and Enlarging

In the last Chapter we considered the characteristics of the various types of printing paper. In the present Chapter we shall deal with the printing operation itself. There are two main ways of making prints: *contact printing* and *projection printing*, the principal difference between the two being in the method of exposing. In contact printing the sensitised paper is literally in contact with the negative, while in projection printing the paper is placed at a distance from the negative, the negative image being projected on to the paper by optical means.

Contact printing
Contact printing is the process of making positive prints the same size as the negative, the sensitised paper being held in contact with the negative during exposure. This form of printing is a more simple operation than projection printing, requiring only the minimum of apparatus and equipment. As the fundamental principles are the same for both methods of printing, experience of contact printing provides a valuable introduction to projection printing.

Papers for contact printing
Contact prints may be made on contact (chloride), bromide or chlorobromide papers (Chapter 21). Contact papers – which, as their name indicates, are specially intended for contact printing – are the normal choice of amateurs. Professional photographers usually make their contact prints on bromide or chlorobromide papers; in this way they are able to obtain the same image colour on both contact prints and enlargements, and thus no difficulty results from the mixing of prints produced by the two methods.

The low sensitivity of contact papers is of advantage to the amateur, in that it enables contact printing to be carried out at a very comfortable level of yellow or orange illumination.

Bromide and chlorobromide papers permit of very short exposure times in contact printing – an important consideration in professional work – but they must be handled and processed at a lower level of illumination than contact papers, a brown or greenish-yellow safelight being required. With modern bromide and chlorobromide papers the actual quality of this light is quite important, and it is essential to use care in the selection of a suitable safelight; the recommendations of the manufacturer of the paper should be consulted. Bromide and chlorobromide papers have the advantage that they are available in a wider range of surfaces than contact papers.

Whichever type of paper is employed for contact printing, a grade appropriate to the contrast of the negative must be selected, as explained in Chapter 21.

Apparatus for contact printing

Contact prints are made using either a *printing frame* or a *printing box*, the latter being essentially a piece of apparatus combining a printing frame with a light source. Printing frames and boxes are intended to ensure as perfect a contact as possible between the negative and the sensitised paper during printing.

A printing frame is the simplest form of apparatus. It is best to choose a frame about two sizes larger than the negative. This makes it possible to mask the negative and to produce pictures with white borders. Using a printing frame, exposures are usually made to an ordinary tungsten lamp one or two feet away, the greater distance corresponding to the larger size of frame. Where maximum sharpness is essential, as when making lantern slides or duplicate negatives, improved definition may be obtained by placing the frame several feet away from the lamp, i.e., far enough for the latter to act as a point source.

For more rapid working than can be achieved using a frame a printing box is used. The chief advantages of a box over a frame are that the source of light is at a constant distance from the negative, and that the darkroom is not illuminated with white light during printing. This enables several operators to work in one room at the same time, and simplifies the calculation of exposure times. Contact printing boxes can be obtained in which both a printing light and a safelight are fitted, the latter being of great assistance in positioning the negative and printing paper. The printing light is automatically switched on when the pressure plate is closed. Printing boxes for the professional and trade worker range in design from robust forms of boxes as described above, to complicated machines devised for the production of long runs, using paper in continuous rolls. In some professional printing boxes it is possible to vary the strength of illumination; this is particularly useful when it is desired to use papers of different speeds. Even when a printing box is employed for normal work, a large printing frame is a valuable standby for printing unusually large negatives.

Exposure times in contact printing

The exposure necessary in contact printing depends upon the power of the light source and its distance from the negative, the presence or absence of a reflector on the light source, the density of the negative, and the speed of the paper. The contrasty grades of paper are usually slower than the soft grades. Hard papers are generally used with thin negatives, however, so that actual printing times do not vary as much as might be expected.

If a printing frame is employed, the most convenient and economical way of ascertaining the correct exposure is to use a *test strip* cut from a sheet of the appropriate grade. This should be exposed in progressive steps, for say 2, 4, 8 and 16 seconds. This is done by exposing the whole strip for 2 seconds, then covering one-quarter of the paper with a piece of opaque card while a further exposure of 2 seconds is made. The card is then moved over to cover half the strip and a further 4 seconds exposure is given. Finally, the card is moved to cover three-quarters of the strip and an exposure of 8 seconds is given (Figure 22.1). If care is taken to move the card quickly and precisely, it may be moved while exposure proceeds, thus avoiding the need for switching the light off and on. The strip is then given standard development, and the correct exposure is assessed on the basis of a visual examination of the four steps in white light.

If the correct exposure appears to lie between two steps, the exposure required can usually be estimated with sufficient accuracy, but if desired a further test strip may be made. If, for example, the correct exposure appears to lie between 8 and 16 seconds, a second strip exposed in steps of 10, 12 and 14 seconds will give a good indication of the exact time required.

Once the exposure time for one negative has been found by trial, other negatives of similar density may be given the same exposure. Further test prints will at first be required for negatives of widely differing density, but with experience it is possible to estimate the exposure required for almost any negative, without resort to test exposures.

When a printing box is employed, it is not usually convenient to expose a test strip in steps; instead, a series of small *test pieces* should be exposed. The exposure should be increased, step-wise, from one piece to the next, and all the pieces should be developed together for the same time.

2 SECS.	2 SECS.	2 SECS.	2 SECS.	1st EXPOSURE
2 SECS.	2 SECS.	2 SECS.	—	2nd EXPOSURE
4 SECS.	4 SECS.	—	—	3rd EXPOSURE
8 SECS.	—	—	—	4th EXPOSURE
16 SECS.	8 SECS.	4 SECS.	2 SECS.	TOTAL

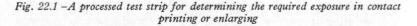

CARD MOVED IN THIS DIRECTION
BETWEEN EXPOSURES

Fig. 22.1 – A processed test strip for determining the required exposure in contact printing or enlarging

Assistance in estimating exposure can be obtained by taking a reading of the density of the negative (in shadows or highlights) with a densitometer and relating this to the density of a negative for which the exposure required has been found by trial, but this procedure is rarely worth while.

Control in contact printing
A certain amount of "holding back" or "printing in" is possible when contact printing in a frame, by interposing an opaque piece of paper or card between the light source and frame. The card, which must be kept moving to avoid forming a hard edge to the shadow cast by it,

permits control of the time during which light falls on the various areas of the negative. If, in a straight print, one area appears too dark, that part of the negative can be shielded by the card for a part of the exposure so that it receives less exposure than the remainder of the negative. If an area appears too light, exposure can be continued beyond the time found suitable for the print as a whole, to give increased exposure to the selected area, the greater part of the negative being shielded by the card. The exposure times required in each case are best found by trial.

If a printing box is employed, "holding back" may be carried out by laying pieces of translucent material – e.g., thin sheets of white paper – on a sheet of clear glass in the printing box an inch or so below the negative. Such pieces of paper are torn to the shapes required – on the basis of tests – and then covered with a further sheet of glass to stop them curling. Since the paper is some distance from the negative, the edges do not usually cast sharp shadows – even though they are stationary. Preparation for shading in this way takes some time, but, once a printing box has been set up, any number of prints may be run off with the assurance that all will be shaded to exactly the same extent. This is invaluable in professional work, where large runs of identical prints are frequently required.

Projection printing

Projection printing is the process of making positive prints by optical projection of the negative image on to sensitised paper. The projected image may be enlarged in scale, the same size as the negative or reduced. When the scale of objects in the print is larger than in the negative, the process is termed *enlarging*; when the scale of the print is smaller than the negative, the process is termed *reducing*. As projection printing is usually employed for the production of enlarged prints, projection printers are usually referred to as *enlargers*, and the term "enlarging" is loosely used to cover all forms of projection printing, whether the image is enlarged in scale, is the same size as the negative or is reduced.

In the early days of photography, printing was done almost entirely by contact. Enlarging was at first difficult because of the slowness of the available printing papers and the lack of suitable artificial light sources. When enlarging was attempted in those early days, daylight was used as the illuminant. With the introduction of faster printing papers, the gasfilled tungsten lamp and other convenient artificial light sources, enlarging became general practice. The tendency was fostered, or even forced, by the increasing popularity of small cameras.

Enlarging is a much more flexible medium than contact printing, enabling control in various directions to be introduced during printing, by, for example:

(1) *Selection of the main area of interest in the negative*, and enlargement of this area to any suitable size. This enables unwanted and possibly distracting areas around the edges of the picture to be eliminated, thus concentrating interest on the main subject.

(2) *Dodging and shading*. This enables detail in highlights or shadows to be brought out, which would otherwise be lost.

(3) *Local "fogging"* by a small external light can be used where dark areas are required, e.g., around a portrait to concentrate attention on the face.

(4) *Modification of the appearance of the image* by use of diffusers, etc. between lens and paper.

(5) *Correction – or introduction – of perspective distortion* by tilting the enlarger easel.

Not all of these controls are peculiar to enlarging, but they are all applied much more readily in enlarging than in contact printing. Details of the techniques involved are given later in this Chapter.

Papers for enlarging
Almost without exception, the papers used today for enlarging are of the bromide or chlorobromide types (Chapter 21). Contact papers are relatively very slow, and, although they have occasionally been used for enlarging with high-power light sources, their use for ordinary work can be completely ruled out.

Apparatus for enlarging
Early enlargers were very similar to lantern-slide projectors, with the optical axis horizontal. To save bench space, some later enlargers were designed with this axis vertical; today, most enlargers are of this type. Not only do vertical enlargers save space, but they are much quicker to use. In some of them, operation is made to be still quicker by means of automatic focusing devices. Horizontal enlargers are, however, still sometimes used, and offer real advantages when "giant" enlargements, for example, are required.

The optical systems of enlargers – whether vertical or horizontal – are of three main types:
(1) Condenser.
(2) Diffuser.
(3) Condenser-diffuser.
The condenser type, based on the lantern-slide projector, was the

earliest form of optical system. More recently, diffuse or semi-diffuse illumination has tended to displace the straightforward condenser type. Whatever the type of optical system, the illumination is nowadays almost invariably provided by an artificial light source.

Condenser enlargers

Figure 22.2 illustrates the arrangement of a condenser enlarger. The purpose of the condenser C is to illuminate the negative evenly. This is achieved, in practice, if the condenser forms an image of the light source S within the enlarging lens L. The latter is employed to form an image of the negative N in the plane of the easel E. The negative effects some scattering of the light, so that a cone of light

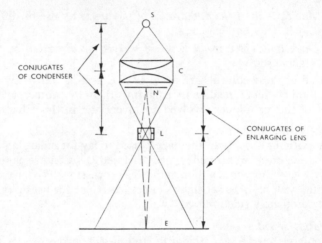

Fig. 22.2 – Optics of condenser enlarger

spreads out from each image point, as indicated by the broken lines in the figure. This cone fills the lens L, but very unequally, the rays passing through the centre of the lens – and due to the non-scattered rays – being more intense than the rays through the outer zones of the lens. One result of this is that stopping down the lens of a true condenser enlarger does not increase exposure times by as much as might be expected (page 381), but tends to increase the contrast of the image.

The required diameter and focal length of an enlarger condenser depend on the size of the largest negative to be used. The diameter must be at least equal to the diagonal of the negative, and the focal length should be about three-quarters of this value.

The choice of focal length for the enlarging lens is restricted by a number of practical considerations. If it is too short in relation to the negative size, it will tend not to cover the negative at big degrees of enlargement. If it is too short in relation to the focal length of the condenser, it will be necessary for the light source to be a long way from the latter in order to form an image of the source within the lens. This will necessitate a big lamphouse. It will also mean that the area of negative illuminated by the condenser will be reduced. If, on the other hand, the focal length of the enlarging lens is too great, the throw from lens to easel will be inconveniently long when big enlargements are required. The best compromise for most work is usually achieved by choosing a lens whose focal length is at least equal to that of the condenser but does not exceed it by more than one-third. This results in a lens of focal length equal to or slightly longer than that of the "normal" camera lens for the negative size covered.

Setting up a condenser enlarger

To achieve optimum illumination in a condenser enlarger, the various parts of the optical system must be so located that the light beam from the condenser converges to its narrowest cross-section within the enlarging lens. Now, when the degree of enlargement is altered, the distance of the enlarging lens from the negative is altered to obtain sharp focus. Since the negative and condenser are fixed in relation to one another, it is obvious that some adjustment of the light source in relation to the condenser must be made if the image of the source formed by the condenser is to be kept within the enlarging lens. This involves "setting up" the enlarger each time the degree of enlargement is changed. The following procedure is recommended:

(1) Insert negative in carrier.

(2) Adjust enlarger to give a sharp image of the desired size.

(3) Stop down to required aperture.

(4) Remove negative (and diffuser, if used).

(5) Examine illumination of easel and adjust the distance of the lamp from the condenser until the illumination is seen to be even. If necessary, adjust the position of the lamp from side to side as well as to and from the condenser.

(6) Replace negative (and diffuser, if used), check the focus and make the exposure.

Diffuser enlargers

Diffuse illumination may be obtained by direct or by indirect lighting of the negative, the two different methods being illustrated in Figure 22.3.

For small negatives, an opal or frosted tungsten lamp with a diffusing screen – opal or ground glass – between lamp and lens is all that is required (Figure 22.3a). This method can be extended to somewhat larger negatives by using a bulb silvered at the tip – or a diffuser specially treated so thatthe transmission of the central part is reduced – to assist in obtaining uniform illumination of the negative. To illuminate a really large negative directly, an assembly of small bulbs must be employed behind the diffuser.

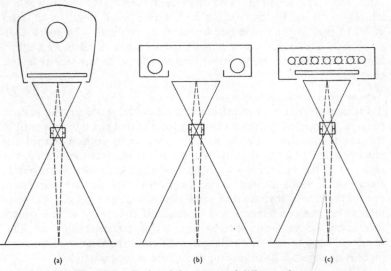

(a)   (b)   (c)

Fig. 22.3 – Optics of three types of diffuser enlargers

The indirect method of illumination illustrated in Figure 22.3b is another method of obtaining diffuse illumination; this is very suitable for large negatives. The light source usually consists of a series of tungsten lamps, although the reflected light from carbon arc lamps is sometimes employed.

A method of obtaining diffuse illumination by means of a mercury vapour lamp or cold-cathode lamp is illustrated in Figure 22.3c. Lamps of this type, in the form of a grid or helix, provide a large intense source of uniform illumination. One type of cold-cathode enlarger for amateur use is fitted with a circular fluorescent tube with a saucer-shaped reflector behind it. The illumination of the negative is obtained indirectly in this case.

Practical differences between condenser and diffuser enlargers
Many negatives can be enlarged equally well on a condenser or a diffuser enlarger. For certain types of work, however – especially in professional photography – the choice of enlarger is important.

The following are the main differences in practice between the two types of enlargers:

Condenser enlarger

(1) Gives maximum tone-separation, especially in highlights.

(2) Is unsuitable for negatives that have been retouched – the ridges of the retouching medium printing as dark lines.

(3) Tends to accentuate blemishes, grain, etc.

(4) Is very suitable for work at a high degree of enlargement, because of its high optical efficiency.

(5) Image contrast is higher than when contact printing or using a diffuser enlarger (see footnote on next page).

(6) Suffers from the inconvenience of requiring readjustment of the lamp position whenever the degree of enlargement is altered appreciably.

Condenser enlargers are therefore often preferred where large prints are required and retouching is unusual, e.g., for commercial and industrial photography.

Diffuser enlarger

(1) Is essential where retouching is used. Since, in retouching, matching is done over an opal diffuser, retouched negatives must be printed under similar conditions for the retouching to yield the desired effect, without being obtrusive.

(2) Subdues scratches, grain, etc.

(3) Is not suitable for work at a high degree of enlargement – unless a high-power cold-cathode or mercury vapour light source is employed – because of the low optical efficiency of the diffuse illuminating system.

(4) Image contrast is similar to that obtained when contact printing, i.e., lower than when using a condenser enlarger.*

---

* In one experiment where the same negative was enlarged in different types of enlargers, equivalent results were obtained with papers of which the log exposure ranges were:

Condenser, clear bulb	1·1
Condenser, opal bulb	1·0
Opal diffuser, clear bulb	0·9
Ground glass and mercury vapour lamp	0·8

(Clerc)

Diffuser enlargers are therefore essential in professional portraiture, where retouching is a routine. There is no reason why the definition obtained with a diffuser enlarger should be inferior to that obtained with a condenser enlarger.

Because of the variation of the Callier coefficient with density (page 229), the tone distribution in the shadows of a print produced with a condenser enlarger may be different from that in a print produced in a diffuser enlarger. The difference is not usually of great practical importance.

Condenser-diffuser enlargers

Many of the popular enlargers of today employ an optical system which includes both condenser and diffuser. For many purposes, especially in amateur work, such a system offers a very practical compromise between condenser and diffuser enlargers. It permits shorter exposure times than a true diffuser enlarger, yet avoids the necessity for adjusting the position of the lamp for each variation in the degree of enlargement as is necessitated in a condenser enlarger. Grain and blemishes on the negative are subdued to a useful extent – even if not as much as in a diffuser enlarger. In most of these *condenser-diffuser enlargers*, diffusion is achieved simply by using an opal or frosted bulb as light source, instead of the point source required in a true condenser enlarger.

Some condenser enlargers are fitted with a removable diffusing screen – usually a sheet of ground glass – between the condenser and the negative carrier. This avoids the necessity for frequent readjustment of the position of the lamp, but exposures are longer. The ground glass is uniformly illuminated by the condenser and its scatter is predominately towards the lens. This action, and the consequent increase in the amount of light passing through the lens (as compared with use of a diffuser without condenser), is the sole advantage of using the condenser in this case. To achieve even illumination to the corners of the negative when a diffusing screen is used in a condenser enlarger, the diameter of the condenser must be somewhat greater than usual, i.e.- a little greater than the diagonal of the negative, instead of equal to it (page 372).

Light sources for enlarging

Three main types of light source are in common use in enlargers:

(a) Tungsten lamps.

(b) Mercury vapour lamps.

(c) Cold cathode lamps.

A single tungsten lamp provides a very convenient and efficient source of light for enlarging, and most of the smaller enlargers employ such a source. A tungsten lamp may be used in conjunction with a condenser or with a diffusing system. An opal or pearl lamp used with a condenser provides, very conveniently, a condenser-diffuser system. Some tungsten lamps are specially designed for use in enlargers. These are usually slightly over-run, to give high efficiency, and specially treated to provide uniform diffuse illumination with minimum absorption by the envelope of the lamp. Care should be taken in selecting a tungsten lamp for use with a condenser that there is no imprint on the top of the bulb, as this may lead to uneven illumination. (The existence of an imprint is unimportant when several tungsten lamps are used to provide illumination by reflection.)

There are a number of types of mercury vapour lamps (page 29). The extended source provided by the larger lamps has certain advantages over tungsten lamps when diffuse lighting is required. Its light is intense, it gives out little heat and it is economical in current. On the other hand, the appearance of the image on the easel is deceptive, and a worker inexperienced with this type of light source is very apt to over-expose. Because the mercury vapour spectrum is not continuous, it tends to yield peculiar results with colour-sensitised papers. With many of these papers, such as the faster chlorobromides, the results are merely softer than usual, and can be corrected by choice of a harder grade of paper. It should be noted that the mercury vapour lamp does not reach its full intensity until about three minutes after switching on, and it should not, therefore, be used until after that period. It is normal practice for mercury vapour enlargers to be left running while in use, exposures being controlled by means of a shutter. Although most mercury vapour enlargers are of the diffuser type, compact source mercury vapour lamps are sometimes used in condenser enlargers.

The cold cathode lamp (page 30) is a comparatively recent and very valuable addition to the range of light sources suitable for use in enlargers. Cold cathode lamps are obtainable in various forms. For use in enlarging they are usually made in the form of a grid or spiral, which provides a large intense source of uniform illumination. All cold cathode enlargers are of the diffuser type. Unlike mercury vapour lamps, cold cathode lamps reach their full intensity almost immediately after switching on and do not require to be left on continuously.

Lenses for enlargers

Lenses especially designed for use in enlargers are usually of the symmetrical type. Apertures are often marked not with f-numbers but with figures such as 1 (maximum aperture), $\times 2$, $\times 4$, $\times 8$, etc., to indicate the relative exposure times required. (But see page 381.) For ease in operation in the darkroom, "click" stops are frequently fitted. Because of the danger of overheating, especially if a condenser enlarger is employed, cementing of the elements of an enlarger lens is sometimes avoided.

We have seen that, for a condenser enlarger, the focal length of the enlarging lens should be similar to or slightly longer than that of the "normal" camera lens for the negative size concerned (page 373). This rule holds good for diffuser enlargers too. If the focal length of a lens used with a diffuser enlarger is too short, it is difficult to obtain uniform illumination at the edges of the field; if it is too long, the required throw becomes inconveniently long – just as with a condenser enlarger.

An exception to the general rule for determining the focal length of an enlarger lens applies when working at or near same-size, or when reducing, e.g., when making lantern slides. The angle subtended by the lens at the negative is then much smaller, and it is possible to use a lens of shorter focal length than normal without running into the dangers of uneven illumination or lack of covering power. In fact, use of a lens of shorter focal length is often essential when reducing in an enlarger with limited bellows extension.

In general, camera objectives may be used quite satisfactorily as enlarging lenses, although some which give a flat field with distant objects do not do so when used in the enlarger; this is because the conjugate distances in the two cases differ widely. Generally speaking, however, this defect can be overcome by stopping down.

Incorporation of a heat filter (page 380) in an enlarger fitted with a tungsten lamp is always an advantage in protecting not only the negative but also the lens from overheating. Possible seats of trouble are the cementing of the elements and the iris diaphragm if made of ebonite.

The use of a mercury vapour light source in an enlarger raises an especial problem in connection with the choice of lens. With such a source, focusing is done by means of the visible (predominantly green) image, whereas the effective rays as far as exposure is concerned are in the near ultra-violet region. It is therefore desirable for a lens used in a mercury vapour enlarger to be corrected to bring the green and near ultra-violet foci into coincidence. (An achromat is normally corrected to bring the green and blue-violet foci into coincidence (page 113).) Lenses especially corrected for use in mercury vapour enlargers are therefore made, although ordinary lenses are sometimes perfectly satisfactory.

Selecting an enlarging lens

When selecting an enlarging lens the following should be considered:

(1) *Focal length.* Is this suitable in relation to the size of negative, focal length of condenser (if employed) and range of bellows extension? The suitability of the focal length of the lens in relation to the negative is a question of covering power. This should be tested when the angle subtended by the lens at the negative is at its greatest. This occurs at large magnifications, when the lens is nearest to the negative.

(2) *Definition.* This should be tested both in the centre and at the edges of the field, at the greatest degree of enlargement likely to be employed in practice, the test being repeated at several apertures. The most useful form of test is to make a series of actual enlargements.

(3) *Range of stops.* Can the markings be read easily or are "click" stops fitted? Is the smallest stop small enough to permit sufficiently long exposures for "dodging" to be done at same-size reproduction, e.g., when making lantern slides by projection?

(4) *If a mercury vapour source is employed,* a check should be made that visual and chemical foci coincide, for the reason given above. For this check, a suitable test negative should be inserted in the enlarger, the easel should be tilted slightly, and the centre of the image focused as sharply as possible. A print should then be made in the usual way, and examined to see where the image is sharpest. If the sharpest part does not lie in the centre of the print, the chemical and visual foci do not agree. The test may be repeated at various stops. A suitable negative for the test is a ruled fogged plate, or a negative of a printed page.

(5) *If an auto-focus enlarger is employed,* a check should be made that the focusing device operates satisfactorily with the lens concerned at all magnifications.

Negative carriers

An important feature of any carrier for film negatives is that it should hold the negative flat. This is often achieved by sandwiching the negative between two pieces of thin glass of good quality, which must be kept scrupulously clean. With very small negatives, e.g., of the 24 × 36 mm. size, the glass can be dispensed with and the negative held between two open frames, which lessens the chance of dust marks on prints. When such glassless carriers are used, there is, however, a tendency for negatives to "jump" from one plane to another under the influence of heat; if this happens between focusing and exposing, the print may be out of focus. Stopping down to increase depth of field helps to minimize the effect of this.

Heat filters

To protect negatives from damage due to overheating, some enlargers are fitted with a heat filter, i.e., a filter which passes visible radiation but absorbs heat rays. The provision of a heat filter is particularly important when a tungsten lamp is employed as the illuminant and exposure times are long, e.g., when big enlargements are being made, or when using colour materials. A heat filter will also protect an enlarger lens from possible danger from overheating (page 378).

Easels and paper holders

When using a horizontal enlarger, the sensitive paper is commonly pinned to a vertical easel – which must be parallel to the negative. For enlargements with white borders, it is necessary to fit some form of masking device to the easel. For vertical enlargers, special paper-holding and masking devices for placing on the bench or bed-plate under the enlarger head, can be obtained commercially. The easels of some vertical enlargers incorporate built-in masking devices.

For enlargements with black borders, prints are first made in the usual way – with or without a white border. A sheet of card, measuring, say, 10 mm less each way than the print, is laid centrally on it and the edges, which are not covered by the card, are fogged to white light for one or two seconds.

Determination of exposure times in enlarging

Of the many factors which affect exposure times in enlarging, the following are probably the most important:

(1) Light source and illuminating system.
(2) Aperture of the enlarging lens.
(3) Density of the negative.
(4) Degree of enlargement.
(5) Speed of the sensitised paper (under given working conditions).

The exposure required will also be influenced by the effect desired in the final print.

The most reliable way of determining the exposure is by means of a test strip. This is made in very much the same way as in contact printing, an opaque card being held between the lens and the paper, close to the latter (page 368). It is not necessary to make a test strip for every enlargement, although it is a wise practice whenever any doubt exists as to the exact exposure required, as, for instance, when an unusually thin or unusually dense negative is being printed. Under normal circumstances, exposure can usually be estimated on the basis of past experience, after due allowance has been made for any variation in lens aperture, density of negative and degree of enlargement.

Effect on exposure of variation of aperture

With a diffuser or condenser-diffuser enlarger, the effect of stopping down on exposure is similar to that experienced in the camera, i.e., the exposure time required varies directly with the square of the *f*-number. In a true condenser enlarger, however, the light reaching the lens from each point on the negative is not distributed evenly in the lens but is concentrated on the axis (page 372). Consequently, stopping down does not reduce the light passed by the lens by as much as might be expected, and exposures do not therefore have to be increased by the anticipated amount. Hence, the customary rule of giving twice the exposure when using the next smaller stop does not apply to the lens of a condenser enlarger. This must especially be borne in mind when using a lens in which the stops are marked with numbers which are intended to indicate the relative exposures required.

Modern enlarging lenses are usually anastigmats giving a flat field and excellent definition at full aperture. Definition may be slightly improved by stopping down one or two stops, but there should not be any necessity to stop down further simply on account of definition. In fact definition in enlarging may sometimes be harmed by excessive stopping down (see page 122). Considerable stopping down will usually be required only:

(1) If a glassless negative carrier is employed and there is risk of the film buckling. Stopping down will then assist by increasing the depth of field.

(2) If the easel has to be tilted to correct – or introduce – perspective distortion. Stopping down will then increase the depth of focus.

(3) If exposure times at larger apertures are too short to enable exposures to be timed accurately or to permit dodging.

Stopping down the lens of a condenser enlarger tends to increase contrast (page 372).

Effect on exposure of variation of degree of enlargement

It might, at first, be expected that the exposure required when enlarging would vary directly with the area of the image, i.e., with m^2, where m is the degree of enlargement (image size/object size). In fact, however, the exposure varies with $(1+m)^2$ – just as in negative making. When the exposure at one particular degree of enlargement has been ascertained, the exposures for prints at other degrees of enlargement, from the same negative, can conveniently be calculated from the table opposite, which is based on the $(1+m)^2$ formula. The required exposure is found from the table by multiplying the known exposure by the factor lying under the new degree of enlargement on the line corresponding to the old.

Enlarging photometers

Various types of photometer have been devised to assist in the determination of exposures in enlarging. The general procedure when

Degree of enlargement for which exposure is known	New degree of enlargement								
	1	2	3	4	5	6	8	10	12	15
1	1	2	4	6	9	12	20	30	40	60
2	1/2	1	2	3	4	5	9	13	20	30
3	1/4	1/2	1	1½	2	3	5	8	10	16
4	1/6	1/3	2/3	1	1½	2	3	5	7	10
5	1/9	1/4	1/2	2/3	1	1⅓	2	3	4	7
6	1/12	1/5	1/3	1/2	3/4	1	1½	2½	3	5
8	1/20	1/9	1/5	1/3	1/2	2/3	1	1½	2	3
10	1/30	1/13	1/5	1/5	1/3	2/5	2/3	1	1⅓	2
12	1/40	1/20	1/10	1/7	1/4	1/3	1/2	3/4	1	1½
15	1/60	1/30	1/16	1/10	1/7	1/5	1/3	1/2	2/3	1

Notes. (1) This table holds only approximately for condenser enlargers where the lamp-to-condenser distance is altered to suit each new magnification, since this has the effect of altering the illumination on the negative.

(2) At very long exposure times, reciprocity failure may assume significant proportions. The higher factors in this table should therefore be used as a guide only; the actual exposure time required when a large factor is indicated may be appreciably longer than that derived from the table.

using such an instrument is to read the luminance of the image on the easel at the desired magnification, with the lens stopped down as required. The reading may be made on either the shadow or highlight areas of the image, provided that the instrument is suitably calibrated. A reading of the luminance of the "shadows", i.e., the brightest part of the image, is usually the easiest to take, and is probably the best guide to the exposure required.

Use of an exposure photometer does not completely solve the problem of print exposure. With subjects of unusual luminance range or unusual tone distribution, the exposure indicated by the photometer will not always be the best. In such a case, the exact exposure must be found by trial, although use of a photometer may assist by giving a first approximation to the exposure required.

Some assistance in estimating exposure can be obtained by reading the density of the negative – shadows or highlights – with a densitometer. The help obtained in this way is not great, however, since allowance must still be made for other variables such as degree of enlargement, aperture, light source, type of optical system employed etc.

Variation in illuminant in enlarger
The output of a tungsten lamp falls off with age. In determining exposures allowance must be made for this, especially when a new lamp is fitted. If the new lamp is of a different type or make from the previous one – although of the same wattage – its output may differ for this reason also, since not all lamps of the same wattage have equal efficiencies.

Voltage fluctuations in the mains supply can make it difficult to achieve accurate exposures in enlarging. For example, a 5 per cent. reduction in voltage lowers the light output by about 20 per cent. and at the same time alters the colour temperature considerably (Chapter 3). Normal supply variations do not usually cause trouble, but, if for any reason the variation is excessive, it may be worth while in professional work to fit some form of voltage regulator to the supply. Both manually controlled and automatically controlled equipment is available for this purpose.

Dodging and shading
We have already stated that one of the advantages of enlarging is that it gives the photographer the opportunity of controlling the picture by intercepting the projected image between the lens and the easel. It is no exaggeration to state that a "straight" enlargement from any

negative is seldom the best that can be obtained, and with the great majority of subjects – landscapes, portraits, architecture or technical – a little local shielding of parts which print too deeply, or the printing in of detail in some especially dense part of the negative, will work wonders. Control of this kind may be used to compensate for uneven lighting of the subject or to give added prominence to any given part of the composition. In many photographs of groups, for example, the front row – or the foreground – prints too deeply in a "straight" enlargement. Such a subject may be greatly improved by shielding the foreground during part of the exposure, with a piece of card held about 100 mm from the easel, the card being kept moving slightly throughout the duration of the exposure.

To bring out detail in a highlight, a card should be used from which has been cut or torn a hole slightly smaller than the part to be treated. After exposing the whole picture in the usual way, the card is employed to shield all parts except that which is to be exposed further. The card is held fairly close to the easel and kept on the move slightly for such additional time as a test or trial enlargement shows to be necessary.

A portrait in which the shadow side of the face becomes too dark before the full details of the other parts are out, can often be improved by using a "dodger". Dodgers may be made from thin card cut to a variety of shapes and sizes, a few of which are illustrated in Figure 22.4, thin stiff wire being threaded through holes in the card. They are

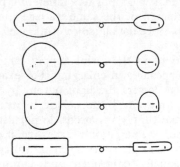

Fig. 22.4 – Dodgers for local control in enlarging

conveniently made to be double-ended as shown, with a twist in the middle of the wire for hanging on a hook in the darkroom. The shape and size of the shadow cast by a dodger can be varied endlessly by tilting it, and by using it at different angles and at different distances from the easel. Professional workers usually find it quickest and simplest to use their hands as dodgers.

Correction – or introduction – of perspective distortion

We saw in Chapter 12 (page 200) that if we tilt a camera upwards in order to include the whole of a building in the picture, we shall achieve the unpleasant effect termed "converging verticals". If we are using a camera without movements such results are sometimes inevitable. The distortion can be remedied to some extent by tilting the easel (in the appropriate direction) when the enlargement is made; this will compensate for the convergence in the negative. Usually, however, only a small degree of distortion can be corrected satisfactorily in the enlarger, and there is always a danger of foreshortening or elongating the image.

In some fields, use is made of the control afforded by tilting the easel to *introduce* distortion.

When the easel is tilted – to correct, or introduce, distortion – it is normally necessary to stop down the enlarger lens as far as it will go, to obtain sharp focus over the whole print. Some enlargers have a tilting negative carrier or tilting head to make it possible to focus sharply over the entire print without stopping down.

Minimizing graininess

Owing to the fact that all photographic images are made up of fine grains of silver of finite size, enlargements – especially if of considerable magnification – may appear "grainy" (Chapter 14). The graininess of a print is primarily a function of the graininess of the negative and the degree of enlargement. It may, however, be modified to a limited extent at the printing stage, e.g.:

(1) *By choice of a suitable enlarger.* Where graininess is serious, condenser enlargers should be avoided as they accentuate the effect; enlargers of the diffuser type are to be preferred in such a case.

(2) *By using a printing paper with a grained or rough surface.*

(3) *By using a diffuser between enlarger lens and printing paper.* See below under "Soft-focus enlargements".

(4) *By setting the enlarger slightly out of focus.*

The following figures indicate *very approximately* the degree of magnification permissible with four common types of film, before graininess becomes apparent on prints held in the hand. They assume correct exposure and development.

The graininess permissible in a print depends very much upon the conditions of viewing. The graininess permissible for a large print to be hung on an exhibition wall is much greater than can be tolerated in a small print to be viewed in the hand. Any figures for permissible

	Type of developer		
Type of film	General-purpose	Fine-grain	Extra-fine-grain
Extreme-speed panchromatic	4 ×	6 ×	8 ×
Fast panchromatic	6 ×	9 ×	12 ×
Medium-speed panchromatic	8 ×	12 ×	16 ×
Extra-fine-grain panchromatic	12 ×	18 ×	24 ×

magnification can, therefore, be only approximate. When preparing "giant" enlargements, critical judgement should not be given until the prints are finally spotted and viewed at the appropriate distance. "Giant" enlargements look extremely coarse and full of imperfections when they are examined prior to mounting and finishing.

Soft-focus enlargements

Subjects of a pictorial nature are often greatly improved by diffusing the image so as to blur its aggressively sharp definition slightly. This may be achieved by breaking up the image by the interposition of a suitable material between the lens and the picture. A piece of black chiffon, bolting silk, fine-mesh wire or crumpled Cellophane may be fitted to a rim which is slipped on to the enlarging lens for part or all of the exposure. Alternatively, an optical "soft-focus attachment" can be employed. The result is to give the image a soft appearance with a slight overlapping of the edges of the shadows on to highlight areas. In addition to giving softer definition, the enlargement also shows slightly weaker contrasts and graininess is minimized. Net-like material or Cellophane stretched over a card cut-out may also be used close to the enlarging paper. The texture effect is then usually more pronounced. Whatever form of diffusing medium is used, at least 50 per cent. of the exposure should generally be made without diffuser. The effect produced when diffusion is obtained in the enlarger is not the same as when a soft-focus lens is used on the camera (page 133).

CHAPTER 23

Developers and Development

THE purpose of development is to blacken those parts of the light-sensitive material which have been influenced by light, i.e., to produce a visible image corresponding to the invisible latent image. Development may be carried out in two ways. In ordinary photographic practice the process of *chemical development* is employed. This involves the reduction of the individual silver halide grains to metallic silver. In this process each grain of the emulsion acts as a unit, in the sense that a grain is either developable as a whole or is not developable. There is a second type of development in which the silver forming the developed image is derived from a soluble silver salt contained in the developing solution itself. This is termed *physical development*. It is described later in this Chapter (page 400).

The individual grains of silver halide in an emulsion are protected against the action of photographic developers by a chemical layer. When light acts upon the emulsion it tends to break down the protective layer at one or more points on each light-struck grain. When a material is bathed in a developing solution the grains are attacked at these points by a *developing agent*, and, in chemical development, each grain which has received more than a minimum exposure is rapidly reduced to metallic silver. The degree of blackening over the surface depends principally upon the number of grains which have been attacked, although it is also influenced to some extent by the fact that some grains which start to develop may not develop to completion in the time for which the developer is allowed to act.

Developing agents are members of the class of chemical compounds termed *reducing agents*. Not all reducing agents may be used as developing agents; only a few are able to distinguish between grains which have been light-struck and grains which have not. With reducing agents that have been found suitable for photographic use, the action of the agent on exposed and unexposed (or insufficiently exposed) grains is distinguished by its *rate*. It is not that unexposed grains do not develop at all, but that exposed grains develop very much more quickly than unexposed grains. The latent image is essentially a catalyst that can accelerate the rate of development but cannot initiate a reaction that would not occur in its absence. Under normal conditions, the proportion of unexposed grains developed is quite small, but with very prolonged development practically all the grains in an emulsion – exposed and unexposed – will develop. Density resulting from the development of unexposed grains is termed *fog*.

Composition of a developing solution

Developing agents are not used alone; a developing solution – usually referred to simply as a *developer* – always contains certain other constituents whose presence is essential for the proper functioning of the solution. A developing solution therefore usually comprises:

(1) *A developing agent (or agents)* – to convert the silver halide grains in the emulsion to metallic silver.

(2) *A preservative* – to prevent (a) wasteful oxidation of the developing agent, and (b) discoloration of the used developing solution with consequent risk of staining of negatives and prints.

(3) *An alkali* (sometimes termed the *accelerator*) – to make the developing agent sufficiently active.

(4) *A restrainer* – to prevent the unduly rapid breakdown of the protective layer surrounding each silver halide grain, and by this means to reduce as far as possible the chance of unexposed grains developing in the normal development time.

In addition, there must be a *solvent* for these ingredients; this is nearly always water.

We shall consider each of these constituents in turn, in detail.

The developing agent

A large number of different substances have been used from time to time as photographic developing agents. Almost all of those in use today are organic substances, derived from benzene, toluene, naphthalene or similar compounds. Not all developing agents behave in exactly the same way, and for certain purposes one agent may be preferred to another. Consequently, a number of different agents are in use for one purpose or another, the characteristics of the most commonly used ones being described below.

Metol

Metol (monomethyl-paraminophenol sulphate), introduced by Hauff in 1891, is a white crystalline powder readily soluble in water. Metol developers are characterized by high emulsion speed (foot speed), low contrast and fine grain. They are valuable when maximum shadow detail is required. Useful soft-working developers may be made up, using metol, sulphite and sodium carbonate, or simply metol and sulphite alone. In general, however, metol is used in conjunction with a second developing agent – hydroquinone (see below), developers containing the mixture having certain advantages over developers based on either developing agent alone. (See page 397.) Metol-hydroquinone developers are usually referred to simply as "M.Q." developers, the letter Q being derived from the word "quinol", a synonym for hydroquinone.

Phenidone

Phenidone (1-phenyl-3-pyrazolidone), the developing properties of which were discovered in the Ilford laboratories in 1940, possesses most of the photographic properties of metol together with some quite unique advantages of its own. A property which it shares with metol is that of activating hydroquinone, so that a Phenidone-hydroquinone (P.Q.) mixture forms a useful and very active developer. Used alone, Phenidone gives high emulsion speed but low contrast, and has a tendency to fog. It is not, therefore, normally recommended for use by itself. Mixed with hydroquinone, however, and with varying concentrations of alkali, Phenidone produces a very wide range of developers of differing types. The activation of hydroquinone requires a much lower concentration of Phenidone than of metol which also possesses this activating property. A detailed comparison of the relative merits of P.Q. and M.Q. developers is given on page 398.

Hydroquinone

Hydroquinone (quinol, para-dihydroxybenzene), whose developing properties were discovered by Abney in 1880, takes the form of fine white crystals, fairly soluble in water. The dry substance should be kept well-stoppered, as there is a slight tendency for it to become discoloured. Hydroquinone requires a strong alkali, e.g., caustic soda, to activate it. Hydroquinone developers are characterized by high contrast. Hydroquinone-caustic developers are mainly used for the development of high-contrast films and plates in graphic arts work. They are not usually suitable for use with fast materials on account of the resulting high fog. Hydroquinone-caustic developers are suitable for low temperature processing (page 417).

Amidol

Amidol (di-aminophenol) is a fine white or bluish-white crystalline powder, readily soluble in water. An amidol developer can be made simply by dissolving amidol in a solution of sodium sulphite, without other alkali. Amidol developer should be made up when required, as it has poor keeping qualities. The solution of amidol and sulphite, while not becoming discoloured to any extent, loses much of its developing power within two or three days. Amidol developing solutions, although not themselves coloured, produce heavy bluish-black stains on fingers and nails. In the dry state, amidol is slowly affected by air and light; it should therefore be kept in well-stoppered bottles. Amidol developers develop rapidly. They were at one time widely used with papers.

Glycin

Glycin (para-hydroxyphenylamino-acetic acid) is a white crystalline powder, only slightly soluble in water but freely soluble in alkaline solutions. Glycin developers are non-staining and have exceptionally good keeping properties, but, unfortunately, they are too slow in action for general use. To obtain as much activity as possible, potassium carbonate is to be preferred as the alkali for glycin developers because it can be used at a greater concentration than sodium carbonate (page 393). Glycin is used in certain warm-tone developers for papers. It is also used, in conjunction with other developing agents, in some fine grain developer formulae of low energy. (See Paraphenylenediamine, below.) The action of glycin is greatly restrained by bromide. The non-staining properties of glycin and its very slow oxidation by air make it very suitable for any process in which the sensitive material is exposed to the air during development. It is thus useful when it is desired to develop a print while still on the enlarger easel, as in some pictorial control processes.

Paramidophenol

Paramidophenol (paraminophenol) is a developing substance which has been widely used for compounding highly concentrated developers. The active agent in these is an alkali salt of paramidophenol, produced by the action of caustic alkali. The solution contains a certain excess of caustic alkali and is diluted with from 10 to 30 times its bulk of water to form the working developer.

Paraphenylenediamine

At one time, many popular fine grain developers were based on paraphenylenediamine (diaminobenzene) as the developing agent (page 400). Paraphenylenediamine itself is poisonous, and used alone requires very long development times. However, it forms complexes with certain other developing agents and some of these complexes are stated to be non-poisonous. To obtain convenient developing times, most paraphenylenediamine developers contain another developing agent, e.g., glycin or metol. In such developers, the paraphenylenediamine probably acts primarily as a silver halide solvent, favouring a physical type of development.

Pyro

Pyro (pyrogallol, pyrogallic acid, tri-hydroxy-benzene) is sold in two forms: as a compact white powder and as bulky light feathery crystals. Pyro, which is very poisonous, is very soluble in water. The image formed by a pyro developer consists not only of silver but also of brownish developer oxidation products which stain and tan the gelatin. This stain, the degree of which depends upon the sulphite content of the developer, has an important effect on the printing quality of the image. If the formula contains a large amount of sulphite the amount of staining is small, but with reduced sulphite the stain becomes appreciable and markedly increases the printing contrast of the negative. Pyro is sometimes used in combination with metol and sometimes with both metol and hydroquinone. Pyro developers were once used almost universally but are rarely used today, the preference being for developers with colourless, soluble oxidation products.

Pyrocatechin

Pyrocatechin (catechol, pyrocatechol, orthodihydroxybenzene) is sometimes used to provide tanning developers and warm-tone developers for certain papers. With caustic alkalis it gives rapid development with high contrast, in a similar manner to hydroquinone.

The preservative

Sodium sulphite is commonly used as the preservative in developing solutions, although potassium metabisulphite is sometimes used as an alternative, either by itself or in addition to sulphite. Sodium sulphite is sold both in crystalline and in anhydrous (desiccated) forms, one part of the latter being equal to two parts of the former. Sulphite crystals should be clear – almost transparent. If coated with a powdery incrustation, they should be quickly rinsed in a very little cold water and mopped dry on a clean cloth or blotter before weighing out. Sulphite crystals dissolve most freely in water at about 40°C, giving a weakly alkaline solution (approx. pH 8·5). Dry, or anhydrous, sulphite is obtained as a powder which dissolves readily in water. Supplies of both crystalline and anhydrous sulphite should be kept in well-closed containers.

Potassium metabisulphite takes the form of transparent crystals, which usually have a slight opaque incrustation. This, however, does not denote deterioration to any appreciable extent. In the dry state, metabisulphite keeps very much better than sulphite. It dissolves fairly readily in tepid water, forming an acid solution smelling of sulphurous acid. As a preservative of pyro in stock solution, metabisulphite is as effective as at least four times the quantity of crystalline sodium sulphite, since its slight acidity has a preservative effect in addition to that of its sulphite content. A similar consideration governs the use of metabisulphite as the preservative of hydroquinone in two-solution hydroquinone-caustic formulae (page 396).

As stated earlier, one of the main functions of the "preservative" is to prevent wasteful oxidation of the developing agent(s) by air. It is convenient to think of the sulphite as removing the oxygen from the air dissolved in the solution or at the surface of the solution, before it has time to oxidize the developing agent. This, however, represents only a simplification of the real state of affairs. The action of the preservative is not simply a matter of preferential reaction between sulphite and oxygen; the rate of uptake of oxygen by a solution of sulphite and hydroquinone, for example, is many times smaller than the rate of uptake by either the sulphite or hydroquinone alone.

The alkali (or accelerator)
In practically all developing solutions an alkali is required to activate the developing agent. By suitable choice of alkali, the pH* of a developing solution can be adjusted to almost any required level, and in this way a range of developers can be prepared of varying activity. In the early pyro developer formulae, ammonia was employed as the alkali. Today, the alkali most commonly used is sodium carbonate, of which there are three forms available commercially: crystalline or decahydrate, containing 37 per cent. of the salt itself; monohydrate, containing 85 per cent. of the salt; and dry, anhydrous or desiccated, containing practically 100 per cent. of the salt. The monohydrate has the advantages of being more stable and more easily dissolved than the other forms. One part of the anhydrous may be replaced in formulae by 2·7 parts of the crystalline form or by 1·17 parts of the monohydrate. Ordinary washing soda is only an impure form of crystalline sodium carbonate, and should *not* be used for photographic purposes. (The "carbonate of soda" sold as a white powder by grocers is a different substance altogether (sodium bicarbonate) and is useless as the alkali of a developer.)

---

* An explanation of the pH scale is given in the Appendix.

In some developer formulae, *potassium* carbonate is used as the alkali. This is supplied as "potassium carbonate, dried". It should be kept securely corked; if left exposed to the air, it rapidly becomes damp or even semi-liquid, in which state its strength is greatly reduced. Potassium salts offer no advantage over sodium salts as the alkali in developers, apart from increased solubility, which permits them to be used, if required, at a higher concentration.

For highest contrast it is usual to employ hydroquinone as the developing agent with caustic soda (sodium hydroxide) or caustic potash (potassium hydroxide). These substances are very strong alkalis and have a corrosive action. If caustic alkali gets upon fingers or clothes, therefore, the affected parts must be washed immediately in cold water. Bottles containing solid caustic alkali or a solution of it should not have glass stoppers, since these tend to stick.

In the high sulphite, low energy class of fine grain developers, borax is the common alkali. The use of sodium metaborate as alkali has been advocated in certain formulae. Identical results are obtained by employing equal parts of sodium hydroxide and borax.

The restrainer

Two main types of restrainer are employed, inorganic and organic, use of the latter being a comparatively recent innovation. The function of a restrainer is to check the development of unexposed grains, i.e., to prevent fog; restrainers also affect the exposed grains to a greater or lesser extent and so affect film speed. The effectiveness of a restrainer in minimizing fog, and its effect on film speed, varies from one developing agent to another, and also depends on the emulsion. It is also influenced by the pH of the developing solution.

Potassium bromide, an inorganic substance, is the most widely used restrainer. Soluble bromide is produced as a by-product of the development process and affects the activity of the developer. Inclusion of bromide in the original developing solution therefore helps to minimize the effect of this release of bromide. For this reason most developer formulae employ bromide as a restrainer, including those formulae which also contain organic restrainers. Among the few developers which do not include bromide are the soft-working M.Q. borax formulae. Developers for papers always include bromide, since with papers any trace of fog is objectionable. High-contrast developers of the hydroquinone-caustic type contain comparatively large amounts of potassium bromide. The purpose of this is to reduce the foot speed in order to obtain a characteristic curve with very short foot, since this leads to higher contrast. Phenidone is much less influenced by bromide than is metol, especially at a low pH.

Of the several organic substances which have been found suitable for use as restrainers, benzotriazole is widely employed. Organic restrainers are especially valuable in Phenidone developers, the activity of most Phenidone formulae being such that to prevent fog with high-speed materials the amount of bromide required as restrainer would be so great that there would be a risk of stain, since bromide when present in excess is a mild silver halide solvent. Use of an organic restrainer avoids this risk. A certain amount of bromide is, however, usually included in Phenidone formulae to help to keep the activity of the solution constant with use, for the reason already explained. Benzotriazole has been found to be very suitable for use as an organic restrainer in Phenidone developers. With contact papers, it combines a blue-black toning action with its restraining action, making it very suitable for use in P.Q. formulae intended for the development of contact prints.

Organic restrainers appear to be capable of restraining fog, without affecting film speed, to a greater extent than inorganic restrainers. For this reason they have come to be widely used as *anti-fogging agents* (anti-foggants), for addition to standard developer formulae whenever there is particular danger of chemical fog or staining. In this rôle, organic restrainers are commonly used:

(1) To minimize the risk of fog and staining on materials subjected to prolonged development or to development at high temperatures.

(2) To help to prevent fog or veiling on materials which have been stored under unfavourable conditions or which are of doubtful age.

The use of anti-foggants is particularly valuable with prints, since fog is more objectionable with these than with negatives. Organic anti-foggants are very potent and must be used with care. Their use in excess may lead to a loss of effective emulsion speed, a slowing of development, and, with prints, to poor blacks.

Water for developers

While distilled water, on account of its purity, is usually the best for the purpose, its degree of superiority is not usually sufficient to justify its extra cost; tap water is normally a perfectly satisfactory alternative. The mineral salts in tap water are usually without photographic effect. If they give rise to calcium sludge, a calcium sequestering agent (see below) may be added to the water before making up the developer.

Miscellaneous additions to developers

Besides the usual four main ingredients (developing agent(s), alkali, preservative, restrainer) a developing solution sometimes contains other ingredients for specific purposes. These may include wetting agents (page 443), silver halide solvents (page 400) and calcium sequestering agents, i.e., water softening agents.

The presence of calcium salts in most ordinary waters often causes a calcium sludge to be precipitated by the sulphite and carbonate in the developer. This may cause a chalky deposit to appear on films and plates on drying. This scum is most likely with developers with a high sulphite content and low pH, e.g., M.Q. borax formulae, especially if hard water is used. (In developers containing caustic alkali, the calcium salts do not generally precipitate.) Calcium scum may be removed by bathing negatives in a 2 per cent. acetic acid solution after washing, and then briefly rinsing them.

The function of a *calcium sequestering agent* (anti-sludge) in a developer is to prevent scum from forming on negatives, by transforming the calcium salts into soluble complexes which cannot be precipitated by the sulphite and carbonate in the developer. Sodium hexametaphosphate (Calgon) is commonly used for this purpose. A suitable concentration in most circumstances is about 3 grammes per litre. This should be added to the water *before* the other developer constituents.

Developer formulae in general use

Many thousands of different developer formulae have been published through the years and a great number of different formulae are still in general use. Nevertheless, the number of basic types of formula employed today is relatively small. Hence those used for negative development, excluding those used in specialized applications of photography, are in the main of three types, as follows:

(1) M.Q. or P.Q. carbonate developers, yielding "normal" contrast.

(2) Soft-working fine grain developers, of the M.Q. borax or P.Q. borax types.

(3) High-contrast developers, of the hydroquinone-caustic type.

The function of each of the constituents of these developers is shown in Table 23.1. Specific formulae of each of the three types are given in Appendix 1, together with other developer formulae.

In the "normal contrast" developer the developing agents are either metol and hydroquinone or Phenidone and hydroquinone. (The differences between these two pairs of agents are described on page 398.) The alkali is carbonate and the restrainer bromide, although P.Q. formulae also require the inclusion of an anti-foggant.

In the fine grain formula the developing agents are again metol and hydroquinone or Phenidone and hydroquinone, but the alkali is borax, giving a lower pH. This produces a soft-working developer, an advantage when fine grain is required. The relatively long development time necessitated by the low activity of this developer permits the sulphite, which is present in high concentration, to have an appreciable solvent action on the undeveloped grains. This further contributes to the fine grain action of the solution. (See also page 400.)

In the third type of developer, the high-contrast formula, use is made of the density-giving powers of hydroquinone at high pH; caustic alkali is therefore employed. Hydroquinone-caustic developers oxidize rapidly and for prolonged storage are best made up in two-solution form, with the alkali in one solution, and the remaining constituents in the other. An acid preservative, metabisulphite, can then be used in preference to sulphite with greater preservative effect. The hydroquinone-caustic formula contains a high bromide concentration, which further assists in obtaining high contrast (page 393).

It will be noted that the two most widely-used types of developer – the "normal" and the fine-grain formulae – are based on mixtures of

Constituents	"Normal" developer, e.g., ID-2 or ID-67	Fine grain developer, e.g., ID-11 or ID-68	High-contrast developer, e.g., ID-13
Developing agent(s)	Metol and hydroquinone or Phenidone and hydroquinone	Metol and hydroquinone or Phenidone and hydroquinone	Hydroquinone
Preservative	Sodium sulphite	Sodium sulphite	Potassium meta-bisulphite
Alkali	Sodium carbonate	Borax	Potassium hydroxide
Restrainer	Potassium bromide and (P.Q. formulae only) organic restrainer	M.Q. formulae: Nil P.Q. formulae: Potassium bromide	Potassium bromide
Approximate pH	10 – 10·5	8·5 – 9·0	11

Table 23.1 – Constituents of three common types of negative developer

metol and hydroquinone, or Phenidone and hydroquinone. Although, for special purposes, other developing agents have found favour from time to time, for general photography nothing has been found to equal M.Q. and P.Q. mixtures in all-round efficiency and flexibility.

Metol-hydroquinone developers

Until the introduction of Phenidone, the general-purpose developers used in practical photography were with very few exceptions compounded with mixtures of metol and hydroquinone. The success of these mixtures depends upon the fact that their photographic properties are superior to those of the components taken separately and are not just equal to their sum or arithmetical mean.

The following experiment illustrates this. If we develop an exposed film, for the normal time, in an M.Q. developer such as ID-2, *omitting the metol*, we obtain a trace only of the highest highlights. Only when development is prolonged to, say, four times the normal do we obtain a negative of normal quality. We describe this by saying that at the degree of alkalinity provided by carbonate, hydroquinone has a very long induction period. If we develop a similar film in ID-2, *omitting the hydroquinone*, we obtain, in the normal development time, a negative which is very flat but does contain detail all over. If in this case we increase the development time fourfold we obtain a negative which is still very soft. We describe this by saying that metol has a short induction period but produces density slowly. It is clear from this experiment that a developer containing both metol and hydroquinone produces density at a rate which is greater than would be expected from a mere addition of the properties of metol and hydroquinone. This is because metol and hydroquinone in combination form a superadditive system.

The mechanism of *superadditivity* in M.Q. formulae is controversial, but may be due to the action of metol in decreasing the induction period of development by the major agent – hydroquinone. "With hydroquinone alone, the first growth of the silver germ is uncommonly slow. But as soon as these germs are somewhat larger, the reduction goes on very quickly. The part of the metol is that it helps in the first period of slow beginning; it shortens the induction period of hydroquinone." (Reinders and Beukers.) It has been suggested that metol is able to do this because as a single-charged ion it reaches the latent-image centres at the beginning of development more readily than the doubly-charged hydroquinone ion.

In M.Q. developers the hydroquinone is oxidized preferentially. This is because the hydroquinone is used up not only in reducing silver halide to silver but also in reducing part at least of the oxidized metol back to the developing agent; i.e., the hydroquinone *regenerates* some of the metol as the latter is oxidized by the silver bromide. Regeneration and superadditivity are two separate phenomena, both of which contribute to the usefulness of M.Q. mixtures.

Phenidone-hydroquinone developers

Phenidone forms a superadditive system with hydroquinone just as metol does, but it is much more efficient than metol in this capacity. Whereas a given weight of hydroquinone requires about one quarter of its weight of metol to activate it, it needs only a fortieth part of its weight of Phenidone. This means that a P.Q. developer is cheaper than its M.Q. equivalent, and highly concentrated liquids can be produced with a P.Q. system without so much danger of the developing agents salting out. The latter feature has led in recent years to a considerable increase in the use of ready-compounded developers in liquid form.

At the same pH, a P.Q. developer is slightly more active than its M.Q. equivalent. Therefore, to attain the same activity as its M.Q. counterpart, a P.Q. developer can work at a slightly lower pH, giving better keeping properties in use and a longer "shelf life". In some formulae, use of a P.Q. mixture in place of an M.Q. mixture avoids the need for the use of obnoxious caustic alkali otherwise required.

In any hydroquinone developer containing sulphite, the first oxidation product of hydroquinone is hydroquinone monosulphonate. With metol, this forms an almost inert system, but with Phenidone it forms a superadditive system of appreciable developing power. This means that a P.Q. developer will last longer in use than its M.Q. counterpart, since, with the latter, development virtually stops when the hydroquinone has been converted to its monosulphonate.

As stated earlier, with the M.Q. system the hydroquinone tends to regenerate the metol. This process, however, has a low efficiency and some of the metol is lost by conversion to an inactive monosulphonate. In P.Q. developers, the regeneration by hydroquinone of the primary oxidation product of Phenidone appears to be much more efficient and is not accompanied by any Phenidone sulphonation. This results in a longer working life. It also simplifies the control of replenished P.Q. developers, since only a small fixed allowance need be made for the loss of Phenidone.

Bromide ion has less of a restraining action on P.Q. developers than on M.Q. ones, especially at a low pH. A very marked difference is apparent in borax-buffered developers. This means that replenisher systems operating on a "topping-up" basis can be worked for longer periods when Phenidone is used (page 403). Further, the P.Q. borax type of negative developer is less likely than an M.Q. borax developer to give the marks known as "streamers" (page 421).

In general, Phenidone is less likely than metol to produce dermatitis on hands which have been immersed in the respective developers. Since the ultimate oxidation product of Phenidone is colourless, P.Q. developers are less liable to cause staining on fingers and clothes than M.Q. developers. Such staining cannot, however, be completely avoided since it partly results from the oxidation products of hydroquinone.

Metol, particularly at high pH, tends to become hydrolyzed to form methylamine, thus giving rise to an unpleasant fishy odour. Phenidone is not open to this objection.

P.Q. developers tend to give a later start to the image formation and subsequently to build up the image rather more quickly than their M.Q. counterparts. This effect is especially noticeable in paper developers.

At the pH levels associated with carbonate buffering, P.Q. developers tend to give fog with high-speed materials. For this reason, it is necessary in most P.Q. developers to include an organic antifoggant such as benzotriazole (page 394). P.Q. borax formulae do not require this.

Fine grain developers

We saw in Chapter 14 that all photographic images have a grainy structure. Although this structure is not normally visible to the naked eye it becomes so on enlarging, especially if high magnifications are employed. The tendency to use smaller negative sizes and make all prints by enlargement aroused interest in the possibility of obtaining a less grainy image than is normally yielded by conventional developers. As a result, special *fine grain* and *extra fine grain* developers have been evolved.

These developers achieve the desired result in several ways. First of all, they are usually soft-working – since this minimizes clumping of the silver grains. Some formulae actually produce smaller individual grains – although this tends to result in reduced emulsion speed. It is considered that the greyish-white nature of the images produced by some extra fine grain developers helps by giving increased percolation of light between grains, resulting in a reduced local variation in density.

Most fine grain developers yield negatives of comparatively low contrast. Although a reduction in contrast serves to minimize the graininess of the negative, it is doubtful whether it contributes significantly to a reduction in the graininess of the final print. Any reduction in graininess achieved by lowering the contrast of the negative is likely to be offset by the increased contrast of the harder paper required to print it.

The fine grain developers in general use today are of four main types:

(1) *M.Q. borax and P.Q. borax developers.* We have already referred to these developers (page 395). They are characterized by low alkalinity and high concentration of sodium sulphite, the sulphite acting as a mild silver halide solvent. One advantage of developers of this type is that no increase in exposure is necessary; another is that development times are not inconveniently long. The scope of M.Q. borax and P.Q. borax developers is not limited to miniature camera work; they are very suitable for use as general negative developers and are quite cheap to make up. This is an important point, and it is probably for this reason more than any other that these are the only types of fine grain developers which have achieved popularity for commercial finishing.

(2) *Paraphenylenediamine developers.* These consist of paraphenylenediamine and sodium sulphite with varying amounts of another developing agent, usually metol or glycin. They produce brownish images which show a very considerable reduction in grain, but require that exposures be increased by a factor of from $1\frac{1}{4}$ to 4, according to the type of developer and negative material. In general, those formulae which give the most striking improvement in graininess require the greatest increase in exposure. The maximum contrast obtainable with these developers is rather low and development times tend to be long.

(3) *Solvent developers.* Certain fine grain developer formulae contain silver halide solvents such as hypo, potassium thiocyanate, etc. With these formulae, development is partly chemical and partly physical (see below), but, whereas in true physical developers the silver for the image comes from the developer, in solvent developers it comes from the emulsion. Solvent developers depend for their success largely upon the fact that the silver redeposited from the solution is in very fine form. They necessarily cause some loss in emulsion speed.

(4) *Physical developers.* Physical developers differ from ordinary (chemical) developers in that they contain silver in solution. An image which has been formed by physical development consists of finely divided metallic silver deposited on the latent image from the silver in solution, instead of being derived from the silver bromide of the emulsion. The best-known physical developers for fine grain are due

to Dr. Odell or are derivatives of his formulae. These give extremely fine-grained images which are finer than those yielded by chemical development and much less dependent on the type of negative material used. Physical fine grain developers have found only a limited practical application because they are rather difficult to use; in particular, there is a tendency for silver to be deposited where it is not wanted. Vessels used for physical development must therefore be chemically clean.

A number of proprietary fine grain developers are on the market. The formulae of these are not published, but most of them are variants of one or other of the four main types of fine grain developer described above.

It should be noted here that the influence of the developer on graininess has been much exaggerated. The most important condition for obtaining negatives of low graininess is the choice of a fine-grained emulsion (page 217). A table indicating very approximately the degree of enlargement permissible with various combinations of film and developer is given on page 386.

High-definition developers

High-definition, or *high-acutance, developers* are solutions which give increased sharpness to photographic images by enhancing the contrast of edges and fine detail in the negative, although the resolving power of the emulsion may not be any higher than ordinarily. This is achieved by use of formulae of high pH and low concentration of developing agents. This promotes the production of adjacency effects (page 421). High definition developers may increase emulsion speed by a factor of one stop or more, but they also increase graininess. They are, therefore, generally recommended for use only with fine grain (i.e., slow or medium-speed) emulsions. Because of their low concentration of developing agents, most high-definition developers should be made up only when required for use and used once only.

Changes in a developer with use

As the function of a developer is to effect a chemical change in the sensitised materials passed through it, it is apparent that the composition of the developing solution itself must change with use. As a developer is often used more than once, in particular when tank development is employed, it is important to know what changes to expect, how these changes affect the function of the solution and what can be done to prevent them or to compensate for them.

The main changes are as follows:

(1) Some developer solution is carried out of the bath with the film,

both on its surfaces and actually in the emulsion. This removes from the bath some of each ingredient. The amount removed depends upon the size of the negative, the type of clip or hanger employed and the time during which developer is allowed to drain back from the film into the tank.

(2) The developing agents are used up: (i) by reducing the silver halide in the negative to silver, and (ii) by aerial oxidation. When the developing agents are used up by reducing silver halide, the products of the reaction tend to cause a *fall* in pH; when, however, the developer is used up by aerial oxidation, the pH tends to *rise*. The reactions involved, expressed in simple form, are as follows:

Exhaustion through use
Developing agents + silver bromide → Oxidized developing agents
+ silver + bromide ions
+ hydrogen ions (acid).
Exhaustion on standing
Developing agents + oxygen → Oxidized developing agents
+ hydroxyl ions (alkali).
With the less alkaline developers, e.g., M.Q. borax and P.Q. borax developers, changes in pH have a very marked effect on the activity of the solution. These changes may be counteracted by incorporating in the developer a so-called "buffer" system in place of the normal alkali (page 404).

(3) The sulphite is used up.

(4) The bromide content of the developer is *increased*, as bromide is liberated from the emulsion itself (see under (2) above).

The main effects of these changes on the working of the developer are:

(1) The development time required to reach a given gamma increases, due to exhaustion of the developing agents and increase in the bromide content. If, therefore, it is desired to use a developer repeatedly, the development time must be increased as more and more material is put through the bath.

(2) The effective emulsion speed produced in the developer decreases owing to the increase in bromide. This speed loss may be partially offset by the increased development time required to maintain contrast.

Complete exhaustion of the solution occurs when the developing agents are entirely used up. Exhaustion of the developing agents is bound up with exhaustion of the sulphite, since, if the sulphite is completely oxidized before the developing agents are used up, the developing agents being then without a preservative will rapidly oxidize too. (The "shelf life" of a developer is usually determined by the sulphite content; its "working life" may be governed either by exhaustion of the developing agents or by exhaustion of the sulphite.) With many developers, the approach of exhaustion is characterized by a brown colour. Since the solution in this condition can stain sensitised materials, developers should not be overworked.

For the amateur, it is a good rule to discard a developer after it has been used once, or, with expensive fine grain developers, after the amount of material recommended by the author of the formula has been passed through it. For the professional who handles large quantities of material, a more economical use of solutions can be achieved by use of a replenishment technique, as described below.

Replenishment

Replenishment, ideally, involves a continuous replacement of part of the used developer by a solution which has been formulated so that the mixture maintains a constancy of photographic characteristics in the material developed. The aim is not to keep the *composition* of the bath constant but its *activity*.

Two methods of replenishment are commonly employed. The first is known as the "topping-up" method and the second as the "bleed" system. In the former, which is used extensively in tank processing in the larger photofinishing establishments, the developing solution is maintained at a constant level either by periodical addition of the replenisher or by a feed system, so that the volume added is equal to the volume of developer carried over by absorption in the gelatin and on the surface of the material being developed. With M.Q. formulae, and P.Q. formulae of high pH, owing to a gradual rise in the bromide content of the mixed solutions, even with no bromide in the replenisher, it is possible to maintain reasonable constancy of characteristics only for a certain period of replenishment. After a given volume of replenisher has been used, therefore, the mixture is discarded and the procedure repeated with fresh developer. P.Q. formulae of low pH, however, are not greatly affected by bromide, so that, with these, replenishment by the "topping-up" method may be continued almost indefinitely.

In the "bleed" system, which is commonly employed for the machine processing of cinematograph film with a circulating developer system, used developer is run off and replenisher fed in continuously, so that the level of the developer and its characteristics remain fairly constant. The bled-off developer, after modifications, is often used for other purposes. The "bleed" system of replenishment is the only one in which it is possible to maintain absolute constancy in the bromide concentration. In certain circumstances, this offers practical advantages.

Formulation of replenishers

The formulation of a satisfactory replenisher for any developer depends largely upon the processing conditions employed and the photographic material being developed. Storage conditions, and the frequency with which the developer is used and its surface agitated during passage of the photographic material, affect the allowance which must be made for aerial oxidation. The coating weight and the average amount of developable silver per unit area of material developed – determined by the exposure and the degree of development – are also factors which must be considered. The carry-over, which depends largely on the type of hanger employed and the draining time, has a very considerable bearing on the formulation of a replenisher. Only for standard conditions of work, therefore, is it possible to recommend a single replenisher, which can be formulated from the data obtained by quantitative study of the chemical changes in the developer solution under working conditions. This procedure is normally followed by the manufacturers of packed developers in devising replenishers for use under standard conditions of processing.

In the absence of a specially formulated replenisher, the developer itself, omitting bromide, may be used as a replenisher solution, but the performance of a bath replenished in this way cannot be expected to maintain constancy of performance over a very long period.

If facilities for analysis of a developer bath are available, addition of individual ingredients may be made to it as required, even under varying conditions of work, and the life of the solution maintained indefinitely. This procedure is adopted in cine processing laboratories where very large volumes of solution are employed and constant performance of the bath is of utmost importance.

Buffering

A solution is said to be *buffered* when it shows only a relatively small change in pH when acid or alkali is added. Water is an unbuffered solution; the pH is quickly and largely affected when only a little acid or alkali is added. Buffering of photographic solutions is commonly achieved by adding relatively large quantities of a weak acid and an alkaline salt of that acid, e.g., boric acid and borax.

Fine grain developers of the high sulphite, low energy class are frequently buffered to prevent changes in the pH of these solutions which otherwise occur in use and on keeping, since such changes have a very marked effect on the activity of these solutions (page 402). Hardening-fixing baths are usually buffered to preserve their hardening properties (page 431).

Compounding a developer

In general, developers should be made up in warm water to speed up the dissolving of the chemicals. With developers containing metol it is recommended that this water should not be at a temperature above 50°C, otherwise, under certain circumstances, the metol may be affected. Developers containing Phenidone can, however, be made up with advantage in *hot* water, at about 50°C, without danger. When making up a developer, only about three-quarters of the required final volume should be employed to start with, so that by adding the remainder after the various chemicals are dissolved, the volume can be made up exactly to the required quantity. This final addition should be of cold water, to help bring the solution down to room temperature again.

The order in which the constituents of a developing solution are dissolved is important. In general, the best order is:

(1) Preservative
(2) Developing agent(s)
(3) Alkali
(4) Other components (restrainers, solvents, etc.)

This order is governed principally by the need to guard the developing agents from wasteful oxidation. Addition of the preservative first, prevents oxidation of the developing agents while the solution is being made up. The rate of oxidation of the developing agents is very much accelerated by the presence of alkali. It is, therefore, usually best for addition of the alkali to be left until both preservative and developing agents are in solution. The other components have little influence on the rate of oxidation of the developing agents and can be left to last.

There are important exceptions to the above general rules:

(1) *Developers containing metol*
Metol is relatively insoluble in strong solutions of sodium sulphite, so that with metol developers and M.Q. developers only a small

quantity of sulphite should be added first as a preservative, then the developing agent and then the balance of the sulphite.

(2) *Developers containing Phenidone*
Phenidone is not as readily soluble as some developing agents, but its solubility is assisted by the presence of alkali. It is, therefore, best added after both sulphite and alkali. (Phenidone does not share with metol the difficulty of dissolving in strong solutions of sulphite.)

(3) *Developers containing glycin*
Glycin is almost insoluble in neutral solution. Hence, it is even more desirable with glycin than with Phenidone to add the developing agent *after* the alkali has been dissolved.

Stirring greatly facilitates solution. On the other hand, when large quantities of chemicals have to be dissolved, they may be contained in a cloth hung from a stick placed across the mouth of the vessel. It will be found that this method brings about complete solution very quickly, and prevents solutions being used while they still contain solid particles – a frequent cause of spots on negatives.

To keep its bulk to a minimum, a developing solution is often made up in a more concentrated form than is required for use. The solution made up in this way is referred to as a *stock solution*. For use, this is diluted by adding a specified quantity of water to make a *working solution*. The working strength for tank use is usually more dilute than the strength recommended for dish use, being commonly half the dish strength. The reason for this is that the development times required using a developer at dish strength are usually too short for uniform development to be obtained under the slight degree of agitation employed in tank work. An exception to the general rule arises with certain soft-working developers, e.g., M.Q. borax and P.Q. borax formulae, which are used at full strength (stock solution strength) in both dish and tank. This is because even when these developers are made up to be as concentrated as the solubility of the chemicals will permit, the required development times are more than long enough to permit uniform development under tank conditions of agitation.

The technique of development
The manipulation of the sensitive material during development depends largely upon the nature of the material – flat films, plates, and roll films each requiring different methods of handling. Details of the procedures recommended with each of these classes of materials are given in the following pages.

Development of flat films and plates
Flat films may be developed in a dish, lying flat – emulsion upwards –
or in a tank, suspended vertically in hangers of special design. For
dish development, the best practice is to place the film in the empty
dish and swiftly but carefully to flood it with developer. The surface
must be wetted quickly and evenly, otherwise developing marks will
result. During dish development, the dish must be rocked continuously to provide agitation. Care must be taken to ensure that the
rocking is not too rapid and that it is varied at intervals – e.g., first
to and fro, then from side to side – to avoid patterns of uneven density
caused by regular ("standing") waves. In tank development, the
agitation provided should be intermittent, and achieved by lifting the
films (in their hangers) from the tank, allowing them to drain to one
corner, and replacing them in the bath – every two minutes. At the
beginning of development, films should be agitated vigorously for
about 30 seconds to dislodge any airbells and ensure even wetting.
Vigorous agitation throughout the whole of the development process
is, however, to be avoided, as it may lead to uneven development
owing to the inevitable variation in the degree of agitation at the edges
of films.

Plates also may be developed either in dish or in tank. The same
recommendations with respect to agitation apply as in the case of
flat films. The rigidity of plates makes their handling during processing particularly easy.

Roll films
Roll films may be developed in an open dish, in specially designed
roll film tanks, or – in photofinishing establishments – in deep
tanks.

Dish development of roll films. Dish development has the advantages
that it requires no special apparatus and is relatively quick. Its disadvantages are that the whole operation must be carried out in a darkroom, and that with panchromatic films the amount of light permissible is so small that great care is needed to ensure that the film is
uniformly developed and that solutions are not splashed about the
room. Now that almost all roll films are of the panchromatic variety,
tank development is usual. However, dish development is still useful
in an emergency. The following procedure is recommended:

Unroll the exposed film and attach a non-corroding (e.g., stainless
steel) clip to the near end of the sensitive film. Continue unrolling the
spool until the far end of the film is reached. Detach this end from
the backing paper and attach to it a second clip. (This operation is

simplified if the first clip – with the film attached – is fastened to a hook on the wall while the remainder of the film is unrolled.)

Dry film is springy, and to make it more manageable in development it is recommended that it should first be thoroughly wetted to make it limp before development starts. To do this, hold the clips – one in each hand – so that the film hangs in a U-shape, and pass the film through a dish of clean water two or three times, lowering the left hand while the right hand is raised, and vice-versa, "see-saw" fashion. This preliminary wetting is more easily managed if the film is held with the emulsion side *down*, although in all subsequent operations the emulsion side must be *up*. When the film is sufficiently limp, drain it for a moment and transfer it to the developer. This may be in an ordinary photographic dish – although a 1 litre jug from a local store makes an excellent alternative. Continue the "see-saw" movement, taking care that the film is evenly and completely covered by the solution from one end to the other.

When the required development time has elapsed, the film should be rinsed in plain water and fixed in a suitable fixing bath, the "see-saw" movement being continued throughout. After fixation, the complete film should be placed in a sufficiently large dish or bowl to wash, the clips being left on the ends of the film to prevent it from curling up on itself. Finally, the film should be hung to dry (page 441).

Tank development of roll films. It is the general practice today, except in photofinishing establishments, to develop roll films in individual tanks. Many different types of tank have been designed for this purpose. Some permit daylight loading, although the majority involve darkroom loading. All are suitably light-trapped to make it possible to carry out the actual developing process in the light. Most tanks accommodate the film in the form of a spiral coil and many devices have been employed to keep the various coils separate. One of the earliest of these took the form of a celluloid apron which was wound up with the film inside. Projections along the edges of the apron held the picture area of the film away from the apron. Nowadays, it is more common to wind the film into a special holder comprising a spool having wide flanges, the inner surfaces of which bear spiral grooves. In some tanks of this type, the distance between the flanges can be adjusted to accommodate roll films of various widths (Figure 23.1).

A darkroom-loading roll film tank is essentially a miniature darkroom. Once the film has been loaded into the tank, all processing operations and the removal of the film may be carried out in full daylight,

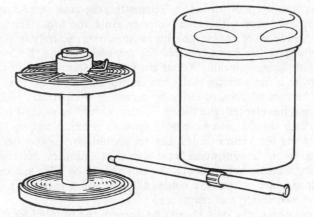

Fig. 23.1 – Roll film developing tank with adjustable spiral

only the actual loading need be done in the dark. No elaborate darkroom is required for this; a cupboard can be used, provided that it is completely dark; very little light indeed is necessary to fog modern high-speed films. It is permissible, of course, to use a suitable safelight during the loading operation, but on the whole it is best to practise loading – using a length of old film – until one becomes so familiar with the operation that it is easy to repeat it in total darkness. The atmosphere of the room in which loading is done must, of course, be free from dust.

The actual loading procedure for the various types of tank varies in detail, and full instructions for loading usually accompany each tank. After loading, the tank may be brought into the light. Developer is usually introduced into the tank through a central light-tight opening in the lid. During development, agitation is obtained by movement of the film through the solution. If the tank is spill-proof this may be achieved by periodic inversion of the complete tank. Alternatively, the holder carrying the film may be rotated in the tank. Rotary action is usually achieved by means of a "twirling rod", which is inserted through the central opening to engage the film-holder spindle; it is recommended that the film should be agitated for 30 seconds at the start of development, followed by five seconds agitation every two minutes. This agitation should be "to-and-fro", since continuous rotation of the film holder in one direction may cause the film partially to leave the spiral.

After development is complete, the solution should be poured from the tank by the spout provided. Thereafter, the tank should be filled and emptied twice with clean water to rinse the film. Throughout these operations, of course, the lid must remain securely in position. After the tank has been emptied for the second time, it should be filled with fixing solution. About ten minutes should be allowed for fixation (in a fresh fixing bath) and during this time the film holder should be rotated once or twice by means of the twirling rod. After this period has elapsed, the fixing solution should be poured from the tank, which should then be placed under a running tap, so that the water enters the central hole. The jet should not be too fierce and washing should be continued for at least thirty minutes. Alternatively, if running water is not available, the tank should be filled and emptied with clean water at least six times, allowing a few minutes to elapse between each filling and emptying.

After washing, the tank should be opened, the film holder taken to pieces and the film removed as carefully as possible. The film should then have a clip attached to each end and be hung by one of these clips in a warm, clean atmosphere and allowed to dry (page 441). The tank should be thoroughly washed, wiped, and placed to dry. It is important that this drying should be thorough and that the wiping should not leave traces of fibrous material in the spiral grooves. Heat should preferably not be used to speed up the drying of the tank, since this may cause it to warp.

Development in deep tanks. In photofinishing establishments, roll films are invariably developed in deep tanks. A common procedure is for a clip to be attached to each end of the film, which is then hung vertically in a tank deep enough for the complete film to be immersed in solution. At the end of development, the film is lifted out by the top clip and lowered into further tanks for rinsing, fixing and washing. Movement of the film from one tank to the next is normally performed mechanically.

Development of 35 mm miniature films

35 mm miniature films are nearly always developed in tanks, the length of a 36-exposure miniature film being such as to make dish development impracticable. Individual tanks are particularly suitable for miniature films because they offer a high degree of protection against blemishes – a most important requirement of miniature film processing in view of the high degree of enlargement normally required with such films. In photofinishing works, 35 mm films are frequently developed in deep tanks, in the same way as roll films, although processing in individual tanks is sometimes obtainable on

request. For development in deep tanks, 36-exposure 35 mm films normally have to be folded on account of their exceptional length. The two ends of the film are held by a clip at the top of the tank, the film having previously been threaded through a weight ring to ensure that it hangs taut.

Pre-soaking
Previous wetting of flat films or plates before development in a so-called "forebath" is not normally recommended. Unless it is done very thoroughly it tends to encourage uneven development in the form of streakiness, instead of preventing it as intended. Use of a forebath may also necessitate a different development time – usually longer than the normal time – a point which is readily overlooked. Pre-soaking is desirable when certain fine grain developers are employed, to discharge backing dyes which would otherwise interfere with development. It is also justified prior to the dish development of roll films, to reduce the tendency of the film to curl.

The required degree of development
When an exposed film is immersed in a developer, the highlights – the most heavily exposed parts of the negative – appear almost at once; then the middle tones appear, and finally the shadow details. If the film be taken out of the developer as soon as the shadows appear, a thin negative of soft gradation will be obtained. If, however, development be continued further, every tone will gain in density, but the highlights and middle tones will gain more rapidly than the shadows. This means that the negative will increase in contrast as well as in density. If neither the emulsion nor the developer contained soluble bromide, no sensible increase in shadow detail would be noticeable on continuing development, but in practice all modern emulsions and most developers do contain bromide, and the result is that on increasing development, shadow detail not apparent on short development appears. Lengthening the time of development can, therefore, be said to increase both the contrast and speed of the emulsion, where, by speed, we mean ability to record shadow detail. There is a limit to which this can be carried. After a certain time in the developer, no further detail appears, the emulsion having reached the maximum speed attainable in the particular developer used. Similarly, after a certain time, contrast reaches its highest value, referred to as gamma infinity. Frequently, speed and contrast increase together, but this relationship varies with different emulsions. Fog and graininess also increase with increasing time of development. (See pages 235–9.)

The point at which development is stopped in practice depends upon the nature of the work being undertaken.

Thus:

(1) In the making of ordinary (continuous-tone) negatives, development is continued until a degree of contrast is achieved which will give negatives of suitable printing quality. (Occasionally, this criterion is abandoned in favour of continuing development until maximum emulsion speed is obtained. This, however, is a specialized technique. See page 421.)

(2) When copying line originals, development is continued until maximum contrast is achieved.

Obtaining the required degree of development

There are two ways by which it may be ensured that a negative is given the required degree of development. The first is *development by inspection*; the second, *development by the time-temperature method*.

Development by inspection

In development by inspection, the film or plate is viewed by light from a suitable safelight and the appearance and growth of the image is watched. Development is stopped when the negative is judged to have suitable densities. This calls for skill and experience. In the early days of photography, development was always by inspection. Adoption of this method was in fact almost essential because, at first, printing papers were available in one contrast only, and it was necessary for all negatives to be of a uniform density range to suit the paper. Development by the time-temperature method does not generally achieve this.

When developing by inspection, use may be made of the fact that, with a normally exposed film or plate, the development time necessary to produce a given degree of development in a specified developer can be expressed as a multiple of the time taken for the first appearance of the image. Suitable factors for different developers were worked out by Alfred Watkins in 1893. Development by inspection with the aid of the appropriate Watkins factor is called the *factorial method of development*. The advantage of the factorial method lies in the fact that it is easier to judge the first appearance of the image than to decide when a certain degree of contrast has been achieved.

The ease with which development by inspection may be carried out depends largely upon the type of safelighting permissible, and thus upon the colour sensitivity and speed of the materials being handled. With blue-sensitive materials the method presents no difficulty. With orthochromatic materials, however, where only a dark red light is permissible, judgement of negative quality is less easy. With fast panchromatic materials any attempt at development by inspection is attended by a risk of fogging,* unless a desensitiser is used (page 423). (It should, however, here be noted that the usual Watkins factor cannot be used if a desensitiser is employed, since use of the latter affects the rate of development.) Use of a transparent developing dish, beneath which a safelight is placed, greatly facilitates dish development by inspection.

The development of continuous-tone negatives by inspection is much less usual today than formerly. The method is, however, still of value whenever correct exposure cannot be correctly assessed, and for subjects of unusually short or unusually long constant range, for which it is desired to compensate in development. It also finds application in the development of negatives on slow blue-sensitive materials – both line and continuous-tone – as, for example, in copying.

Development by inspection has considerable application in the development of papers (Chapter 21).

Development by the time-temperature method

Development of negatives today is normally performed almost entirely by the *time-temperature method*. The basis of this method is that a standard developer formula is used and a development time is given which it is known will produce a given degree of contrast. The time given is based either on the recommendations of the manufacturer for the emulsion employed, or on the user's experience. This method of development does not permit of compensation for variation in subject range or for errors in exposure, but, provided reasonable care is taken in determining exposure, the latitude of the photographic process is such that satisfactory results are usually achieved. Development by the time-temperature method may be carried out in total darkness, and is thus well suited to the development of modern negative materials, which are almost invariably panchromatic.

The development time required to obtain a given contrast (e.g., gamma or average gradient) with a given material depends principally upon:

(1) The particular film or plate used.
(2) The developer used, its dilution and its state of exhaustion.
(3) The temperature of the developer.
(4) The degree of agitation employed.

---

* This risk is at its least if a very dark green safelight is used, for a short period only, towards the end of development.

The effect of each of these factors is discussed below.

Film or plate used. Materials differ appreciably in the rate at which they develop. This was referred to in Chapter 15 (page 235).

Developer. The effects of variations in the composition of a developer on the development time required to reach a given gamma have been referred to earlier in this Chapter.

The temperature of the developer. Rate of development is profoundly affected by the temperature of the developing solution, the activity of the solution increasing with temperature. For photographic processing it is usually best to work at a temperature in the region of 18 to 21°C. This represents a compromise between low temperatures which lead to inconveniently long development times, and high temperatures which lead to uncontrollably short development times, an undesirable amount of fog or stain, and undue swelling of the emulsion with its attendant difficulties such as frilling, reticulation, etc. Published development times are usually related to a standard temperature of 20°C, a temperature selected as easily maintainable (in temperate climates) all the year round. It is recommended that where possible the temperature of the developing solution should be maintained at this figure. Where conditions are such that working at 20°C, or even within the range 18 to 21°C, is not practicable, development of most materials may be carried out satisfactorily at any temperature from 13 to 24°C, provided that the development time is adjusted accordingly. At temperatures below 13°C, development in the usual solutions is inconveniently slow, and above 24°C special precautions have to be taken because of the risk of softening the emulsion.

Within the range 13 to 24°C, the development time required may be ascertained approximately by multiplying the published time – related to 20°C – by an appropriate factor.

The factor to be used in any given circumstances will depend upon the *temperature coefficient* of the developing agent employed. This is defined as the ratio of the development times required to give the same contrast at two temperatures 10°C apart. With many M.Q. and P.Q. developers the temperature coefficient is between 2·5 and 3·0 Development-time factors corresponding to a temperature coefficient of 2·75 are given in Table 23.2.

Calculation of development times for the time-temperature method is facilitated by use of curves in which temperature is plotted against time of development for a given gamma. Such curves, referred to as *time-temperature curves*, are usually plotted with a linear temperature scale and a logarithmic development-time scale, because the "curves"

Temperature of developer	Factor
13°C	2·02
14°C	1·83
15°C	1·66
16°C	1·50
17°C	1·35
18°C	1·22
19°C	1·11
20°C	1·00
21°C	0·90
22°C	0·82
23°C	0·74
24°C	0·67

Table 23.2 – Development-time factors for use when development time is known at 20° C

then take the form of straight lines. A *time-temperature chart* usually comprises a series of such curves, each related to a different value of gamma. Such a chart is shown in Figure 23.2. This chart, like the development factors given in Table 23.2, is based on a temperature

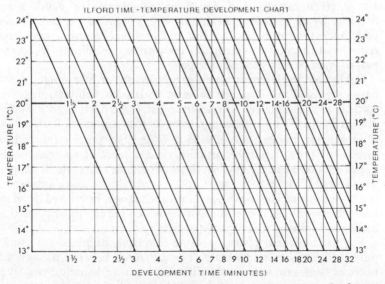

Fig. 23.2 – Time-temperature development chart for M.Q. and P.Q. developers of normal composition

coefficient of 2·75. It will be noted that in the chart the slopes of all the curves shown are the same. The slope, which depends directly on the temperature coefficient, is, in fact, more-or-less constant for all emulsions in any one developing agent, although it varies from agent to agent. Use of a time-temperature chart avoids the calculation required with development-time factors.

To use a time-temperature chart one has first to find the development time required at the published temperature – usually 20°C – and then follow the diagonal line corresponding to this time until it cuts the horizontal line representing the temperature to be used. The point on the horizontal axis immediately below the intersection gives the development time required.

Degree of agitation. The degree of agitation employed in the development of a film or plate affects the development time required; the more vigorous the agitation, within limits, the shorter the development time required. Thus, the continuous form of agitation recommended in dish development permits the use of development times about 20 per cent. shorter than those required when developing in a tank with intermittent agitation.

The basis of published development times

For a given material and developer, the degree of development required by an ordinary (continuous-tone) negative depends principally upon the nature and lighting of the subject (subject luminance range) and, to a lesser extent, on the printing conditions to be employed (type of enlarger, etc.; see page 375).

Published development times assume a subject of average brightness range and are designed to give, with such subjects, negatives suitable for printing (in a condenser-diffuser enlarger) on a middle grade of paper. This usually corresponds to a gamma of 0·65 to 0·80 or an average gradient ($\overline{G}$) of 0·55 to 0·70. (The times published for general-purpose developers usually yield a level of contrast at the upper limit of the range quoted; those quoted for fine grain developers usually yield a level of contrast at the lower limit.) With subjects of below-average or above-average luminance range, published development times will usually yield negatives which require to be printed on harder and softer grades of paper respectively.

For flat films and plates, separate development times are usually published for dish and tank use. The difference between the two sets of times takes into account the differing forms of agitation employed in the two cases. If the recommended tank dilution of the developer differs from the dish dilution, the change in dilution is also allowed for.

Development times for roll films and 35 mm miniature films are usually given only for tank development (with intermittent agitation). In the event of it being desired to develop a roll film in a dish (with continuous agitation), the published time should be reduced by 20 per cent.

Published development times for high-contrast materials used for the photography of line subjects are designed to be sufficient to produce the maximum contrast that the material is capable of yielding.

Where a specific value of gamma is required, the published gamma-time curve (page 237) for the material and developer concerned will give an indication of the required development time, provided that the user's working conditions are similar to the conditions under which the curve was determined.

Development at low temperatures

The activity of all developers slows down at low temperatures and development times must be increased accordingly, the increase required depending on the temperature coefficient of the developer used.

With M.Q. and P.Q. developers, however, development at temperatures below 13°C is slowed down to an extent greater than would be expected from the temperature coefficient. This is because the superadditivity of these mixtures is markedly reduced at low temperatures, an M.Q. developer, for example, behaving in these circumstances as if it contained metol only. In practice, therefore, M.Q. and P.Q. mixtures should not normally be employed at temperatures below about 13°C.

It should be noted, however, that although metol and Phenidone fail to activate hydroquinone at low temperatures, the developing action of hydroquinone itself, in, for example, a hydroquinone-caustic solution, is not impaired, although development times have to be increased to allow for the temperature coefficient. Hydroquinone-caustic solutions are in fact recommended for low temperature work in preference to other formulae, and have been used with success at temperatures below 0°C, an anti-freezing compound being added to prevent solidification of the solution.

Obtaining very uniform development

Uniform development is always desirable, and the normally recommended methods of development are designed to give a good degree of uniformity. Some slight unevenness is commonly obtained using these methods, but in normal photography this is not detectable. For certain types of work, however, a much higher degree of uniformity than usual is desirable, as in the processing of colour separation negatives, spectrographic plates, sensitometric strips etc. The following points should then be noted:

(1) Use of a considerable amount of developer in a large dish, e.g., a size larger than the negative to be processed, helps to minimize the risk of uneven development at the edges, which arises if a dish of the same size as the film or plate is used.

(2) Since the degree of agitation affects the degree of development, variation in the degree of agitation received by different areas of the negative will tend to yield unevenness in development. This problem can be overcome in dish development by employing a degree of agitation so great that further increase does not affect the degree of development.* In sensitometric work, the required degree of agitation is therefore commonly obtained by "brush development" (in which a felt or camel hair brush is used to brush the sensitive surface in all directions during the whole of the development period), or by use of a wiper which moves rapidly to and fro about 1 mm above the negative.

(3) When more normal methods of agitation are employed, i.e., rocking in a dish or intermittent agitation in a tank, uniform development is assisted if the dilution of the developer is so arranged that the development time required is not less than 5 minutes in a dish or 10 minutes in a tank.

(4) Employment of a material whose contrast is such that it is possible to work near gamma infinity will help to ensure uniformity, because near gamma infinity small changes in the degree of development affect density least. Further, variation of emulsion speed due to variation in the amount of bromide in the developer – which may arise from ageing of the developer (especially if in a tank) – is smallest near gamma infinity.

(5) If a developer of low pH is to be employed, use of a P.Q. formula is to be preferred to an M.Q. formula (page 398).

Water-bath development
Water-bath development consists in immersing an exposed film or plate alternately in developer and water, according to a planned schedule. It is of particular value for records of subjects of extremely long brightness range, which, if developed normally, would yield

---

* This principle cannot be applied in tank development because in a tank a high degree of agitation leads to uneven development, because of interruption in the flow of developer by hangers, racks etc.

unprintably hard negatives. Water-bath development operates on the principle of "rationing" the amount of developer available, by limiting this to what is soaked up by the sensitive layer. The developer is therefore exhausted in heavily exposed areas before it is exhausted in less exposed areas, and, consequently, the overall contrast of the negative is restricted. To be of greatest value, water-bath development must be carried out by inspection. To permit a useful level of illumination for this, desensitisation is normally necessary (page 423).

Two-bath development
The aim of two-bath development is the same as in the water-bath method, i.e., to limit the density range of the negative. Two-bath development is carried out by bathing the negative first in a solution containing the developing agent, preservative and restrainer, and then in a solution containing only the alkali. Unlike water-bath development, in the two-bath method the negative should be agitated continuously in both baths.

Monobaths
The term *monobath* is applied to a single solution which combines the actions of development and fixation. Solutions of this type have attracted interest for many years but it is only recently that the problems associated with their formulation have been solved. The main problem is the loss of emulsion speed which results if the exposed silver halide is dissolved away by the fixation process before development can take place. To prevent this, developing agents of high activity are required and a low concentration of fixer. Modern monobaths usually contain Phenidone and hydroquinone as developing agents, and sodium thiosulphate as fixing agent.

Monobaths have the advantages of simplifying and speeding up processing, but it is usually necessary to provide a specially balanced monobath formula for each emulsion or group of similar emulsions. For these reasons, monobaths have found their main application in fields in which rapid access to photographic records is important, as in data and trace recording, etc., and where the inflexibility of the system is not a disadvantage.

Reversal processing
As we have seen, normal methods of processing involve the production of a negative from which a positive is produced on another material by a separate printing operation. It is, however, possible to carry out

these two operations on the one material, producing the positive image by what is called the *reversal method*. This technique is most frequently employed in colour work and in narrow-gauge cinematography. In reversal processing, a negative image is first obtained in the usual way by development of the original latent image. This negative image is then dissolved away in a bleach bath, and the silver halide remaining is exposed and developed to provide the required positive image. The second exposure may or may not be controlled. The second development is usually followed by fixing in a hypo bath, although, if the second exposure has been sufficiently great, little undeveloped silver halide usually remains to be fixed out. The first developer normally contains a silver halide solvent which may be ammonia, sodium thiosulphate, or ammonium thiocyanate. Inclusion of a solvent is necessary when it is desired to reverse a material the shoulder density (D_{max}) of which is greater than the maximum density required in the final positive. For the final developer, any normal formula may be used. In some methods of reversal processing, the second exposure and final development are replaced by a chemical fogging treatment.

Films especially designed to be processed by reversal methods are supplied by some manufacturers. Many, although not all, negative materials may also be reversal processed, but the procedures to be followed for best results will vary from one material to another. Manufacturers should be consulted for details of materials suitable for reversal processing and for appropriate processing procedures.

Control of effective emulsion speed in development
With all the aids to exposure assessment available today (see Chapter 20), the photographer who concerns himself only with normal subjects should not obtain seriously incorrectly-exposed results. There are, however, occasions when mistakes happen, or when underexposure is inevitable and it is desired to correct for the error, as far as possible, in development. In such cases, control is possible in the following ways:

(1) *Variation of development time*
Although the main effect of alteration of development time is on contrast, with modern emulsions there is also an appreciable effect on speed. Shortened development decreases the effective speed; lengthened development increases it (page 411). The limit to the control of speed possible by varying development time is set largely by the accompanying variation in contrast; development must not be such that negatives are too soft or too hard to be printed on the available papers. The maximum development time may also be limited by

graininess and fog, both of which rise with increasing development. The practice of continuing development to obtain maximum speed is sometimes referred to as *development to finality*. Since this technique yields a high gamma, it is generally suitable only for negatives of subjects of short luminance range.

(2) *Choice of developing agent*
Since the effective speed of an emulsion depends upon the developing agent employed, known errors in exposure can sometimes be compensated by suitable choice of developing agent. For example, if maximum speed is required a plain metol developer is preferred. On the other hand, if it is desired to lose speed, a paraphenylene diamine or solvent developer may be employed.

(3) *Variation of potassium bromide content of developer*
A quite considerable degree of over-exposure can be corrected by "doctoring" an M.Q. developer with potassium bromide. The amount of bromide required may be worked out by comparing two test exposures, e.g., wedges, one developed in the normal developer and the other in the "doctored" developer. The amount required will vary both with the developer and with the emulsion used. (In one experiment, the addition of 2·5 grammes of bromide per litre of ID–11 reduced the effective speed of HP3 flat film to one-quarter of its normal value. The development time required to be increased from 12 to 30 minutes, in tank, at 20°C, to obtain suitable contrast.)

Adjacency effects
The action of development results in the production of soluble bromide, which is liberated in proportion to the amount of silver developed. Since bromide restrains development, local concentrations resulting from still development would render the whole process very uneven. Agitation during development is designed to prevent such local concentrations of exhausted developer. If, however, insufficient agitation is given, a number of *adjacency effects* may arise. These are sometimes all given the general title of *Eberhard effects*, although this term is properly applied to one particular manifestation of these effects, described below.

Adjacency effects may take the following forms:

(1) *Streamers*
Insufficient agitation of films developed in a vertical plane, leads to light *bromide streamers* from heavily exposed areas and dark *developer streamers* from lightly exposed areas. If a film is developed in a

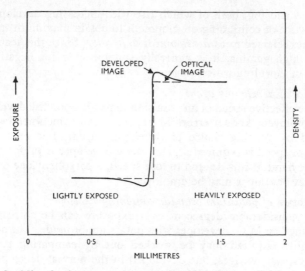

Fig. 23.3 – Microdensitometer trace across boundary between lightly exposed and heavily exposed areas of a negative

horizontal plane the effect may take the form of "mottle", a peculiarly distressing form of uneven development.

(2) Mackie lines

This effect is sometimes seen where there is a sharp boundary between two areas having a large difference in density. The passage of relatively fresh developer from a lightly exposed area to a heavily exposed area accelerates the growth of density at the edge of the heavily exposed region, while the diffusion of bromide in the reverse direction retards development at the edge of the lightly exposed area. The result is a dark line just within the edge of the heavily exposed area and a light line just within the lightly exposed area, the two being called *Mackie lines*. The effect is illustrated in Figure 23.3, which shows a micro-densitometer trace across a boundary between a lightly exposed area and a heavily exposed area.

(3) Eberhard effect

The density of a developed image of small area is influenced by the actual size of the area and upon the density of adjacent image areas. Further, the density of an image area may vary from point to point, even though exposure has been constant all over the area. This is known as the *Eberhard effect*. It is due to the same causes as the Mackie lines.

(4) *Kostinsky effect*
Not only the density but the actual *size* of a small image area may be reduced by the presence of an adjacent image area. The effective separation between the two areas is therefore increased (Figure 23.4). This is known as the *Kostinsky effect*, after the astronomer who first noticed it.

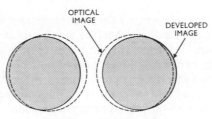

OPTICAL
IMAGE

DEVELOPED
IMAGE

Fig. 23.4 – Kostinsky effect

Sabattier effect
If an exposed film or plate be developed and washed (but not fixed), and then given a second overall exposure and redeveloped, certain parts of the original image may be found to be reversed. This is known as the *Sabattier effect*. The effect is often observed when films or plates are developed in an unsafe light. It is believed to result partly from optical shielding by the image produced by the first exposure and development, and partly from a desensitising effect resulting from the first exposure and development.

The Sabattier effect is sometimes used to obtain special effects in pictorial photography, where it is commonly – but incorrectly – termed "solarization". (Reversal due to the Sabattier effect should not be confused with true solarization, i.e., reversal due to use of the region of reversal of the characteristic curve.) Amidol developer is stated to exhibit the Sabattier effect to a marked degree.

Desensitisation
Desensitisers have the power of reducing very considerably the sensitivity of silver halide grains without seriously affecting the latent image produced by the camera exposure. Use of a desensitiser thus makes possible the development by inspection, at a comfortable level of illumination, of panchromatic and fast orthochromatic materials – which normally have to be handled in total darkness or at a very low level of illumination.

A desensitiser is preferably used as a pre-bath, although it may, in some cases, be added to the developer itself. From two to three minutes are required for the desensitising action to take place, whether in pre-bath or in developer, and this operation must be carried out with the normal safelight, or, preferably, in total darkness. After this period has elapsed, more light may be used to inspect the negatives. It is not safe to use white light; a controlled light from a bright green safelight is all that is permissible – but this light can be quite bright enough to work by.

Today, when development by the time-temperature method is the rule, the number of occasions when the development of negatives by inspection is desired is far less than in the early days of photography; consequently, desensitisers are now rarely used.

Certain modern materials do not respond satisfactorily to the action of desensitisers; speed and/or contrast of the emulsion are seriously affected. In the case of doubt, a practical test should be carried out with an unimportant or trial exposure.

Development of papers
See Chapter 21.

CHAPTER 24

Processing Following Development

As soon as a film has been developed it bears a visible silver image, but it is not yet in a condition to be brought into the daylight or be used in the further operation of making positive prints. In the first place, the silver halide grains which were not affected by exposure – and which have not undergone reduction by the developer – still remain in the emulsion, making it difficult to print from the negative. Further, these silver halide grains are still light-sensitive and will gradually print out, changing colour and masking the image to a greater and greater extent as time goes on. Then, again, the gelatin is in a swollen condition and has absorbed a considerable amount of the developing solution. This is still capable of developing action unless quickly stopped.

The purpose of *fixation* is to remove the unwanted silver halide without damaging the silver image, and, at the same time, to stop development. The fixing operation may also be used to harden the gelatin, to prevent further swelling.

Rinse bath

A *plain rinse bath* is very commonly employed between development and fixation to *slow* the progress of development, by removing all the developing solution which is merely clinging to the surface of the film. A rinse bath does not completely *stop* development – because it leaves more-or-less unchanged the developer actually in the swollen emulsion layer – but it does remove much of the gross contamination of the film by the developing solution. Rinsing is carried out by quickly immersing the material in clean plain water. To ensure that it does not become loaded with developer, a rinse bath should be changed frequently – or running water should be employed.

Rinsing in plain water must be followed by fixation in an acid fixing bath to *stop* development. The rinse bath then serves not only to slow development, but also to lessen the work that has to be done by the acid in such a fixing bath. Rinsing thus "protects" the fixing bath.

Acid stop bath

Although a plain rinse bath is all that is commonly used between development and fixation, a better technique is to use an *acid stop bath*, the function of which is not only to remove the developer clinging to the surface of the film, but also to neutralize developer carried over in the emulsion layer, and thus to stop – not merely slow – development. It does this by virtue of the fact that developing agents fail to act in acid solution. An acid stop bath is of particular value when a highly alkaline developer such as a hydroquinone-caustic formula is used.

In selecting an acid to acidify a stop bath it must be remembered that some of the bath will be carried into the fixer as films and plates pass through it. This rules out use of the stronger acids (e.g., sulphuric acid), since these would cause precipitation of sulphur in the fixing bath. Solutions of potassium metabisulphite ($2\frac{1}{2}$ per cent.) or acetic acid (1 per cent.) are commonly used. Acetic acid, the acid present in vinegar, is available in pure form as "glacial" acetic acid. This is a colourless liquid which freezes at a temperature of about 16°C. It is this freezing propensity which gives it the description of "glacial". Impure or dilute samples of acetic acid freeze at a lower temperature. Acetic acid crystals expand on melting, so that if a bottle of the substance has frozen hard, warmth should be applied first near the top – to avoid a burst bottle. It should be noted that in its concentrated, or glacial, form acetic acid is an exceedingly strong irritant to the skin.

Fixing baths

Although, as stated earlier, a *fixing bath* may perform several functions, its characteristic action is the removal of unexposed silver halide from the emulsion. Fixing baths, therefore, always contain a solvent for silver halides – whatever else they may contain. For use in photographic processing, the solvent must be one which forms a complex with silver which can be washed out, it must not damage the gelatin of the emulsion and must not attack the silver image to any great extent. Of the possible solvents for the silver halides, only the thio-sulphates are in general use – all the others have disadvantages of one kind or another. The alkali cyanides and thiocyanates, for example, although more rapid in action than the thiosulphates, exert a softening action on the gelatin and have a fairly considerable solvent action on the silver image. The cyanides have the additional disadvantage of being highly poisonous. They are still generally used, however, in the wet collodion process (page 208), where the image is largely silver iodide.

By far the most widely used silver halide solvent is sodium thiosulphate – known to photographers as "hypo". In early days, this substance – whose true chemical name is sodium thiosulphate – was wrongly named "hyposulphite of soda", and in abbreviated form the name stuck. Besides being a solvent for silver halides, hypo has a weak solvent action on the silver image itself – more so in acid solution than in neutral solution – and while this action is negligible during the time required for fixation, prolonged immersion in the fixing bath may result in reduction in the density of the image, the effect being most marked where fine grain negative emulsions and printing papers are concerned. In the latter case, image colour may be affected as well as image density (page 358).

The fixing bath removes the residual silver halide by transforming it into complex sodium argentothiosulphates. These substances are more or less unstable and, after fixation, must therefore be removed from the emulsion by washing. If left in the emulsion, they will in time break down to form an all-over yellowish-brown stain of silver sulphide.

In the presence of a high concentration of soluble silver, or low concentration of free thiosulphate, as when the fixing bath is nearing exhaustion, there is a tendency for the complex sodium argentothiosulphates to be "adsorbed", or "mordanted", to the emulsion, in which condition they are difficult to remove by washing. Fixation in an exhausted bath is therefore attended by risk of subsequent staining, as a result of the breakdown of the silver complexes remaining in the emulsion, however efficient the washing process.

To avoid the danger of such staining, the best practice is to use two fixing baths in succession, according to the following procedure. Initially, two fresh baths are prepared and materials are left in the first bath until they are just clear, being then transferred to the second bath for an equal period. In the course of time, the clearing time in the first bath – which is doing practically all the work of fixation – will become inconveniently long. When clearing requires, say, double the time required in a fresh bath, the first bath should be discarded and replaced by the second, which, in turn, should be replaced by a completely fresh bath. This process is repeated as required, with the result that the second bath is always relatively fresh. Adoption of this procedure ensures that all films leave the second fixing bath in good condition from the point of view of subsequent permanence; as good in fact as if they had been fixed throughout in a fresh bath. The method is also economical, in that it enables all the hypo in turn to be worked to a point far beyond that at which a single bath would have to be discarded.

A fixing bath for negatives is usually made to contain between 20 and 40 per cent. of crystalline hypo. A bath intended for papers is not usually made stronger than 20 per cent.; a stronger bath will be attended by the risk of bleaching the image on prolonged fixation, and will also aggravate the problem of removing hypo from the paper on washing, a problem which with papers is more serious than with films and plates, owing to the absorbent nature of the base. As the average coating weight of papers is only about one-quarter of that of negative materials, fixing times for papers are shorter than those required by negative materials, and the times required in the weaker bath are not excessive. (For the fixing of papers see also Chapter 21.)

Plain fixing bath

A solution containing hypo alone is termed a *plain fixing bath*. If such a bath be used immediately following development, or with only a plain rinse between development and fixation, there is a very considerable danger of staining resulting from the carry-over of developer in the emulsion layer. This staining may be of two kinds. Organic stains may result from oxidation of the developer, since the concentration of the preservative is now lowered by dilution. More serious, silver stains may result from the fact that any development which takes place in the fixing bath does so in the presence of an excess of a silver halide solvent.

If, therefore, it is desired to use a plain fixing bath, it must be preceded by an acid stop bath. In practice, it is more common to combine the stop bath with the fixing bath to form an *acid fixing bath* (see below).

A plain hypo bath, without a previous stop bath, is used when it is desired to get the maximum amount of staining with a pyro developer, which for this purpose is made with a low concentration of sulphite (page 391). When a plain hypo bath is used, white light must not be switched on until fixation is complete.

Acid fixing bath

For the reasons stated above, the addition of a suitable acid to the hypo solution provides a more satisfactory bath than a plain fixing bath. An additional convenience when an acid fixing bath is used is that white light may be switched on shortly after the sensitive material has been placed in the bath, provided that the material is completely immersed and agitated for the first few seconds after being placed in the bath.

The stronger acids cause hypo to decompose with the formation of minute particles of sulphur which cause the solution to become milky in appearance. This reaction is enhanced by the presence of sulphur, with the result that once sulphur has appeared in it the solution deteriorates rapidly. The presence of sulphite in the solution, however, tends to prevent this decomposition of the hypo. Acid fixing baths are therefore usually made up either:

(1) By the addition to the hypo solution of potassium metabisulphite, or

(2) By the addition to the hypo solution of a weak acid such as acetic acid, together with sodium sulphite. (A stronger acid than acetic – for example, hydrochloric acid or sulphuric acid – would destroy the hypo even in the presence of sulphite.)

When amidol is used as the developing agent, it is more than usually important that the fixing bath should be acidic, since amidol continues to develop even in neutral solution.

Hardening

When, for any reason, it is necessary to process in warm solutions or to carry out rapid drying by the application of heat, it is an advantage – sometimes essential – to harden photographic materials. Even at ordinary temperatures hardening has important advantages:

(1) It checks swelling and consequent softening of the emulsion layer. A hardened film is thus less easily damaged in subsequent processing operations. Further, since less water is taken up by a hardened emulsion, there is less to be removed on drying – which in consequence is more rapid.

(2) Hardening raises the melting point of the emulsion. It thus allows a slightly higher temperature to be used for drying. For this reason, and because there is less water to be removed, hardening makes possible a considerable speeding up of the drying operation.

The extent to which an emulsion swells, i.e., takes up water, is limited if it is in a solution containing a high salt concentration. In normal processing, therefore, only a limited amount of swelling takes place in the developer and fixer, and this is not usually serious. There is a tendency for further swelling to take place in the rinse between developer and fixer, but provided the rinse is brief this swelling is not serious. On finally washing in plain water, however, an unhardened gelatin layer will swell considerably and it is then that the film is in its weakest state. This is illustrated in Figure 24.1. The use of extremely soft water aggravates this swelling, because of its low salt concentration. From this it is seen that for hardening to be of value it must take place before washing begins.

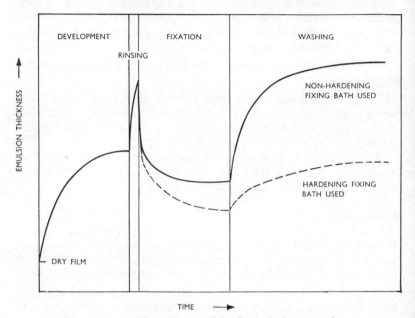

Fig. 24.1 – Swelling of an emulsion layer during processing.

In practice, it is usually most convenient to combine the hardening process with fixation, and this is done by the addition of a *hardening agent* to the fixing bath, to form a *hardening-fixing bath*. This avoids the need for an additional processing operation.

The degree of swelling of an emulsion increases with temperature. In tropical climates, therefore, even the partial swelling which takes place in the developer may assume significant proportions. It is then common practice to harden the film *before* development.

Typical hardening agents are ordinary alum – sometimes called white alum or potash alum – and chrome alum. These are respectively sulphates of aluminium and chromium with a certain proportion of potassium sulphate. Hardening by means of these agents is a chemical process in which aluminium or chromium combines with the gelatin and makes the latter more resistant to water, to heat and to abrasion.

Both chrome alum and potash alum are widely used in hardening-fixing baths. Chrome alum acid hardening-fixing baths can be made up with a higher concentration of hypo (up to 40 per cent.) than potassium alum baths (maximum of 30 per cent.). This does not, however, make it possible to process more quickly in the former, because, for efficient hardening with chrome alum, the film must be in the bath for about 10 minutes at 20°C, as opposed to the 5 minutes required in a potassium alum bath. It is stated that chrome alum is capable of yielding a greater degree of hardening than potash alum. However, the hardening properties of a chrome alum hardening-fixing bath diminish with age, becoming negligible after two or three days, whether the bath is used or not. For these reasons, chrome alum is most useful when a hardening-fixing bath is required for use over a short period only, soon after mixing; when a hardening bath is required for continuous use, potassium alum is to be preferred. Potassium alum is always to be preferred when it is required to harden prints, because with chrome alum some papers have a tendency to acquire a slight greenish tint which will not wash out. Chrome alum is commonly used when a hardening rinse bath is required between development and fixation, as when processing is carried out at high temperatures. A chrome alum bath containing no fixer retains its hardening powers indefinitely unused, although hardening falls off in a few days once the bath is used.

A fairly careful adjustment of the acid activity of the solution is required in both chrome alum and potash alum hardening-fixing baths. If the pH is too low there is a danger of sulphurization; if too high of sludging. A safe range is 4 to 6·5. For optimum hardening, the pH should be at about the middle of this range. Hardening-fixing baths are therefore made to contain ingredients which ensure good buffering properties (page 404); this prevents carry-over of developer from affecting the pH too much.

Formalin is sometimes used as a hardener of photographic materials when a hardening rinse bath is required, as, for example, when processing under tropical conditions. To obtain maximum hardening with formalin, the solution must be alkaline. A formalin bath is generally employed either before development or after fixation, depending upon circumstances. It should not be employed immediately after development, since developer carried over in the emulsion layer may combine with the formalin to soften, rather than harden, the emulsion layer. Formalin is not suitable for use in combined hardening-fixing baths.

Making up fixing baths
The principal ingredient of most fixing baths is hypo. This is available in three forms: pea crystals, rice crystals and anhydrous. Pea crystals are fairly clear hexagonal crystals of about the size of a pea; rice crystals are smaller and thus have the advantage that they dissolve more readily. Anhydrous hypo is a white powder. Crystals of hypo – pea or rice – contain 36 per cent. of water and only 64 per cent. of the salt, whereas anhydrous hypo contains practically 100 per cent. of the salt. It is common practice to specify the concentration of fixing baths in terms of crystalline hypo. Thus, a 40 per cent. hypo bath contains 40 grammes of crystalline hypo per 100 ml of solution, or 25 grammes of anhydrous hypo.

The making up of fixing baths is effected most rapidly if the hypo is first dissolved in *hot* water. This is especially advantageous when crystalline hypo is employed, since solution of this form of hypo is accompanied by a fall in temperature. (Anhydrous hypo gets slightly warm on dissolving.) Where large quantities are involved, the hypo may conveniently be placed in a muslin bag suspended just below the surface of the water, and left overnight. This method obviates the need for stirring.

When an acid hypo fixing bath is required, the metabisulphite should be added to the *cool* hypo solution. If metabisulphite is added to hypo in a hot solution the hypo may decompose.

The formulae of acid-hardening fixing baths are more complicated than those of ordinary acid fixing baths, and greater care is therefore needed in making them up. The procedure to be followed in making up a hardening-fixing bath will depend on the particular formula employed; detailed instructions are given with each formula and packing. Provided that these instructions are carefully followed no difficulty should be experienced. One general rule that may be noted in making up potassium alum hardening fixers supplied as single-powder mixtures is that the water used should not be above 27°C; if hot water is used the fixer may decompose.

Time required for fixation
Rate of fixation depends principally upon the following factors:
(1) *Type of emulsion and thickness of coating*
Other things being equal, fine grain emulsions fix more rapidly than coarse ones, and thin emulsions more rapidly than thick ones. Silver chloride fixes more rapidly than the bromide.
(2) *Type and degree of exhaustion of the fixing bath*
Where hypo is employed as the clearing agent, a concentration of

about 75 per cent. (of crystalline hypo) gives the most rapid rate of fixation; concentrations above or below this value give slower rates of fixation. The concentration may, however, be reduced to about 20 per cent. before fixation is seriously slowed. As stated earlier, the concentration usually employed in practice is between 20 and 40 per cent. A partially exhausted bath fixes more slowly than a fresh bath, not only on account of reduction in concentration of hypo, but also, if used for fixing negatives, because of the accumulation of soluble silver and of iodide (page 434). For special work, fixing agents which clear more rapidly than hypo may be employed (page 436).

(3) *Temperature of the bath*
Increase in temperature gives increased rate of fixation.

(4) *Degree of agitation*
The rate of fixation is controlled by a diffusion process, so that agitation materially reduces the time required.

(5) *Degree of exposure*
The heavier the exposure, the less the amount of unused silver halide to be removed in the fixing bath, and hence the more rapid the rate of fixation.

As a general rule, a material may be considered to be fixed after approximately twice the time required for *clearing*. In a fresh acid fixing bath of normal composition, fixation of films and plates may be regarded as complete in about 10 minutes at 20°C. Fixation is complete when all visible traces of the silver halide have disappeared, but as the exact moment of clearing is not easily determined it is good practice to give double the apparent clearing time. With papers, clearing of the image is even less readily observed, but fixation may be regarded as complete in about 5 minutes in a fresh bath. Hardening takes place slowly and usually requires longer than clearing. To be efficient, hardening is therefore assisted by allowing materials to remain in the fixing bath for twice as long as they take to clear.

The temperature of the fixing bath is by no means as critical as that of the developing solution, but it should normally lie within a few degrees of the temperature of the developer, to avoid the danger of reticulation of the gelatin.

Changes in a fixing bath with use
The composition of a fixing bath, like that of a developer, changes with use. We can best understand the reasons for these changes by considering the sequence of events following development, assuming that an acid-hardening fixing bath is used, preceded by a plain rinse.

(1) The rinse bath removes much of the gross contamination of the film by the developing solution, and thus slows development.

(2) The film is transferred to the fixing bath where the acid neutralizes the alkali of the developing solution in the emulsion layer and stops development.

(3) The hypo converts the silver halide in the emulsion to complex sodium argentothiosulphates which gradually distribute themselves throughout the fixing bath.

(4) The hardening agent soaks into the gelatin and begins its hardening action.

As the bath is used, more and more of the alkaline developer is carried over and the acid will become exhausted. A good guide to the degree of acid exhaustion is provided by an indicator paper. The pH of the bath should preferably not be allowed to rise above about 6·0. If the bath becomes definitely alkaline, it will not stop development quickly enough, and consequently there will be risk of staining. If the bath is a hardening one, there will also be a serious falling-off in hardening power. If a hardening-fixing bath becomes very alkaline, sludge may be formed from the interaction of the hardening agent and the alkali. This will tend to deposit itself on negatives in the form of scum, which may be difficult to remove. (The white scum from potash alum will usually wash off while the negative is wet, but not when dry. The bright green scum from chrome alum will frequently not wash off at all.) (See also page 431.)

Not only does the acidity of the bath fall off as the bath is used, but the clearing action itself becomes slower. This is partly due to exhaustion of the hypo, but, with negative materials at least, is also due to a concentration of iodide – derived from the emulsion – which builds up in the bath. Silver iodide, present in small amount in many negative emulsions, is extremely difficult to dissolve in hypo, and has the effect of depressing the solubility of silver bromide and so retarding the clearing process as a whole. We thus have a symptom of apparent "exhaustion" which is brought about by the piling up and resisting action of an end-product. Among other end-products which build up in the bath with important results are the complex sodium argentothiosulphates. These retard clearing, too, but their most important effect is upon the permanence of the negatives and prints (page 427).

A further cause of exhaustion of a hardening-fixing bath could be exhaustion of sulphite, but the quantity employed is usually sufficiently large to ensure that trouble from this source is rare.

Lastly, since a small volume of water from the rinse bath is carried into the bath on each film, while a small volume of the fixing solution is carried out, the fixing bath becomes progressively diluted on use. This, also, leads to an increase in the clearing time required.

Useful life of a fixing bath

A fixing bath is usually discarded when its useful life is considered ended. This life depends upon several factors, of which the number of films passing through is but one. For this reason, it is not possible to state with any high degree of precision the number of films or plates which may safely be fixed in a given bath. The following figures may, however, be taken as a rough guide:

$$\left.\begin{array}{l} \text{4 No. 120 roll films} \\ \text{4 35 mm miniature films (36-exposure)} \\ \text{14 } 102 \times 127 \text{ mm flat films or plates} \end{array}\right\} \begin{array}{l} \text{in 600 ml of 20 per} \\ \text{cent. hypo solution.} \end{array}$$

We have just noted that as a bath approaches exhaustion, the time it takes to clear a film increases for a variety of reasons. It is common practice to discard a bath when the clearing time has risen to double the time required by the bath when fresh. When a bath is used solely for papers this rule is not readily applicable, since it is not easy to tell when a paper is cleared. In this case, the bath should be discarded when a known area of paper has been passed through. This, of course, necessitates the keeping of some sort of record.

Replenishment of fixing baths

Although, at one time, a fixing bath was invariably discarded when exhausted, it has increasingly come to be recognized that this is unnecessarily wasteful of both hypo and silver, and the possibility of replenishing a fixing bath has therefore been studied. The first property of a fixing bath to fall off with use is its acidity; then, usually, its hardening properties. The life of a bath may, therefore, be usefully increased by the addition of a suitable acid mixture. If this is made to contain a hardener, both acidity and hardening power can be restored to a certain extent. This process cannot, however, be continued indefinitely because of the accumulation of iodide (usually) and silver in the bath. It is not, therefore, worth while to attempt to replenish a fixing bath by the addition of hypo, unless some means of removing the silver is available, as, for example, by electrolytic silver recovery (see below).

Where silver recovery *is* being practised a bath may be replenished by adding fresh hypo and hardener (say, 10 per cent. of the amount used initially) when the initial clearing time is exceeded by about

50 per cent. Following this, the acidity of the bath should be restored by adding, with stirring, 50 per cent. acetic acid solution until a pH of about 5·0 is achieved. This may be checked with an indicator paper. It is desirable, before replenishing, to draw off a quantity of the solution to ensure that the bath does not overflow on replenishment.

Silver recovery

The recovery of silver from a fixing bath is attractive because of the high value of silver, quite apart from the possibility of replenishing the fixing bath. The various methods of silver recovery commonly practised today may be divided into two main groups:

(1) Sludging methods.
(2) Electrolytic methods.

In sludging methods, chemicals are added to the spent fixing bath to deposit the silver – either as a metallic sludge, or as a compound such as silver sulphide. For a sludging method to be applied, the solution must be taken out of service and normally no attempt is made to use it again.

With electrolytic methods, on the other hand, there is no difficulty in using the solution again after silver recovery, and electrolytic recovery apparatus may even be designed to operate in such a way that the solution is kept in service while recovery proceeds.

Ammonium thiosulphate fixers

Many materials – in particular those with a high iodide content, such as fast negative materials – clear more rapidly in a solution of ammonium thiosulphate than in hypo. This is the basis of most rapid fixers on the market. Ammonium thiosulphate is not very stable in powder form and is therefore usually supplied as a liquid.

The fixing capacity of an ammonium thiosulphate fixer is greater than that of a hypo bath, and there is consequently more likelihood of its becoming heavily laden with silver. Care must therefore be taken not to allow clothes to be splashed with used rapid fixer; such splashes will form dark silver stains on exposure to light and heat.

Rapid fixing

We have seen earlier (page 432) that rate of fixation is influenced by a number of factors. Rapid fixing is normally achieved in three ways: by using hypo at its optimum concentration, by using fixing agents which clear more rapidly than hypo, and by raising the temperature of the bath. If it is desired to raise the temperature above about 24°C, special precautions must be taken to prevent the emulsion layer from swelling unduly.

For rapid fixing, the optimum concentration of hypo (cryst.) is about 75 per cent. (page 433). The concentration normally employed in practice is only 20 to 40 per cent., but the reduction in fixing time that can be achieved by working hypo at a higher concentration is not very great. As already noted, however, ammonium thiosulphate clears many materials much more rapidly than hypo. If a shorter fixing time still is essential, ammonium thiocyanate may be employed. This solvent, like ammonium thiosulphate, is particularly effective with emulsions containing silver iodide. For ultra-rapid processing, thiocyanate is sometimes employed at high temperatures with specially hardened films, under which conditions it clears in a few seconds. Some of the products of fixation with thiocyanate are, however, insoluble in water and darken rapidly on exposure to light. If, therefore, permanent records are required, fixation with thiocyanate must be followed by immersion in a hypo bath.

Substitutes for hypo

In times of scarcity, interest has been aroused in substitutes for hypo. The most successful method appears to be to replace part of the hypo by ammonium sulphate. Instead of using 400g hypo per litre, for example, we may use 100g of ammonium sulphate and 250g of hypo. The ammonium sulphate converts some of the hypo (sodium thiosulphate) into ammonium thiosulphate, which clears film more rapidly than hypo. The clearing time of this bath is similar to a 40 per cent. hypo bath – the increase in clearing time that would be expected from the decrease in the amount of hypo being balanced by the acceleration of clearing due to the presence of the ammonium salt.

Washing

The purpose of the washing operation is to remove all the soluble salts left in the emulsion layer after fixing. The important salts to be removed are hypo and the complex silver salts. If hypo is allowed to remain, it can cause the silver image to discolour and fade, the sulphur in the residual hypo combining with the silver image to form yellowish-brown silver sulphide. If the complex silver salts are allowed to remain they also may decompose to form silver sulphide, which will be especially noticeable in the highlights and in unexposed areas.

Glass negatives may be washed in several ways, the choice depending upon whether only one or two or a large number must be handled simultaneously. A single negative placed under a gentle spray of water from a rose will be washed in as little as three to four minutes. The plan of placing negatives in a shallow inclined trough, down which water runs from a perforated tube at the upper end, is nearly as expeditious. Both methods, however, are wasteful of water.

Where consumption of water is a consideration, and many plates are to be washed, the best appliance on the whole is a tank fitted with a siphon, by which the water running into the tank from a tap is almost completely drawn off every time the tank becomes full. A loose rack for such a tank will accommodate a dozen or more negatives, and patterns may be obtained which take several sizes. A washing time of 30 minutes is generally advised in a tank. With tanks employing continuous flow, proper circulation must be maintained – with no stagnant spots.

Flat films should be kept in their hangers and washed in a tank with a siphon. Roll films, which have been dish-developed by the see-saw method, may be stretched out base side downwards in shallow trays with weights at each end to keep them from curling. Films which have been developed in roll film tanks may usually be washed in the same tanks, as described in Chapter 23.

For efficient washing of films, plates or papers, running water is best, the reason being that this ensures that fresh water is continuously brought to the gelatin surface. In practice, this method is very wasteful, and satisfactory washing can be obtained by using several changes of water. The removal of hypo from an emulsion layer is a simple process of diffusion of soluble salt from the layer to the water, the rate increasing with the difference between the concentrations of salt in the layer and in the adjacent water. If the concentration of salt in the water becomes equal to that in the emulsion layer no further diffusion of salt from the emulsion can be expected. From this, the advantage to be gained by frequent changes is easily seen. Agitation during washing is very advantageous, since it displaces water heavily loaded with soluble salt from the emulsion surface and replaces it with fresh water. For quick and efficient washing of films and plates, six changes, each lasting for two minutes with rocking, will usually prove satisfactory. (With *extreme* agitation, three changes of half-a-minute will provide adequate washing for many purposes.) Without rocking, six changes of five minutes each may be given. The "number-of-changes" system is, in effect, employed in tanks fitted with siphon devices to give periodic emptying.

Washing is even more important with prints than with negatives, because paper emulsions are of finer grain than negative emulsions and consequently fade much more readily in the presence of hypo.

Chloride paper emulsions are more susceptible to fading than bromide emulsions. Further, whereas in the fixation of films and plates only the gelatin layer becomes impregnated with hypo, with prints hypo permeates the base and becomes held in the paper fibres and baryta coating, from which it is very difficult to wash out. For normal purposes, washing times of 30 minutes for single-weight papers and 1 hour for double-weight papers are adequate. However, even with these times of washing, traces of hypo are retained in prints which are sufficient in time to cause fading under certain storage conditions, in particular high temperature and high humidity. If the highest degree of permanence of prints ("archival permanence") is required, use of a hypo eliminator is necessary (see below).

Since the ill-effects of faulty washing (and faulty fixation) appear only after the image has been stored for some considerable time, there is a tendency for the dangers inherent in such faulty processing to be overlooked. It is, however, most important that these stages of processing should be treated seriously; all the work that goes into the making of a photograph rests upon them.

Hypo eliminators and washing aids

Water-washing, properly carried out, is, with negative materials at least, all that is usually required for permanence. Good washing removes practically all the hypo, and, provided the negative has been properly fixed, the unwanted silver compounds too. With papers, however, a small trace of hypo may be detected in a print even after 60 minutes good washing.

When permanence is more than usually important, the last trace of hypo may be destroyed by a *hypo eliminator*, essentially an oxidizing agent which converts the thiosulphate to sulphate, which is inert and soluble in water. Various hypo eliminators have been suggested, such as potassium permanganate, sodium hypochlorite, persulphate, iodine and potassium perborate, but probably the best method is to immerse the well-washed material in an ammoniacal solution of hydrogen peroxide for five minutes, following this with ten minutes further washing.

As already stated, the use of a hypo eliminator appears to be justified only when it is impossible to remove the hypo by washing, a situation which normally arises only with prints. Hypo elimination is not intended as a short cut to do away with washing.

There are, however, occasions when it is desired to shorten the washing time, and this can be achieved by the use of washing aids, sometimes referred to as "assists". These are based on an observation that the consitution of processing solutions can greatly influence the rate of removal of hypo from a photographic material during the final wash. One recommended technique is to rinse the material being processed briefly after fixation and then bathe it for two minutes in a 2 per cent solution of anhydrous sodium sulphite. By the use of this technique, the subsequent washing time can be reduced to one-sixth of that normally required.

Tests for permanence
It is sometimes desirable to test the completeness of the fixing and washing of negatives and prints. Two tests are required: one for the presence of unwanted silver salts, the other for the presence of hypo. If either of these is present the permanence of the negative or print cannot be assured (page 437).

Test for residual silver
A simple test for the presence of injurious residual silver compounds is to apply a drop of 0·2 per cent. sodium sulphide solution to the clear margin of the negative or print after washing and drying (or squeegeeing). After two or three minutes the spot should be carefully blotted. If silver salts are present, silver sulphide will be formed. Any colouration in excess of a just-visible cream indicates the presence of unwanted silver salts. For careful control, a comparison standard may be made by processing an unexposed sheet of material through two fixing baths and making a spot test on this sheet. The presence of unwanted silver salts may be due to too short an immersion in the fixing bath, use of an exhausted fixing bath, or to insufficient washing.

Test for residual hypo
Tests for residual hypo are of many kinds; some are intended to be applied to the wash water, others to the photographic material itself. A test applied to the wash water gives an indication of the readily diffusible hypo in the emulsion layer, but no indication of the amount of hypo held by paper fibres or baryta coating. Such tests may therefore be useful with films and plates but are of no value with papers. With all materials, a test of the residual hypo in the photographic material itself is to be preferred.

One of the usual solutions for detecting the presence of hypo in the wash water is an alkaline permanganate solution. The procedure for the use of this is as follows: Dissolve 1 gramme of potassium permanganate and 1 gramme of sodium carbonate (anhydrous) in 1 litre of distilled water. Add one drop of this solution to each of two vessels, one containing drops of water from the washed film or plate and the other an equal quantity of water straight from the tap. If the colour persists for the same time in both, then washing has been satisfactory. If, however, the colour of the water drained from the washed material clears first, washing is incomplete. (The tap water control is required because tap water itself may contain substances which decolorize permanganate.)

The detection of hypo in the processed photographic material may be carried out quite simply by applying one spot of a 1 per cent. silver nitrate solution to the clear margin of the negative or print after washing and drying (or squeegeeing). After 2 or 3 minutes the negative must be thoroughly rinsed to remove excess reagent, which if not removed will darken on exposure to light. If hypo is present, silver sulphide will be formed where the spot was applied. Any colouration in excess of a pale cream indicates the presence of an unsafe amount of hypo. This test is suitable for use with films, plates and papers.

A very accurate test for the presence of hypo in the processed material is given in British Standard 1153 : 1955. (See Appendix.) A square inch of the material is placed in 10 ml of a mercuric chloride-potassium bromide solution, and, after 15 minutes, the turbidity is compared with the turbidity produced in a series of standard solutions. This test accurately measures quantities of hypo in films as low as 8 mg per square metre. The mercuric chloride test is suitable for use with films or plates, but not with papers, since it gives no indication of the amount of hypo in the paper base. Silver nitrate, used in the preceding test, reacts with all the hypo in film or print.

Drying

After washing, the film or plate should preferably be given a final rinse for a minute or two in a bath containing a few drops of wetting agent (page 443). This will improve draining and so help to prevent the formation of tear marks on drying. The material should then be taken straight from this bath and placed to dry. Surplus moisture from the surface of the material may be wiped off with a clean, soft chamois leather or a viscose sponge dipped in water and wrung dry.

For satisfactory drying, care should be taken to avoid placing films or plates too close together, as this will prevent effective access and circulation of air, with the result that negatives will dry slowly from the edges, the centre being the last to dry. If a negative be removed to hasten the drying of the central damp patch, the latter will dry with distinctly greater density and form an irremovable mark. This effect is probably due to variation with drying rate of the packing, or orientation, of the grains in the emulsion layer. If, despite all precautions, it is found that, say, a row of plates on a rack is drying very slowly, no attempt should be made to remove the plates and dry them separately; the plates should be left to finish their drying naturally. Flat films and roll films are best dried by clipping them on a line in such a manner that they cannot touch one another if blown about by a draught.

Rapid drying by heat is not recommended except in properly designed drying cabinets; even if the films have been hardened, quick drying involves risk. Good circulation of clean air is much more expeditious than drying by heat. The air stream must not, however, be too violent – a steady current is all that is required. Under normal conditions, a roll film hung to dry about five feet from an electric fan will dry in about 20 to 30 minutes. Care must be taken to maintain the flow of air until drying is complete, for the reason explained above. A fan must not, of course, be used in a room where it is likely to raise dust. If there is a risk of this, it is a good plan to leave negatives to dry naturally overnight, when there is least likelihood of trouble from dust.

Where rapid drying of a large number of films is required, as for example in the x-ray department of a hospital, the use of heated drying cabinets is usual. When such cabinets are employed, it is desirable that ducting be used to lead to the outside of the building the heated moisture-laden air that emerges from the cabinet.

Glass negatives may be quickly dried by immersion for 2 or 3 minutes in a bath of industrial alcohol and water, containing not more than 80 per cent. alcohol. Such a bath should be used in ample quantity and frequently renewed, as it takes up water from each negative. These negatives can then be dried in a few minutes in a brisk current of air. The same procedure can be followed with films, although it should be noted that, if immersion of the film in the spirit is unduly prolonged, there may be a risk of obtaining streaky negatives, owing to action of the spirit on plasticizer in the film base.

Stabilization processing

A method of processing in which an exposed material is developed, "fixed" without intermediate rinsing, and then dried without washing has been evolved in recent years. In this process, known as *stabilization*, the silver halide remaining in the sensitive layer is converted into compounds which are relatively stable to light. It can be shown, in fact, that the image on an unwashed print is more stable than an incompletely washed print – although by no means as stable as a completely washed print. The fixing – or, rather, stabilizing – agent employed may be ordinary hypo, although many other compounds have also been suggested.

Stabilization processing has come to be widely used with the introduction of materials – in particular, papers (page 365) – in which a developing agent is incorporated in the emulsion. Such materials develop in a few seconds in caustic alkali and, by combining this rapid development with the use of a rapid-acting stabilizing agent, such as ammonium thiocyanate, semi-dry prints can be produced in as little as 10 seconds. The two solutions are applied to the material by immersion or surface application, in a machine through which the material is transported by rollers.

The life of stabilized prints is not as great as that of conventionally processed prints, but they will not normally show significant fading for some months and can, in any event, be fixed by normal methods at any time after stabilization.

Uses of wetting agents in photography

Wetting agents are compounds which, when added in small amounts to liquids, enable them to spread more easily. Their use is of value whenever a dry photographic surface has to be wetted or a wet surface has to be dried. Special wetting agents are available for photographic purposes. They are particularly useful:

(1) *For minimizing water marks when drying films or plates*
The washed films or plates should be immersed for about 1 minute in a bath containing wetting agent, and then placed to dry in the usual way.

(2) *For improving the glazing of prints*
The washed prints should be immersed for about 1 minute in a bath containing wetting agent, and then glazed in the usual way.

(3) *For promoting the flow of developers*
A few drops of wetting agent, added to the developer, will help to prevent the formation of airbells.

(4) *For facilitating the application of water colours, opaques, etc.*
A few drops of wetting agent should be added to the water used to make up the water colour, etc.

Photographic wetting agents are usually supplied as concentrated liquids, a few drops of which should be added to the solution concerned. Wetting agents are not usually suitable for addition to fixing baths.

CHAPTER 25

After-treatment of the Developed Image

TREATMENT of the image after processing is occasionally useful to correct, at least partially, errors in exposure and/or processing of black-and-white negative materials. The process of lowering the density of a developed image is referred to as *reduction* and that of increasing it as *intensification*.

Sometimes it may be desired to change the colour of a photographic image, be it on film, glass plate or on paper. The process of effecting such a change is referred to as *toning*.

Reduction

The process of reduction is concerned with the removal of some of the silver from the various parts of the image. Chemically it is not a process of reduction at all, but one of oxidation: the silver is converted into a soluble silver compound or into an insoluble compound which dissolves in some other constituent of the reducer.

Classification of reducers

Many reducers and intensifiers of differing performance have been evolved. They may usefully be classified in general types according to their relative action on the various densities of the image, best displayed by the characteristic curve. The nomenclature commonly adopted follows the general lines of a system described by R. Luther in 1910.

The main classes of reducers according to this sytem are as follows:

(1) *Proportional*

All the densities of the image are reduced in the same ratio (Figure 25.1a). The action of a proportional reducer may be regarded as "development in reverse".

444

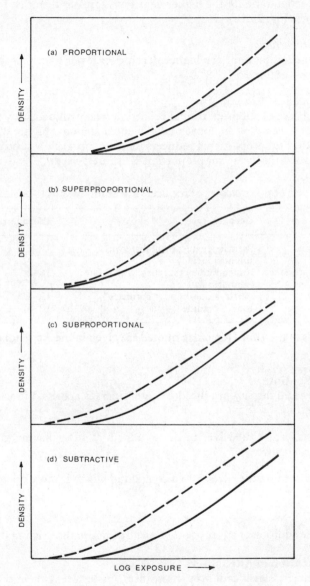

Fig. 25.1 – The effect of various types of reduction

(2) *Superproportional*
The reduction ratio for the higher densities is greater than that for the lower ones (Fig. 25.1b).

(3) *Subproportional*
The reduction ratio for the higher densities is lower than that for the lower ones (Figure 25.1c).

(4) *Subtractive* (*"cutting"*)
A special case of subproportional reduction where all densities of the image are lowered by an approximately equal amount (Figure 25.1d). All practical subproportional reducers tend to approach a subtractive action so that the term "subproportional" is rarely used.

Examples of these classes of reducers are as follows:

Class	Chemical type	Ilford formula
Porportional	Permanganate-persulphate with sulphuric acid	IR–3
Superproportional	Ammonium persulphate with dilute sulphuric acid	IR–2
Subtractive	Ferricyanide-hypo ("Farmer's")	IR–1
	Iodine-cyanide	IR–5

Details of the Ilford formulae quoted are given in the Appendix.

Intensification
The increased density produced by intensifiers is achieved in varying ways, e.g.:

(a) by converting the silver image to a form of silver having greater covering power,

(b) by converting the silver into a compound which is more opaque to light,
or

(c) by the addition of silver or other metal atoms to the existing image.

Classification of intensifiers
A convenient classification of intensifiers, in terms of their relative action on the various densities of the silver image is as follows:

(1) *Proportional*
All the densities of the image are increased in the same ratio (Figure 25.2a). The action of a proportional intensifier may be regarded as "increased development".

(2) *Superproportional*
The intensification ratio for the higher densities is greater than that for the lower ones (Figure 25.2b).

(3) *Subproportional*
The intensification ratio for the higher densities is lower than that for the lower ones (Figure 25.2c).

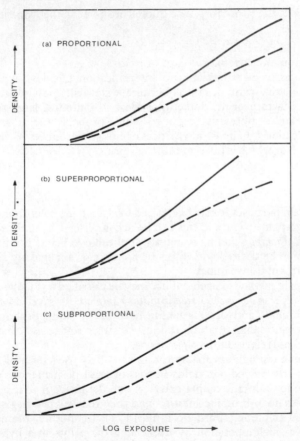

Fig. 25.2 – The effect of various types of intensification

Examples of these classes of intensifiers are as follows:

Class	Chemical type	Ilford formula
Proportional	Chromium	IIn–3
	Mercuric chloride – bromide bleach with silver nitrate – potassium cyanide redeveloper ("Monckhoven's")	IIn–4
Superproportional	Monckhoven's intensifier with slight excess of potassium cyanide in the redeveloping solution	—
Subproportional	Uranium	IIn–5

Details of the Ilford formulae quoted are given in the Appendix.

Reduction and intensification of prints

The processes of reduction and intensification find less application with prints than with negatives because it is usually possible to repeat an unsatisfactory print. Sometimes local reduction of large prints is justified and a subtractive reducer is then probably the most useful. Intensification by almost any process generally produces a change in image colour which is unacceptable in a print.

Toning

For certain purposes it may be desired to change the colour, or *tone*, of a photographic image, and this can be accomplished by various means of *chemical toning*. Toning is mainly applicable to prints but may also on occasion be desired with films or plates, e.g., for making slides or other forms of transparency.

The main methods in general use may be classified as follows:

(1) *The silver image is converted into silver sulphide (or silver selenide)*
Silver sulphide and silver selenide have brown and purple colours, much warmer than that of the usual silver image, so that these processes are referred to as *sepia toning*.

Sulphide toning is probably the most widely used form of toning, and properly carried out yields images of great permanence. Various formulae for sulphide toning exist: in one the image is first bleached in a ferricyanide-bromide solution and then redeveloped in a solution of sodium sulphide (Ilford Formula IT–1). In another, toning takes place in a single operation by immersing the prints in a hypo-alum bath at 50°C (Ilford Formula IT–2).

(2) *The silver image is replaced by means of a series of chemical reactions producing a compound of some other metal*

The compounds produced are usually ferrocyanides and the metals used have included:

Metal	Tone
Copper	Reddish-brown
Iron	Prussian blue
	(Ilford Formula IT–6)
Uranium	Orange-brown
Vanadium	Yellow

(3) *The silver image is replaced by means of colour development producing a dye image*

This process is essentially similar to the production of the dyes in the three layers of a colour film. Black-and-white prints produced in the normal way are bleached and redeveloped in a colour developer, i.e., a developing solution containing colour couplers (see Chapter 28). A wide range of tones may be produced by such processes of colour development.

CHAPTER 26

Faults in Negatives
and Prints

NEVER destroy a faulty negative until the cause of the fault has been ascertained. You will be wiser as the result of your investigation and may save yourself much trouble and annoyance in the course of further work.

It is, of course, impossible to mention *every* fault which may occur, but we propose to deal with as many as possible – usual and unusual. In order to facilitate identification, description of the appearance of the negative is given as a heading, and beneath it are listed the various faults which may be the cause of this appearance (see index on pages 464–7). Many faulty negatives are illustrated, but it will be appreciated that it is impossible to reproduce on paper the true appearance of any transparency and, moreover, with faults such as over-exposure and light-scatter, which are likely to produce very dense negatives, the density has been reduced in our reproductions so that the other characteristics of the negatives may be seen. At the same time, the illustrations will generally be found to give a better understanding of the nature of a particular kind of fault than the most careful description, and for this reason frequent reference should be made to them.

In arriving at the cause of any particular fault, the first step should be to narrow down the field of investigation by reference to the index on pages 464–7. By following up the references to text and illustrations in the index, it should be possible to classify the fault as one of exposure or of development, and then, from the evidence available, it should be a simple matter to identify the cause. The majority of faults can occur in *all* types of material, but where any faults are peculiar to, or most likely to occur with, one particular type of material or camera this fact is mentioned.

The cause of faulty negatives is rarely traceable to the material. Reputable photographic materials are made with such scrupulous care, and subjected to such rigorous testing, that it is rare indeed for even a minor defect to escape the vigilance of the examiners.

Unsharp negatives

Unsharpness is of several kinds. It may arise from the image being out of focus, due to misjudgement of distance, incorrect setting of the focusing scale or to approaching nearer than three metres from the subject when using a fixed-focus camera. More rarely the unsharpness may be due to a faulty focusing scale, incorrect register of the film or plate or to the components of the lens being misplaced. In the case of a miniature camera with coupled rangefinder and focusing scale, unsharpness may be due to the coupling being out of adjustment. This is unusual, but it may happen if the camera is dropped or knocked violently.

With reflex cameras and other cameras focused by means of a ground glass screen, unsharpness will result if the ground glass screen is removed and replaced with the ground side away from the lens. Frequently, some part of the subject will be sharp, but not the part which ought to have been in best focus.

Occasionally, when a folding camera has been used, fuzzy unsharpness may be found to exist more at one side of the picture than at the other. The fault is due to the front of the camera having been bent slightly forward or backward, or to its having become loose on its runners through wear, with resulting backward sag.

If the fuzziness exists more in the centre of the picture than at the sides, then the fault may be due to the camera (if of the folding type) having been opened too quickly, and the film sucked forward out of the plane of focus by the partial vacuum so formed.

Another kind of unsharpness is caused by unsteady holding of the camera during exposure, resulting in several images of the subject being recorded, each shifted slightly from the others. A magnifier will usually show these separate outlines, which serve to distinguish this kind of fuzziness from that mentioned above, as does also the fact that camera-shake generally causes unsharpness of everything in the picture. This can be prevented by holding the camera very steady and *pressing* the shutter instead of *jerking* it. A "time" exposure with the camera held in the hand will result in unsharpness from this cause.

The beginner who uses a miniature camera, and very often, too, an experienced photographer who has just changed to a miniature camera, may have trouble with camera-shake when using slow snapshot exposures – 1/30th second or longer. This is due to the fact that a degree of camera-shake which would pass unnoticed in a quarter-plate negative, is a serious fault in a negative measuring only 24 × 36 mm, which must subsequently be considerably enlarged. Miniature camera photography calls, in fact, for greater care and precision throughout.

Sometimes the blur caused by camera-shake will be found to exist over only a part of the negative. This may be due to one of two causes. In the case of a miniature camera, or reflex camera fitted with a focal-plane shutter, the shake may have occurred when the slit in the blind had already travelled across half the width of the film.

The alternative explanation, which is applicable to any type of camera, is that one hand of the photographer moved while the other remained still, thus one side of the camera moved more than the other – usually it is the hand which presses the shutter release which is the more likely to shake.

It should not be overlooked that camera-shake can occur when the camera is used on a tripod if there is any vibration due to wind, to a passing vehicle or to carelessness on the part of the photographer. If the tripod legs slip or slide, too, the same effect will be seen in the negative.

There is also another kind of unsharpness, which is really diffusion of a sharp image, and may be caused by dirt on the lens, or by the lens becoming clouded when brought from a cold atmosphere into a warm one. This produces a softness over the whole picture.

An unsharpness somewhat similar to camera-shake is obtained, in the case of moving objects, if the shutter is too slow; the image of the moving object has time to move on the film or plate while the shutter is open. This occurs chiefly with objects crossing the line of sight and, of course, affects the moving parts of the subject only.

This fault can be prevented in three ways:

(a) By giving a faster shutter speed and using a wider lens aperture.

(b) By swinging the camera carefully so that the image of the moving subject remains in the same place in the picture area, and the movement is imparted to the background. This technique – termed "panning"– helps to suggest speed and is a most effective trick.

(c) By standing near the line of approach of the subject.

There is no remedy for unsharpness of the negative, but it can often be covered to some extent by printing on a grained surface paper.

Thin negatives

Insufficient density of the negative as a whole arises from under-exposure or under-development (or both). Some idea of the cause may be obtained by noticing the occurrence of detail and the density of the highlights (sky) relative to the shadows. If there is detail everywhere, though faint in the shadows, and if the shadows are free from veil (almost clear when the negative is laid face down on white paper), the cause is under-development, i.e., for too short a time, or in a solution which is cold or partly exhausted. The negative is weak (thin, rather than flat) and clear. The chromium intensifier will increase the density to give very much the same effect as though development had been continued for the proper time.

If the negative shows detail throughout, including the shadows, but is veiled all over (so that the picture appears to be buried in fog when the negative is laid face down on paper), the cause is over-exposure followed by under-development. Beginners sometimes make the mistake of stopping development when they see the picture "going black". It is not easy to remedy an over-exposed and under-developed negative satisfactorily, but intensification will often make a marked improvement. Unless the negative is excessively thin, it is worth while to reduce it slightly with ferricyanide-hypo before intensifying. This requires considerable care, but the negative can then be intensified with a better chance of success.

If the negative is thin only in the half-tones and shadows, which are badly lacking in detail, but of fair density in the sky or other highlight, the cause is under-exposure. The negative may look hard, owing to the highlight density, but the other parts are wretchedly flat. It is made worse by the usual intensifier, but is often improved sufficiently to yield passable prints by treatment with the uranium intensifier.

In the case of negatives which are weak or flat from under-development, satisfactory prints can frequently be obtained by using a contrasty paper.

Dense negatives

Excessive density of negatives results from over-development, but the character of the negative varies very greatly according to whether the exposure has been reasonably correct, too much or too little. The means for improvement likewise differ in the respective cases.

In the case of negatives which have had reasonably correct exposure, over-development results in increased contrast. The heavier deposits grow more in density relative to the faint deposits in the shadows. The negative looks hard and grainy. If this contrast is excessive, the range of densities will be too great to be rendered in the print, which will then be lacking in gradation of either the lightest tones or the darkest ones. The remedy is to reduce the negative with a solution which, so to speak, will undo the action of the developer. No reducer does this exactly, but Farmer's reducer is fairly satisfactory if used very weak. The permanganate-persulphate reducer, though nearer the ideal in action, is more troublesome to make up.

In the case of over-exposure, continued development will give a negative which is very dense and black all over, yet may be as perfect as one correctly exposed, except that much longer time is required for printing. This arises from the latitude of the emulsion. But if exposure has been grossly excessive, the negative, though dense, will be flat. In either case it is best to treat with Farmer's reducer until density is reduced to a degree suitable for printing. For negatives judged to be of satisfactory contrast, the reducer should be used weak; if the negative is thought to be flat, a stronger solution should be used. (It is a good plan to make certain by taking a print before reducing.) Then, if necessary, the negative is brought to satisfactory contrast by intensification. Really extreme over-exposure may result in reversal of the negative to an imperfect positive.

Over-development of a negative which has been much under-exposed results in excessive density, chiefly in the highlight and heavier deposits, which become opaque and almost unprintable. The best reducer is ammonium persulphate, but it is often difficult to remedy a negative of this very hard or "chalky" character.

Fog

Fog – ranging from a thin uniform deposit (called "veil") which causes the negative to print flat, to a heavy one which obliterates the picture – may be due either to general action of light other than that from the lens, or to chemical action.

The condition of the edges of the film, or other portion protected from the action of light in the camera, provides a clue to the probable cause. If these, or parts of them, are practically free from fog, the cause must be sought among things which can possibly happen to the film in the camera, whereas fog which covers every part of the negative is probably due to action of light before or after exposure, or to chemical action.

Fog in the camera arises from gross over-exposure (e.g., use of a shutter set by accident to "time" instead of "instantaneous"); from the scattering of light caused by a dusty or dirty lens or reflection of light from the bellows (slight veil); from a scattering of the light which often occurs when the camera is pointed directly against a strong light; or from leakage of light into the camera, in which case the fog often occurs as a band or streak, the position of which gives some indication of the point of leakage, such as a loose-fitting camera back.

Fog or veil over the whole surface may arise from some accidental exposure to white light, or to unsafe darkroom light (handling films and plates too close to the lamp). Fog may even occur from exposure of negatives to white light before they are completely fixed, especially if a plain (not acid) fixing bath is used. Apart from improper action of light, wrongly compounded developer or the contamination of developer with fixer may cause the defect. Materials which show persistent fog should be tried with freshly compounded developing solutions. Fog along the edges of roll film is caused by the spool becoming loose, and light penetrating between the spool paper and the metal flanges of the spool. Such fog extends sometimes right across the width of the film.

Light fogging of miniature camera films while in the camera is unusual, but the possibility of light leakage in the cassette should never be overlooked. If a cassette with a velvet-edged light lock has been used several times and the nap flattened, light is likely to leak in and fog the film at the beginning.

As a rule nothing can be done to remove fog, whatever its cause.

General stain

Yellowish or brownish colour of negatives seldom occurs with modern emulsions and developers. When it does, the cause is almost always a stale or oxidized condition of the developer, due to the use of sulphite of poor quality, to a stock solution having been kept too long, to using a developer for too many films or plates, or to "forcing" a negative in the developer. It is most liable to occur with pyro, pyro-metol, and hydroquinone developers. When using hydroquinone developer, a yellow stain is liable to occur if negatives are not well rinsed between development and fixing. The acid fixing bath corrects the tendency to the occurrence of stain.

A very effective method of removing the heaviest developer stain is by use of the bleaching solution worked out some years ago by Ilford Limited, viz.:

Potassium permanganate	6g
Sodium chloride (common salt)	12·5g
Acetic acid, glacial	50 ml
Water to make	1000 ml

This solution oxidizes the stain to a soluble substance, and at the same time converts the silver image into silver chloride. The negative is immersed in it for ten minutes with constant rocking, rinsed and soaked in a solution of potassium metabisulphite (50 g in 1000 ml water) until the negative is white when viewed from the back. It is then re-developed fully with any normal M.Q. or P.Q. developer.

Owing to the very acid character of the bleach, it is well to harden the film first by immersion for a few minutes in a solution of chrome alum (10 g in 1000 ml water).

Dichroic fog

Dichroic fog is a stain which appears green when looked at and reddish when looked through. It is caused by contamination of developer with hypo, ammonia or other solvent of silver bromide or by keeping films in an impure atmosphere or by the use of alkaline hypo or by one film lying upon another in the hypo bath. It is removed by very weak Farmer's reducer.

Transparent spots

The two chief causes are air-bells clinging to the emulsion surface during development, and particles of dust on the emulsion surface during exposure and/or development. Spots of the two kinds may be distinguished by holding up the negative to the light and examining with a pocket magnifier. Spots from air-bells are all almost circular in shape. They generally arise from air-bubbles in the developer. Water drawn from pressure mains is usually highly aerated, and when used for diluting stock solutions is very liable to cause a crop of bubbles. For this reason as well as for chemical reasons it is most desirable to use boiled water for the preparation of photographic solutions.

Dust spots, under the magnifier, are seen to be of all kinds of shapes, much smaller than spots made by air-bells, and of sharp outline. The dust causing this trouble is almost always present in the camera before loading, and spool chambers, cassettes, film or plate holders, and the inside of the camera should regularly be wiped with a damp cloth. These spots are often caused by closing or opening cameras of the strut pattern very suddenly when an unexposed film is in place. Any dust on the inside of the bellows is forced on to the sensitive surface.

Clear spots on a negative may also be caused by dirty dishes or by impurities in tap water. Clear spots and "smudges" may be caused, too, by the adherence of scum to the surface of the emulsion during development. This scum is found on the surface of tank developers which have been much used, and should be removed with a strip of paper before films or plates are inserted. The formation of scum and oxidizing of the developer are greatly reduced if a floating lid is used.

Clear spots arising from causes other than the above are very seldom met with. Developer which has become stale from age or use, or is contaminated with wax or grease, is liable to cause light spots of irregular shape. In tropical countries, similar spots may be formed by bacteria which have found the damp gelatin a suitable culture medium. In temperate climates, cases are occasionally met with in which the gelatin coatings of negatives have been eaten into minute holes by insects.

Light spots of comet shape on a ground of heavy fog are also rare, and may be a puzzle until their cause is found. They arise from leakage of light from some point which causes rays to graze the emulsion surface. Particles of dust on the latter cast shadows which, in the negative, form the comet-like spots on the ground of fog.

Clear spots on negatives cannot be rectified other than by physical retouching.

Dark spots
Dark spots – caused by undissolved particles of the developing agent (amidol, hydroquinone, etc.) in the developing solution; settlement on the emulsion coating of particles of metol, amidol, etc., suspended in the air of the darkroom from previous weighings of the dry chemicals (spots produced by metol dust are very characteristic – they are clear with dark edges); dark, insoluble particles of oxidized developer formed in old or used developing solutions.

Particles of solid matter in tap water may also settle upon the gelatin emulsion and cause spots.

Yellow or brownish spots
The cause of spots of this type is air-bells still clinging to the emulsion surface in the fixing bath and thus obstructing the action of the hypo. If noticed soon after fixing, they can usually be removed by returning the negatives to the fixing bath, but since the air-bells will in all probability have been present in the developer the process of fixation will simply fix out the undeveloped silver bromide and leave clear spots.

Light bands and patches
Light bands and patches are usually less easy to diagnose than dark ones. Some of these defects are of very obscure origin. The following may be noted:

A light or clear band across one end of the negative usually means omission to draw the slide of the film or plate holder fully out or that the projecting baseboard of the camera is obscuring the field of view of the lens.

A clear patch on a roll film negative, with three straight edges and one irregular edge, may be due to the sealing paper having been torn off and having become lodged in the body of the camera. An irregular shaped patch may be caused by a small, loose fragment of such paper.

Band of lesser density along one side or end of the negative – fixed but unrinsed negative left projecting from the water in the washing tank. Patches of lighter density may also occur on film negatives left to fix with parts above the surface of the hypo bath.

Areas of lighter density may also be due to uneven flooding of the film with developer, the light areas having remained dry longer than the remainder. This is a common fault when only a very small quantity of developer is used.

Small, round light patches – finger tip markings – are produced if the emulsion is touched before development with slightly greasy or chemically contaminated finger tips. The finger print pattern usually provides a clue to the cause of this defect. Splashes of fixer on the sensitive material before development will cause clear patches or patches of lighter density.

If it is necessary to repack plates (e.g., between exposure and development), the original wrapping papers should be used. Exposed plates should never be stacked face to back between exposure and development, but always face to face and preferably with the separator slips replaced.

A light patch surrounded by an edge of greater density is likely to be a drying mark caused by a drop of water remaining on the emulsion after the remainder was dry. Drying marks may also be caused on film negatives by drops of water remaining on the base side. A blank, undefined area at one edge of the negative may be due to part of the picture being cut off by the photographer's finger over part of the lens. Blank areas at the corners of the negative are caused by the lens not covering fully: if only the top corners are affected the fault may be due to the use of excessive rising front. A fault of similar appearance may be caused by a badly fitting or unsuitable lens-hood.

When only a part of the end negative of a roll film is developed and the image ends with a more or less defined edge, the cause is insufficient solution in a vertical developing tank.

Blank areas or areas of low density on a roll film may be due to two films having been in contact during development, one film preventing the solution from reaching the other.

Dark bands and patches

Almost always, this type of fog is due to leakage of light into the camera. If the fog has the appearance of a ray originating at one edge of the film or plate, the cause may be sought in a small point of leakage somewhere in the camera back.

In a roll film camera, looseness of the camera back may be responsible while, in the case of a large format camera, a leakage in the film or plate holder, bad fitting of the holder, or worn condition of the velvet surfaced light traps, may cause the trouble.

A central circular patch of fog may be caused by accidental release of the shutter with the camera ("folding pocket" or miniature types) closed. Light penetration of the leaves of a between-lens shutter, if these are of ebonite, by long exposure to intense light (more liable to occur on panchromatic films or plates, which are sensitive to the reddish light transmitted by thin ebonite) will cause a similar defect. A round or oval patch may be a "flare spot", more especially if the picture has been taken against the light. Light reflected from bright metal parts inside the camera or in the lens or shutter may cause similar trouble.

Lens flare is comparatively rare, but scattering of light and reflection of the shape of the lens diaphragm are seen fairly frequently when pictures have been taken against the light. Because of the greater number of reflecting surfaces which they incorporate, compound lenses are more liable to produce this fault than simple lenses.

A patch of fog of irregular shape may be caused by pouring developer on to the centre of a plate while the plate is in the dish.

Splash markings of greater density may be caused by water or developer which has been splashed accidentally on to the sensitised material before development. Similar markings of rather less density may be caused by water splashing on to the dry negative.

Dark finger-print patterns occurring on the negative are caused by touching the sensitive material with developer-contaminated finger-tips before development.

Dark or degraded edges of the negative are caused by storage of the sensitive material in a damp place. The fault is usually accompanied by some degradation over other parts of the negative.

Irregularly shaped streak marks of greater density extending from the end (or ends) of a roll film for from six to nine inches are due to the film being held by the hands during development by the see-saw method. Developer warmed by the fingers runs down the film each time one end is raised and produces greater density in the parts it touches. To avoid this, always hold the ends of the film in non-corroding clips. Dirty or corroded clips, however, are liable to cause markings similar to those just described. Defined dark markings on a plate or flat film negative may be caused by contamination from a dirty developing dish.

A peculiar kind of fog may very occasionally be found on a plate which has been used in a new wooden dark-slide or has been in contact with the wooden surface of a drawer or bench. Frequently the wood grain is seen and the cause is chemically active substances in the wood. Nothing can be done to remove this fog from the negative, but it can be prevented by repainting the inside of the dark-slide "dead black". Paint containing turpentine must not be used, because this spirit is very liable to fog photographic emulsions.

Chemically active substances are also present in some printing inks and for this reason sensitised materials should never be wrapped in printed paper. The ink used to print lettering and numbers on the backing paper of roll films is made from substances which are inactive in this respect.

Yellowish or reddish patches, usually not occurring until some time (days or weeks) after the negative has been finished, are caused by incomplete fixation. In the case of films, they may be due to part of the negative floating above the surface of the fixing bath or to one film pressing on another. If the patch has a straight edge the latter cause is indicated.

Line markings

Fine, clear lines running the length of a band of roll film are caused by friction of the emulsion surface against rough guide rollers or against dust or grit on the latter; they may also be caused by the guide rollers being jammed and failing to revolve as the film is wound across them.

Similar "tram-lines" may occur along the length of a miniature camera film due to the film having been rolled or pulled too tightly, or to the velvet light trap of the cassette picking up grit which causes scratches as the film is drawn through the camera.

Irregular lines may be caused by the film being allowed to touch the working bench – almost any form of friction on the sensitive surface is liable to cause such abrasion marks. A tiny "arrowhead" mark may be caused by the film being allowed to "kink".

A dark line round an outline where (in the subject) dark objects come against a light background sometimes occurs in tank development when the solution is allowed to remain without movement for the whole period of development. Solution in contact with a heavy deposit becomes exhausted, while that on an adjoining light deposit (largely unexhausted) runs over to the former, adding further density all along the edge.

So-called "streamer" lines, i.e., bands of extra density running from the image of a narrow, dark object such as a chimney, a flagstaff, etc., result from downward diffusion of largely unexhausted solution in stagnant tank development. The same type of fault can occur when roll and miniature camera films are developed in spiral tanks, but in this case the streamers will run across the *width* of the film and, with miniature films, are likely to be most intense adjacent to the perforations. Streamers will not occur unless the agitation of the developer is insufficient. To prevent this fault, the spool bearing the film must be rotated at regular intervals throughout the course of development. (See also page 421.)

The cause of tangle markings, i.e., a tangle of dark lines, sometimes covering the entire negative, is a pinhole in the body or between-lens shutter of the camera. On carrying the latter about in bright sunlight, the pinhole forms an image of the sun on the emulsion surface, and the position of this image changes continuously as the position of the camera changes. The result is a continuous line, running here and there, according to the directions in which the camera was pointed. When lighting is diffused, the indication of a pinhole in the bellows will be small, dark patches on the negative, with heavy centres and undefined edges. A pinhole in the blind of a focal-plane shutter will cause a line of slightly greater density across the negative.

Short "hair-line" marks occurring all over roll film negatives are called "cinch marks", and are caused by winding the spool too tightly after removing it from the camera and before sealing.

Halation

Halation takes the form of a spread of density from the image of bright parts of the subject on to surrounding portions, obliterating detail in the latter. Common examples are the blur of fog round the windows in interiors and from the image of the sky on to that of tree branches. It is largely prevented by the use of backed films and plates.

Irradiation

Irradiation may also occur in such cases. This is due to reflection of the image of a bright part of the subject *within* the sensitive emulsion and, of course, backing is powerless to prevent it. Negatives showing halation or irradiation are difficult to remedy, but can be improved in many cases by rubbing down the affected parts with a fine abrasive preparation such as Frictol, or by bleaching as for chromium intensification, washing thoroughly and developing for a short time only in a strong developer. The negative is then re-fixed and washed.

Positive instead of negative

At times, the image (when finished in the usual way) will appear as a positive instead of a negative; usually a greatly fogged positive. Frequently, part only of the subject is positive and the remainder negative. The reversal is generally caused by "forcing" an under-exposed film or plate by protracted development in an unsafe darkroom light (see page 423). The defect is very seldom met with, but cases sometimes occur in which one or two negatives on a spool of film are perfect, while the others are reversed, the exposure to the darkroom light having been greater in the part of the spool affected.

Reticulation

Reticulation takes the form of a fine irregular grain which occurs over the whole negative, but is most pronounced in the heavier densities. It arises from a physical change in the gelatin caused by sudden swelling on transference from a cold to a warm solution, or by sudden contraction when transferred from a warm to a cold solution.

Frilling and blisters

These defects are manifestations of poor adhesion of emulsion to the base. Frilling usually occurs at the edges whereas blisters may be found at any point on the surface of the negative. Neither trouble is likely to be met with except perhaps when processing is carried out under the worst tropical conditions and when the various solutions are used at widely different temperatures. Frilling may, however, be caused by transference of negatives from a strongly alkaline to a strongly acid bath, and may also result if negatives are held by the edges with warm fingers.

Blisters can be largely removed by pricking with a needle when the emulsion is half dried. Frilling can be corrected to some extent by replacing the loosened emulsion carefully so that it will dry in position.

Mottle

This may be caused by age deterioration of the sensitive material, by deterioration caused by chemical fumes or by exposure to the air as in the case of a roll film left in a camera for a period of months. Another form of mottle may be caused by the growth of bacteria or fungus in the gelatin in hot and humid climates. Stagnant developer is the cause of yet another type of mottle.

A mottle which is more or less defined all over the picture will arise if a backed plate is inserted into the dark-slide the wrong way round, so that the light forming the image has to pass through the backing before reaching the emulsion – the picture will also be reversed left to right. Similar mottling will occur if a backed plate is left face downwards on the darkroom bench long enough for the darkroom lamp to fog the emulsion.

Dull image

When the dullness of the image is due to insufficient density of the negative and to a certain amount of veil which extends over the margins, the cause is probably exhausted or contaminated developer. The presence of stain on the negative confirms this. This dullness also may be due to incorrect compounding of the developer. The weakness of the developer is responsible for the weakness of image, and "forcing" or contamination of the solution is liable to produce the chemical fog and stain. Such a negative can be improved by *slight* reduction followed by chromium intensification.

Dullness of the image of a negative of good density may be due to inadequate fixation. Undissolved silver salts remain in the negative and obscure the clear parts. Re-fixing and washing is usually successful.

Dullness of the image may also be due to dichroic fog, which is dealt with on page 456, or to veiling of the picture by slight general light fog, to scatter from the lens or to chemical fog.

Do not overlook the possibility of dullness being due simply to over-exposure or to under-development, which are explained on pages 452–4. The subject, too, may have been poorly and flatly lit, when only a dull reproduction can be expected.

Other faults

The reasons for some photographic failures are so obvious that they need hardly be described. For example, the blurring and mingling of the image which occurs when the emulsion melts is unmistakable and can be attributed only to the use of hot solutions or to drying at too high a temperature.

If the picture slants within the picture space and this fault is found to occur frequently, it is likely that the viewfinder of the camera is bent or, if of the swivelling type, may not have been fully turned into position.

When pictures overlap on a roll film the fault is under- or over-winding. This may be met with in cameras giving 12 exposures on No.120 roll film if the winding indicator is not very precise.

Torn and/or cockled edges of a roll film are caused by misalignment in the camera. Often this fault is accompanied by edge fog, due to light entering where the spool paper was torn. The misalignment may be due to a bent or broken spool chamber spring, or to one or both of the small guide rollers being bent or moved cut of the true position owing to wear of the bearing ends.

One must not be dismayed by the foregoing formidable list of the failures which may occur in negative making. The aim has been to put into small compass descriptions of most of the defects which may arise, not excepting many which are of most uncommon occurrence and all the more puzzling on that account.

Index to faults in negatives

The index on the following pages is included to assist you in the speedy identification of negative faults. It must, however, be used in conjunction with the general evidence in your possession – type of material, type of camera used, etc. It attempts to sum up, very briefly, the information given in the foregoing pages, and reference should be made to these pages, and to the following illustrations.

Appearance of negative	Fault	Information	Illustration
		Page	Page
Unsharpness			
Fuzzy definition	Out of focus	451	470
Blurred all over	Movement of camera	451	472
Blurred image of part of subject	Movement of subject	452	470–1
Too dense all over			
Flat and much shadow detail	Over-exposure	454	472
Contrasty	Over-development	453	472
Too thin all over			
Lacking shadow detail	Under-exposure	452	471
With shadow detail but lacking contrast	Under-development	452	471
Dark markings			
Dark areas with images of lens diaphragm	Light scatter	454	473
Black "blobs" with images of lens diaphragm	Lens flare	459	
Black "splashes"	Light leak in camera	454, 459	473
"Splashes" of greater density	Water or developer splashes before or after development	459	475

Appearance of negative	Fault	Infor-mation	Illus-tration
Dark markings (continued)		Page	Page
Black finger marks	Developer-contaminated finger tips	459	
Black edges (roll film)	Edge fog	455	474
Black circle in centre	Accidental exposure with folding camera closed	459	473
Dark or degraded edges	Damp storage	459	474
Uneven dark streaks	Dirty dishes	460	474
Black streaks, usually from one corner	Light leaks in holder, adapter or camera back	454, 459	476
Fine black lines	Abrasion marks		476
Dark streamers from light parts of negative extending on to dark parts	Tank development – insufficient agitation	461	477
Black spots	Chemical dust	457	477
Dark ribbon-like tangle	Sun tracks	461	476
Tiny dark ↓ -shaped mark, accompanied by dimpling of film negative	Kink mark	460	
Very short, rather faint hair lines close together all over roll film negative	Cinch marks	459	
Dark streamer marks, intense at end of roll film and fading off down length of the film	Chemical fog caused by dirty film clips or holding film with fingers during development	459	
Wood grain markings	Fog from wooden dark-slide	460	478
Printed characters superimposed on image	Newsprint fog	470	478
Light markings			
Clear areas or areas of lower density	Fixer contamination	458	475
Sharply defined blank area	Paper in camera	458	478
Clear finger marks	Greasy or contaminated fingers	458	475
Sharply defined irregular areas of lesser density	Uneven covering with developer	458	478
Irregular clear spots	Developer scum	456	478
Picture fades into transparency at corners	Lens not covering	458	482
Clear scrape marks – emulsion removed	Abrasion by finger nail or by other negatives		480
Emulsion removed or loosened at edges	Frilling	462	480
Large spot of lighter density with greater density at edges	Drying mark	458	481

Appearance of negative	Fault	Infor- mation Page	Illus- tration Page
Light markings (*continued*)			
Line of lighter density	Loose thread on blind of focal plane shutter		482
Irregular lines of lighter and greater density	Too vigorous brushing before development		479
Irregular shaped small clear spots	Dust on material during exposure	456	484
Round spot either clear or of lighter density	Air-bells during development	456	481
Undefined clear area at one edge of negative	Hand partly covering lens	458	482
Clear curved margin at one of the longer edges of roll film negative taken with bellows-type camera	Cut-off due to rapid opening of camera		483
Mottle			
Dappled marking which can be seen also by reflected light	Old material	462	
Defined mottle without physical marking of surface	Exposure or fog through backing	462	485
Defined pattern with physical marking of surface	Reticulation	462	483
Irregular streaky mottle	Insufficient agitation during development		485
Dull image			
Insufficient density with some veil over shadows	Exhausted developer	463	484
Brownish appearance of back	Inadequate fixation	463	484
Reddish stain when looked through – greenish stain when looked at	Dichroic fog	456	
Obscuration of the picture to a greater or lesser extent	Light fog or chemical fog	454	
Distortion			
Converging upright lines	Camera tilt		486
Exaggerated perspective	Short focus lens used too near subject		486
Miscellaneous faults			
Dark halo around highlights	Halation or irradiation	461	487
Two images on same negative	Double expsoure		486

Appearance of negative	Fault	Infor-mation	Illus-tration
		Page	Page
Miscellaneous faults (continued)			
Blurring and mixing of the image accompanied by irregularities in emulsion surface	Melting of emulsion	463	487
Positive or partial positive instead of negative (normal density)	Reversal due to fogging by unsafe darkroom lamp during development	462	488
Positive or partial positive instead of negative (extreme density)	Reversal caused by extreme over-exposure	454	489
Picture slanting on negative	Bent viewfinder	463	
Two images over part of the negative	Over- or under-winding of film spool	463	487
Torn or cockled edges (roll film)	Misalignment in camera	463	

Faults in prints

Abrasion or stress marks

These defects, in the form of fine lines, hair-like markings or grey patches, sometimes make their appearance when the sensitive paper has been roughly handled before development. The printing apparatus may have some protruding metal part, or the corner or edge of the negative may have scratched the emulsion surface. To remove the dark markings, pass the prints through a weak reducer such as ferricyanide and hypo or rub the surface of the dry prints with a soft rag dipped in a mixture of equal parts of methylated spirit and ammonia.

Blisters

These may be caused by wide variations in temperature of developer, fixing bath and washing water, by too strong a fixing bath or by too long immersion in it. Blisters on sulphide-toned prints may be caused by too strong a sulphide solution. Hypo-alum toned prints may blister if the prints are put straight from the hot toning bath into cold washing water instead of through an intermediate bath of tepid water. Mechanically produced blisters are caused by creasing or folding the paper, or by the strong local action of water in washing.

Colour of image unsatisfactory

Prints on bromide or contact papers which are greenish in colour indicate under-development following over-exposure, too great a proportion of potassium bromide in the developer or too much dilution of the developer. The latter, especially, applies to contact papers.

Contrast excessive or lacking

Excessive contrast generally indicates the use of the wrong grade of paper. Specially soft grades of paper are made for printing from hard or contrasty negatives. Excessive contrast may also be caused by under-exposure and over-development of the print.

When contrast is lacking, the cause may also be the wrong choice of paper. Thin, flat negatives require printing on hard or contrasty papers and will give prints of normal contrast in this way. Another cause of poor contrast is the use of a partially exhausted or improperly compounded developer, or the use of a developer at too low a temperature. Poor contrast may also be caused by over-exposure, followed by short development.

Deposits on dry prints

When caused by the use of hard water the deposit can usually be removed by wiping the surface of the wet print before drying. Prints which have been insufficiently washed after fixing may show a deposit of white powder or crystals. Prints toned in the hypo-alum bath may dry with a bad surface unless well sponged when removed from the toning solution. Sulphide-toned prints will show patchy alkaline deposits if inadequately washed after toning. Deposits can also be removed mechanically by applying to the surface of the dry print a little metal polishing paste on a piece of soft rag, followed by polishing with a clean rag. Beeswax dissolved in petrol, or ordinary wax floor polish, will often improve a bad surface.

Fading or tarnishing

Incomplete removal of the unused silver salts by the fixing bath or failure to remove all the hypo may cause fading or tarnishing. Impurities in the mount or the use of an acid mountant may also cause fading. Keeping the prints in an impure atmosphere may cause yellowing or tarnishing.

Fog or degraded whites

A grey veil over the surface of a print may be caused by:

(a) Exposure to light or an unsafe darkroom light before or during printing or developing.

(b) Prolonged development beyond the usual time, or with the developer at too high a temperature.

(c) Using an incorrectly made up developer, or one with insufficient potassium bromide.

(d) Storing the sensitive paper in an unsuitable place.

Mottle or patches
Bad storage of the sensitive paper, or failure to keep the print moving in the developer, fixing or other bath, may cause these defects. In the case of prints on contact papers, patches are usually caused by failure to move the developed prints as soon as they are first placed in the fixing bath, especially if the acid content of the fixer is exhausted.

Spots
White spots, other than those caused by defects on the negative, are the result of air-bells forming on the surface of the print during development. Particles of chemicals, either as dust or solution, particularly of hypo, falling on the surface of the paper may cause black or white spots. Dark spots are usually caused by air-bells during fixing.

Stains
The yellow stains which sometimes make their appearance, particularly on contact papers, are caused by prolonged development, by too long exposure to the air between development and fixation, by imperfect fixing or by insufficient acid in the fixing bath. A mere trace of hypo in the developer or on the fingers when handling the print previous to development may cause stains.

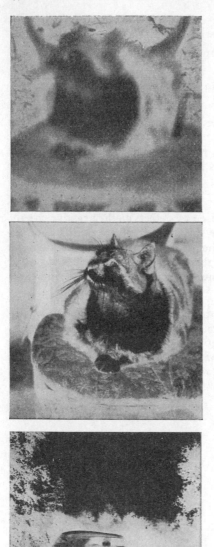

1 Image out of focus

When a simple "fixed-focus" camera is used, the subject must not be nearer than 3 metres from the camera, or the picture will have this appearance.

2 Image brought into focus

If a portrait attachment is fitted to a "fixed-focus" camera it is then possible to approach to 1 metre from the subject to obtain a sharp image.

3 Movement of subject

The shutter exposure must be brief enough to "arrest" the image of any moving parts of the picture area. In this case the car was travelling at 30 km/h and was photographed in 1/30th second.

4 Movement of subject

The car was also travelling at 30 km/h when this picture was taken, but a shutter exposure of 1/125th second has given a reasonably sharp image.

5 Thin negative

Caused in this case by **under-exposure.** There is little shadow detail in the negative and only the highlights are recorded.

6 Thin negative

Caused in this case by **under-development.** It is characteristic that shadow detail is present, but that the highlights lack adequate density.

7 Dense negative

The denseness here is caused by **over-exposure.** There is an abundance of shadow detail, but the very dense negative is flat.

8 Dense negative

In this case the negative is **over-developed,** and although it is much denser than the normal the outstanding characteristic is extreme contrast.

9 Camera movement

This is undoubtedly the most common photographic fault, and is caused by the camera being held unsteadily at the moment of exposure. (The car in this picture was stationary.)

10 Light-fogged areas

Light-fogged areas like this are caused by scattering of the light by reflection from the air-glass surfaces of the lens when the camera is pointed directly against strong light.

11 Accidental exposure

This circular black patch is characteristic of accidental exposure with a folding camera, with the bellows closed. The accidental exposure may not be noticed at the time, but the next picture taken will show this defect.

12 Light leak in camera

Rays of light may enter a pinhole in the bellows of a folding camera and produce characteristic areas of light fog like this. The defect, however, may appear only occasionally, many negatives taken in the same camera being unblemished.

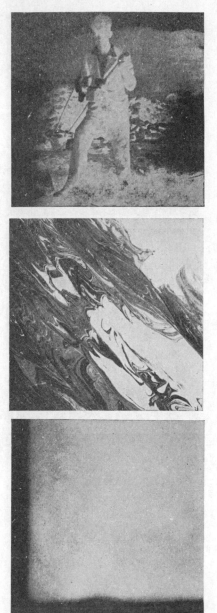

13 Edge fog

Due to loose winding of a roll film. Light has penetrated between the edges of the backing paper and the metal ends of the spool.

14 Dirty dish markings

These are caused by a form of contamination from residual chemical impurities remaining in the bottom of a dish, or having been absorbed into the material of which the dish is made.

15 Damp storage

Damp storage may result in fogging around the edges of the material when developed, and is often accompanied by veil or mottle all over the negative.

16 Fixer contamination

Splashes of fixer have fallen on the surface of the material before development and removed some of the sensitive silver salts.

17 Water splashes

Marks caused by water splashes on the sensitive emulsion before development.

18 Finger marks

These are caused by handling the sensitive material with greasy or chemically contaminated fingers before development.

19 Abrasion marks

If sensitised material is scratched or scraped, a line or mark will appear on development. In extreme cases a little of the emulsion may actually be removed.

20 Loose camera back

Marks like this are due to light fog caused by loose fitting of the camera back or film or plate holder. Similar markings may be caused when replacing the sheath of a film or plate holder by inserting one corner first.

21 Sun tracks

This tangle of ribbon-like markings is caused by the image of the sun formed by a pinhole in the camera body or bellows. This image moves about as the camera is carried.

22 Chemical dust

Chemical dust which may be floating in the atmosphere may settle on the sensitive surface of the material and produce spots like these on development. Never prepare developing solutions in the darkroom.

23 Water splashes

Water splashes on the negative after drying.

24 Development streamers

Insufficient agitation of 35 mm films during development in a spiral tank may produce this effect.

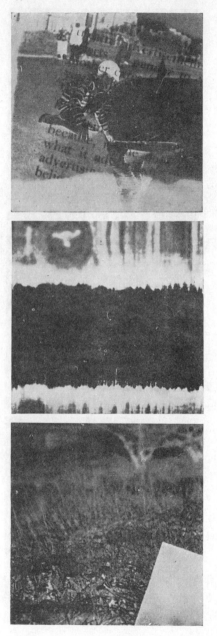

25 Newsprint fog

Many printing inks are chemically active and can cause this characteristic fogging. Therefore, films and plates should never be wrapped in newspaper. Special inactive printing inks have to be used for the numbering and printing of roll film backing papers.

26 Fog from wood

Caused by chemical action from the wood of a new wooden dark-slide.

27 Loose paper masking

Due to the presence of paper inside the camera. Loose roll film banding labels or plate separator slips are the most frequent causes of this trouble.

28 Uneven development

These areas of light density are characteristic of the use of insufficient developer. The material is not fully covered by the solution at once, and some parts receive more development than others.

29 Scum

Scum on the surface of the developer may cling to the surface of the emulsion in places and prevent the action of the developer. The illustration also shows light fog caused by a defective dark-slide.

30 Brush marks

Brush marks caused by too vigorous use of the dusting brush on a plate before exposure or before development.

31 Abrasion marks

Abrasion marks may be caused on roll film or miniature camera film when tension of the film across the guide rollers is too great, or when there may be friction of the sensitive surface with part of the camera body or cassette, or with grit on the velvet light trap of a cassette. In some instances the marks are light; in others dark.

32 Abrasion during washing

An area of the gelatin emulsion removed by scraping with a finger nail or the edge of another film or plate.

33 Frilling

This is caused by the edges of the emulsion becoming loosened from the support, owing to careless handling in warm weather, to the use of hot solution, or to washing in a strong current of water. The trouble is almost exclusively confined to plates.

34 Air-bell marks

Tap water is often highly aerated, and air-bells may form on the surface of the sensitive material, thus preventing the developer from reaching it at those points.

35 Air-bell marks magnified

This is what air-bell marks look like when viewed through a magnifier.

36 Drying marks

These may occur when the negative is taken directly from the washing water and dried by heat. Isolated drops of water keep small areas of the emulsion wet for a time, after the rest of the material is dry, and uneven contraction of the gelatin will result in marks such as that seen in the sky of this negative. They may be avoided by careful swabbing of the emulsion surface when the material is removed from the washing water.

37 Cut-off

This is due to the lens not fully covering the area of the sensitive material, and is caused by the use of excessive rising front movement (cut-off at top corners), or by the use of a lens of insufficient covering power (cut-off at all four corners).

38 Cut-off

Due to the hand being held partly over the lens during exposure.

39 Loose thread on focal-plane shutter

A loose thread on a focal-plane shutter may trail across the sensitive material, causing a line to receive less exposure than the remainder. A light line results (between the leading aeroplanes). Conversely a pinhole in the shutter blind causes a dark line.

40 Bellows vacuum

If a folding roll film camera is erected with a jerk a partial vacuum may be formed inside, causing the sides of the bellows to cave in. This may be unnoticed at the time, and part of the picture is consequently cut off.

41 Reticulation

This occurs when the negative is removed from a very warm solution and placed directly into a cold one. The gelatin emulsion which has expanded is suddenly contracted. This sudden contraction is uneven, and produces a crinkled surface all over the negative.

42 Reticulation

This is the appearance of reticulation when the negative is examined with a magnifier.

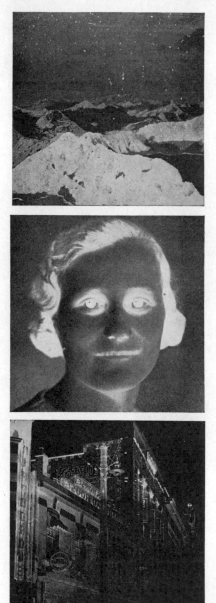

43 Dust

Dust on the sensitive material during exposure prevents light action and results in clear spots on the negative.

44 Stale or exhausted developer

The developing action is too weak to give adequate density to the highlights and is also likely to cause a deposit over the shadows by chemical fog.

45 Inadequate fixation

Inadequate fixation is characterised by a brownish appearance of the back of the negative.

46 Irregular density

Irregular density such as is seen here is the result of the developer being insufficiently mixed, of insufficient agitation of the solution during dish development, or a combination of both causes.

47 Exposure through backing

Due to loading a plate in the dark-slide incorrectly, with the backed surface facing outward.

48 Fogging through backing

Caused by exposure to an unsafe darkroom lamp, through the backing of a plate. When a plate is exposed back to front in the camera similar mottle appears, but without veiling of the shadows (see illustration above).

49 Camera tilt

When the camera is tilted in order to include the whole of a tall subject, distortion like this will result; it can be avoided by setting the camera quite level and using the rising front movement. If rising front is not available the camera should be held level and moved further away from the subject until the top is included.

50 Foreshortening

This exaggeration of perspective is caused by the use of a camera with a short focus lens very near to the subject. It can be avoided by using a more distant viewpoint; a correspondingly smaller image is obtained if the same lens is used, but a larger image can be obtained with a lens of longer focal length.

51 Double exposure

Caused by failure to wind on a roll film, or to change a film or plate holder.

52 Partial double exposure

Due to over-winding or under-winding a roll film or miniature camera film, and caused by carelessness in winding or possibly by inaccuracy of the winding device.

53 Halation

This is caused by rays of strong light passing right through the film or plate, and being reflected from the back surface of the support. The reflected image exceeds the boundaries of the true image, and forms a halo of density around it.

54 Melting

The sad fate of a negative dried by the use of excessive heat.

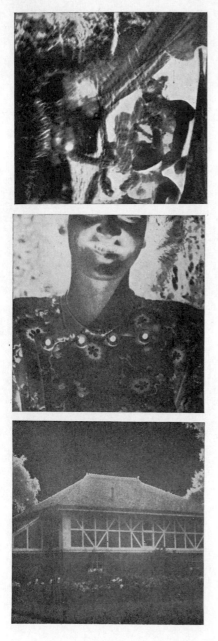

55 Melting

Melting due to using the hot water tap by mistake when washing.

56 Untruthful viewfinder

Incorrect aiming of the camera caused by bent viewfinder or incomplete erection of a folding finder.

57 Reversal

Caused by an unsafe darkroom lamp. A faint negative image is developed before fogging starts, and this image is then "printed" by the unsafe light on to still sensitive silver salts beneath it. Thus the "negative" is partly negative and partly positive.

58 Reversal

Partial reversal (note the sky) caused by extreme over-exposure.

CHAPTER 27

Principles of Colour Photography

Colour vision

More than three hundred years ago Newton discovered that sunlight could be made to yield a variety of colours by allowing it to pass through a triangular glass prism. A narrow beam of sunlight was *dispersed* into a band showing the colours of the rainbow. These colours represent the visible spectrum, and the experiment is shown diagrammatically in Figure 27.1. It was later found that recombination of the dispersed light by means of a second prism gave white light once more.

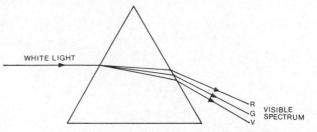

WHITE LIGHT

R
G
V

VISIBLE
SPECTRUM

Fig. 27.1 – Dispersion of white light by a prism

Later experiments showed that by masking off parts of the spectrum before recombination, a range of colours could be produced. Young in England, and Helmholtz in Germany showed that if small parts of the spectrum were selected in the blue, green and red regions, then a mixture of appropriate amounts of blue, green and red light appeared white. Variation of the blue, green and red contents of the mixture resulted in a wide range of colours. Almost any colour could be produced, including *magenta*, which did not appear in the visible spectrum. The results of mixing blue, green and red light are listed in Table 27.1 and illustrated in Figure 27.2.

490

Colours of light mixed	Visual appearance
Blue + green	Blue-green, or *cyan*
Blue + red	Magenta
Green + red	Yellow
Blue + green + red	White

Table 27.1 – Mixing blue, green and red light

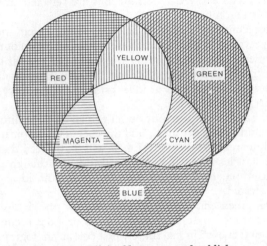

Fig. 27.2 – Mixing blue, green and red light

The results of mixing blue, green and red light suggested that the human eye might possess three types of colour sensitivity, to blue, green and red light respectively. This triple sensitivity theory is called the *Young-Helmholtz theory of colour vision*. It provides a fairly simple explanation for the production of any colour from an appropriate mixture of blue, green and red light.

The colours blue, green and red are called *primary colours* because the other colours can be matched by mixing the appropriate proportions of these primaries.

Colour reproduction

The colours of most objects around us are due to a multitude of dyes and pigments. No photographic process exists which can form an image from these original colorants, but colour photography can produce an acceptable *reproduction* of colours in the original scene. Such a reproduction reflects or transmits mixtures of light which appear to match the original colours although in general they do not have the same spectral energy distributions. Different spectral energy distributions which give rise to an identical visual sensation are termed *metamers,* or *metameric pairs.*

Because of this phenomenon of metamerism it is only required that a colour photograph shall be capable of giving appropriate mixtures of the three primary colours. We shall now consider the methods by which blue, green and red spectral bands are selected and controlled by colour photographs.

The most convenient way of selecting blue, green and red light from the spectrum for photography is to use suitable colour filters. We may thus select bands in the blue, green and red regions of the spectrum, and this selective use of colour filters is illustrated in Figure 27.3 which shows the action of ideal primary colour filters, and their spectral energy distributions.

The spectral density distributions of primary colour filters available in practice differ from the ideal, and the curves of a typical set of such filters are illustrated in Figure 27.4. It will be noticed that the filters shown transmit less light than the ideal filters, although the spectral bands transmitted correspond quite well with the ideal filters previously illustrated.

The blue, green and red filters available for photography are thus able to give three separate records of the original scene, and such filters were in fact used in making the first colour photograph.

The first colour photograph

Clerk Maxwell in 1861 prepared the first three-colour photograph as an illustration to support the three-colour theory of colour vision. He took photographs of some tartan ribbon through a blue, a green and a red filter in turn, and then developed the three separate negatives. Positive lantern slides were then produced by printing the negatives, and the slides were projected in register. Provided the positive corresponding to a particular taking filter was projected through a filter of similar colour, the three registered images together formed a successful colour reproduction and a wide range of colours was perceived. Maxwell's process is shown diagrammatically in Figure 27.5.

Methods of colour photography which involve the use of primary colour filters at the viewing stage, in similar fashion to Maxwell's process, are called *additive* methods. In the context of colour photography the colours blue, green and red are sometimes referred to as the *additive primaries.*

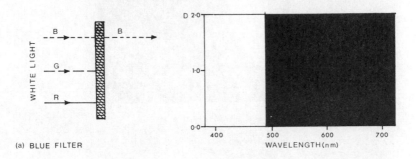

(a) BLUE FILTER

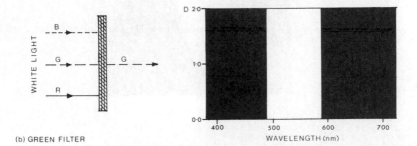

(b) GREEN FILTER

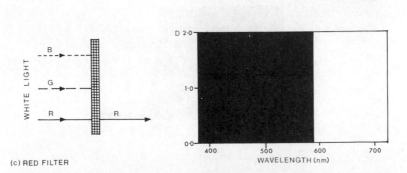

(c) RED FILTER

Fig. 27.3 – The action of ideal blue, green and red filters, and the corresponding spectral density distributions

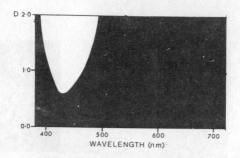

(a)   BLUE FILTER

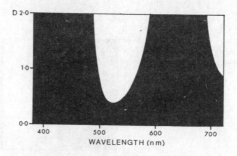

(b)   GREEN FILTER

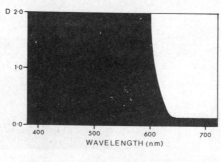

(c)   RED FILTER

Fig. 27.4 – The spectral density distributions of primary colour filters used in practice

In Maxwell's process the selection of spectral bands at the viewing stage was made by the use of saturated primary colour filters. The control of the amount of each primary colour projected onto the screen was achieved by means of the silver image developed in the positive lantern slide.

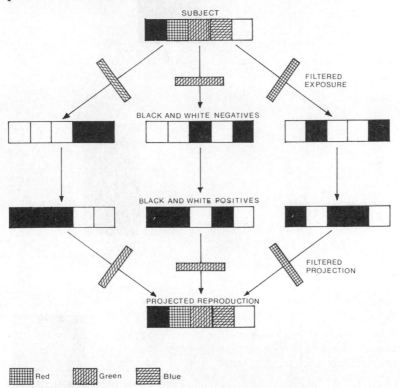

Fig. 27.5 – Maxwell's method of colour photography

An alternative approach to the selection of spectral bands for colour reproduction is to utilise the complementary colours yellow, magenta and cyan to absorb independently light of the three primary colours – blue, green and red. The action of ideal complementary filters is shown in Figure 27.6.

Whereas the ideal primary colour filters illustrated in Figure 27.3 may transmit up to one-third of the visible spectrum, it will be seen that complementary colour filters transmit up to two-thirds of the visible spectrum – they *subtract* only one-third of the spectrum.

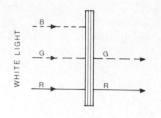

(a) YELLOW FILTER

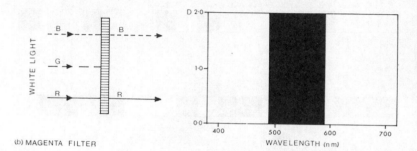

(b) MAGENTA FILTER

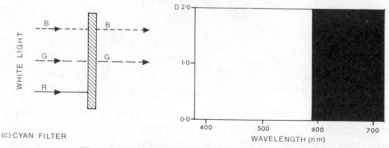

(c) CYAN FILTER

Fig. 27.6 – Ideal yellow, magenta and cyan filters

As with primary colour filters, the complementary colour filters available in practice do not possess ideal spectral density distributions, and examples of such filters are shown in Figure 27.7.

Combinations of primary colour filters appear black because they have no common bands of transmission, so such combinations cannot

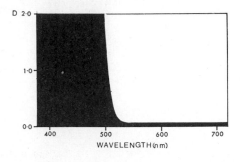

(a)   YELLOW FILTER

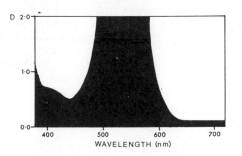

(b)   MAGENTA FILTER

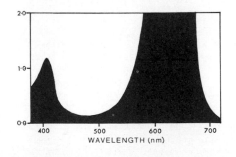

(c)   CYAN FILTER

Fig. 27.7 – Typical yellow, magenta and cyan filters

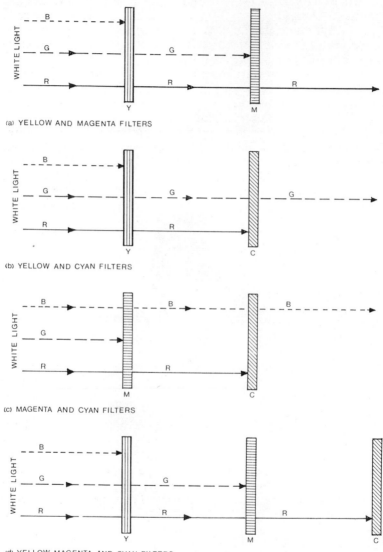

(a) YELLOW AND MAGENTA FILTERS

(b) YELLOW AND CYAN FILTERS

(c) MAGENTA AND CYAN FILTERS

(d) YELLOW MAGENTA AND CYAN FILTERS

Fig. 27.8 – Combinations of complementary colour filters

be used to control the colour of transmitted light. With the complementary colour filters the situation is quite different. Despite the imperfections of practical complementary filters it remains substantially true that each absorbs only about one-third of the visible spectrum. Consequently such filters may be used in combination to control the colour of transmitted light. The effect of combining complementary colour filters is shown in Figure 27.8.

In principle, the positive lantern slides used in Maxwell's additive method of colour photography can be made as positive dye images. If we make the colour of each positive complementary to that of the taking filter – the positive record derived from the negative made using a blue filter being formed by a yellow dye and so on – then the three positives can be superimposed in register and projected using only one projector. Such methods, which involve the use at the viewing stage of dyes which *subtract* blue, green and red light from the visible spectrum, are called *subtractive* processes. The preparation of a subtractive colour reproduction from blue, green and red light records is illustrated in Figure 27.9.

We have examined the principles of operation of the *additive* and the *subtractive* methods of colour photography, and will now consider the operation of some practical examples of each type of process.

Additive processes

As we have seen, the first three-colour photograph was made in 1861 by an additive process. The viewing system alone required the use of three projectors and the entire process was too unwieldy for general photography.

By the first decade of the twentieth century, however, an ingenious application of the additive system made possible the production of plates yielding colour photographs by a single exposure in a conventional camera.

In order to achieve analysis of the camera image in terms of blue, green and red light, the exposure was made through a mosaic, or *reseau*, comprising very many blue, green and red filter elements. Depending on the manufacturer, the reseau was either integral with the photographic material, or, in some cases, was placed in contact with it. Materials which employed an integral reseau were then reversal processed, while those using a separate reseau were negative processed and then printed to yield a positive which was subsequently registered with a colour reseau screen.

In each case, projection yielded a colour reproduction of the original scene and the method is exemplified by the Dufaycolor process. In

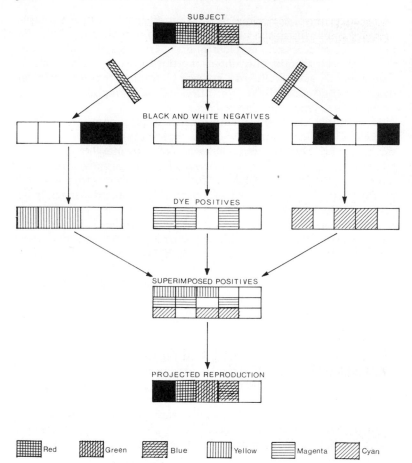

Fig. 27.9 – A subtractive colour photograph

this process the reseau was integral with the film and the system is shown in Figure 27.10.

Exposure was made through the film base, the reseau being coated on the base beneath the emulsion. After first development the silver image was completely removed using a potassium permanganate bleach solution, and the residual silver halide was fogged and developed to metallic silver. After fixing, washing and drying, the reproduction could be viewed.

In such additive processes, whether employing an integral or separate reseau, the colour mosaic was present at the viewing as well as

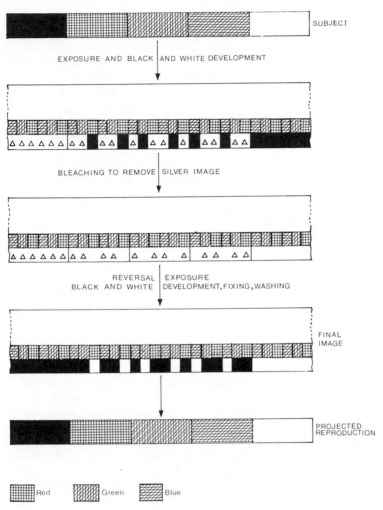

Fig. 27.10 – The Dufaycolor system

the taking stage. This meant that the brightness of reproduction of white was limited by the light absorption of the reseau. Only about one-third of the light striking the film could be transmitted and consequently the minimum density was at least 0·5. Such methods therefore wasted about 70 per cent. of the available light and generally gave a dim picture.

Additive methods employing three separate analysis negatives and the corresponding positives can give very good colour reproduction and a bright image owing to the use of three separate light sources. Such methods are cumbersome in operation and suffer from registration difficulties. The more convenient methods employing reseaux suffered from the loss of light at the projection stage, and definition difficulties due to the reseaux. Even if the reseau employed were so fine as to be unobjectionable in the reproduction, further generations of reproduction, such as reflection prints, were likely to be unsatisfactory.

The registration and light-loss problems inherent in additive methods of colour photography led to the adoption of methods based on the subtractive system.

Subtractive processes

Subtractive systems use yellow, magenta and cyan image dyes in appropriate concentrations to control the amounts of blue, green and red light transmitted or reflected by the reproduction. Thus white is reproduced by the virtual absence of image dyes, grey by carefully balanced quantities of the three dyes, and black requires a high concentration of each dye. Colours are reproduced by superimposed dye images of various concentrations. The effects of superimposing pairs of subtractive dyes are identical to the combination of filters of the same colours and have been illustrated in Figure 27.8.

The possibility of preparing subtractive dye positives from blue, green and red separation negatives has already been referred to. If such dye positives are used then it is possible to superimpose the yellow, magenta and cyan images to obtain a reproduction that may be projected using one projector only.

Although such a separation system suffers from registration difficulties when the positives are superimposed, two important commercial processes still operate in this manner. In each case separation positives are made which are able to absorb dye in an amount depending upon the image density. Each positive then carries the dye and is made to deposit it on a receiving material which retains the transferred dye. The three dye images are laid down in sequence to build up the required combination. The positive transmission or reflection prints made in this way can be of very high quality provided accurate image registration is maintained. The two processes which operate by this method are the Kodak Dye Transfer method of making reflection colour prints, and the Technicolor method of preparing motion picture release colour prints.

Integral tripack

While, as we have seen, it is possible to produce subtractive dye images separately, and to superimpose them to form a colour reproduction, this method finds limited application. Most colour photographs are made using a type of material which makes blue, green and red records in discrete emulsion layers within one assembly. This specially designed emulsion assembly is called an *integral tripack*.

The latent-image records within the three emulsion layers are then processed in such a way that the appropriate dye images are generated in register within the emulsion layers by colour development. The processing chemistry is such that the blue, green and red records are made to generate yellow, magenta and cyan images respectively. We shall look further at this type of process in Chapter 28.

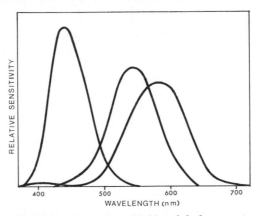

Fig. 27.11 – Spectral sensitivities of the human eye

Imperfections of colour processes

Additive system

Typical spectral sensitivity curves of the eye are shown in Figure 27.11 and it is clear that the sensitivities of the three colour receptors overlap considerably. While the red receptor alone can be stimulated by light of a wavelength of 650nm or greater, there are no wavelengths at which unique stimulation of the blue or green receptors is possible. A good approximation to the ideal can be achieved by using a wavelength of about 450 nm for the blue stimulus, but the best that can be done for the green is to select light of a wavelength of about 510nm. Even at this wavelength there is still considerable red and blue sensitivity in addition to the green.

In practical systems of additive colour photography shortage of light usually dictates the use of fairly wide spectral bands. The green record will thus elicit a significant response from the blue and red sensitive receptors as well as from the green receptor. The green light then appears to be mixed with some blue and red light, and in consequence appears a *paler* green. Reproductions of greens thus appear paler than the originals. Similar, but less severe, *desaturation* of blues and reds is also encountered owing to the broad spectral bands used in practice. The overall effect is to make colours less vivid, to desaturate them, effectively, by the addition of white light.

This impossibility of achieving separate blue, green and red stimulation of the retina is in fact common to all three-colour systems of colour reproduction, whether additive or subtractive.

Subtractive system

The subtractive system not only shares the limitations of the additive process in the reproduction of colours, but also suffers from defects introduced by the use of subtractive image dyes.

Ideally, each subtractive dye controls one-third, and only one-third, of the visible spectrum. If the regions controlled were made narrower than this, it would not be possible to reproduce black, or saturated colours, owing to uncontrolled transmission in one or two bands of the spectrum.

The subtractive system thus uses blue, green and red spectral bands that are broader than those used in the additive system and the reproductions of vivid colours are accordingly more desaturated. This would result in reproduced colours appearing markedly paler than the originals, if certain steps, detailed later, were not taken to improve matters.

In addition to the inherent inferiority of the subtractive system when compared with the additive, a further difficulty arises from the imperfections of the image dyes. It is found in practice that magenta and cyan image dyes especially, have additional absorptions in regions of the spectrum other than those required. Typical effects on colour reproduction include the darkening of blues, greens and reds, together with an overall lack of colour saturation.

Correction of deficiencies of the subtractive system

Various means are adopted to minimise the deficiencies of the subtractive system. One common procedure is to construct the photographic emulsions so that the blue, green and red sensitivities have steeper peaks which are more widely separated than those of the eye. A comparison between typical colour film sensitivities and those of the eye is shown in Figure 27.12. This expedient improves the saturation of many colours but may introduce marked errors, either through the emulsion sensitivities extending beyond those of the eye, or through a gap in the film sensitivities such as that shown at a wavelength of about 580nm in the illustration.

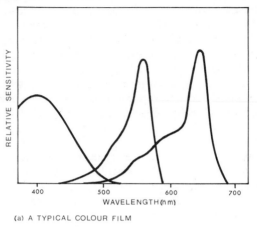

(a) A TYPICAL COLOUR FILM

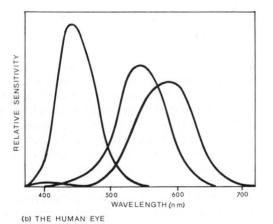

(b) THE HUMAN EYE

Fig. 27.12 – Spectral sensitivities of a typical colour film, and the human eye

The extension of emulsion sensitivity further into the ultra-violet than that of the eye may result in blue skies being reproduced at too high a saturation, and distant views appearing pale and blue. If these faults are encountered, the remedy is usually to employ an ultra-violet absorbing filter over the camera lens. At the long wavelength end of the spectrum, the extended sensitivity of the colour film compared with that of the eye may lead to an interesting effect. Flowers which reflect blue light often possess also a high reflectance close to the long wavelength limit of retinal sensitivity. The result is that in colour photographs it is frequently found that these flowers appear pink or pale magenta instead of blue. The light reflected by the flowers records in both the blue- and the red-sensitive emulsion layers. There is no simple remedy for this fault because filters which cut-off the extended sensitivity region adversely affect colour reproduction within the visible region.

It is found that the desaturation of colour reproductions described above is reduced by adopting a higher emulsion contrast than would be objectively ideal. The reproduction then possesses a higher contrast than the original and this results in an increase in colour saturation together with a departure from objectively correct tone reproduction. In most cases faults due to the increased tone contrast are outweighed by the superior colour saturation. It is, however, often advisable to keep the lighting ratio of the subject low in colour photography, if the increased tone contrast of the reproduction is not to be objectionable.

In the processing of colour materials it is often found that development of the record of one colour inhibits the development of an adjacent emulsion layer. This is called an *inter-image effect* and is in many ways similar to the Eberhard effect encountered in black-and-white processing (page 422); the products of development of the colour record diffuse into adjacent emulsion layers and inhibit development. An important difference lies in the fact that the action of the Eberhard effect extends parallel to the film base whereas useful colour inter-image effects are perpendicular to the film base in action.

The inter-image effects found in colour processes may be promoted by design of the system and harnessed to improve colour reproduction. The development of the record of any colour is made to inhibit the development of other colour records. Thus the neutral scale reproduction may possess a contrast which is much exceeded by the contrast of the reproduction of colours, such a situation being illustrated in Figure 27.13. Successful use of inter-image effects gives increased colour saturation with little distortion of tone reproduction, and can lead to very acceptable results.

Compensation for deficiencies of the subtractive system achieved by these means may be successful in a first generation reproduction. This category embraces colour transparencies produced by reversal processing of the original camera film. In many cases further generations of reproduction are required. Such further reproductions include reflection prints made from colour negatives or reversal transparencies, and also duplicate positive transparencies.

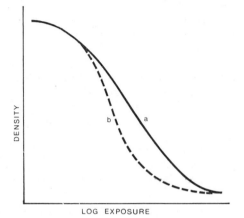

Fig. 27.13 – *The characteristic curve of the red-sensitive layer of a colour reversal film:*
(a) in the case of a neutral exposure
(b) in the case of a red exposure

It is generally true that further reproduction stages accentuate the departures from ideality of the first generation. Saturated colours become darker and may change hue, pale colours become paler and lose saturation, and tone contrast increases so that highlight detail is lost while the shadow areas become totally black. From the point of view of colour reproduction, therefore, it is usually preferable to make the camera record on negative film which can be made relatively free from deficiencies of colour and tone reproduction. The method used to achieve this freedom from deficiencies of colour reproduction is called *colour masking*.

Masking of colour materials

The spectral density distribution of a typical magenta image dye is shown in Figure 27.14. The characteristic curve of the green-sensitive emulsion which generates the dye is shown alongside and represents the green, blue and red densities of the dye image. It will be seen that the density to green light increases with exposure as would

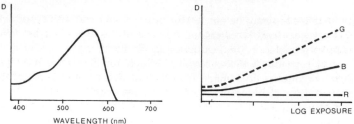

(a) SPECTRAL DENSITY DISTRIBUTION AND CHARACTERISTIC CURVE OF THE MAGENTA DYE IMAGE

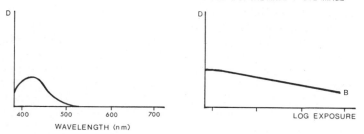

(b) SPECTRAL DENSITY DISTRIBUTION AND CHARACTERISTIC CURVE OF THE YELLOW MASK

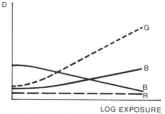

(c) THE IMAGE AND MASK CHARACTERISTIC CURVES

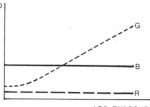

(d) THE COMBINED CHARACTERISTIC CURVES OF THE MASKED GREEN-SENSITIVE LAYER

Fig. 27.14 – Elements of masking the blue absorption of a magenta dye:
(a) spectral density distribution, and characteristic curve of the magenta dye image
(b) spectral density distribution, and characteristic curve of the yellow mask
(c) image and mask characteristic curves
(d) combined characteristic curve of the masked green-sensitive layer

be expected, and that the unwanted blue and red absorptions of the dye are shown by the increase in blue and red densities over the same exposure range.

At the printing stage an unmasked negative record employing this dye will convey spurious information to the printing paper about the distribution of blue and red light in the camera image. This is undesirable and results, for instance, in bluish greens in the print reproduction.

In order to compensate for the variation of blue density with the magenta dye content of the negative, it is merely necessary to prepare a corresponding positive yellow dye record as shown in Figure 27.14b. The yellow positive is then superimposed in register with the negative as shown in (c). Provided the blue density characteristic curve of the positive is of the same contrast as that of the negative, the combined effect of the mask and the unwanted secondary density of the image dye is as shown in (d). The printing effect of the unwanted absorption of the magenta image dye has been entirely compensated at the expense of an overall increase in blue density.

Making separate coloured masks is usually inconvenient and the most useful masking systems rely on the formation of masks within the negative colour film. This is called *integral masking*, and is widely used in colour negative films. The overall orange-brown appearance of such negative films results from the yellow mask of the magenta dye together with the reddish mask required by the cyan image dye. The yellow image dye is usually sufficiently free from unwanted absorptions that masking is unnecessary.

It should be noted that the overall coloration due to integral masking precludes the use of this process in reproductions which are to be viewed. The eye does not adapt to the overall orange appearance, and consequently masked images are unacceptable for viewing and can only be used as intermediates in the production of final prints.

In the next Chapter we shall examine the methods by which subtractive dye images are produced in a variety of practical processes.

CHAPTER 28

The Chemistry of Colour Image Formation

W E have seen that the image of a subject may be analysed in terms of blue, green and red light contents. It is usual in colour photography to control these three portions of the visible spectrum by means of yellow, magenta and cyan dyes respectively. In this Chapter we shall be concerned with three important methods of producing the dye images commonly encountered in colour photography. The methods rely on the generation of dyes, the destruction of dyes, and the migration of dyes respectively. We shall consider each of them in turn.

Chromogenic processes

Generation of dyes

The majority of commercial colour processes employ a processing step in which the generation of image dyes takes place. This dye forming development gives the name *chromogenic* – colour-forming – to such processes. Such a dye-forming solution is called a *colour developer* and in this solution image dyes are generated alongside the development of metallic silver. Two important chemical reactions take place in a colour developer:

(1) Silver halide grains which have been rendered developable by exposure to light, or otherwise, are reduced to metallic silver and the developing agent is correspondingly oxidized:

Developing Agent + Silver Bromide →
　　　　Developer oxidation products + Silver metal + Bromide ion

(2) Developer oxidation products react with chemicals called *colour formers* or *colour couplers* to form dyes. Colour developing agents of the substituted paraphenylenediamine type are used on practice, and the colour of the developed dye depends mainly on the nature of the colour former:

Developer oxidation products + Colour former →Dye

510

Colour photographic materials

The dye-forming development reaction allows us to generate dyes of the required colours, yellow, magenta, and cyan, to control blue, green and red light respectively. To take advantage of colour development it has been necessary to make special photographic materials of what is called the *integral tripack* variety. This means that light-sensitive emulsions are coated in three layers on a suitable support; the construction is shown in Figure 28.1. The records of blue, green and red light are made independently in the three emulsion layers.

The sensitivities of emulsions used in camera speed films are illustrated in Figure 28.2, from which it will be clear that no independent record of blue light can be achieved without special steps being taken.

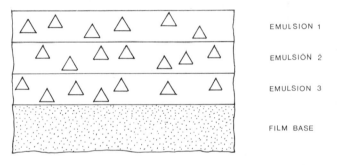

Fig. 28.1 – Cross-section of an elementary integral tripack film

What is usually done in practice is to coat the film as shown in Figure 28.3, with the blue-recording layer on top of the other two, and with a yellow filter layer between the blue-recording and green-recording layers. The supercoat is added to protect the emulsions from damage. The filter layer absorbs blue light sufficiently to suppress the natural blue sensitivities of the underlying emulsions. The resulting layer sensitivities are illustrated in Figure 28.4.

We have examined the method used to obtain separate blue, green and red latent-image records in an integral tripack. Now we shall consider the methods by which the colour developer oxidation products evolved in an emulsion layer are arranged to react with a colour former to yield the appropriate image die. As the colour developing agents are mobile in solution and diffuse rapidly through the swollen

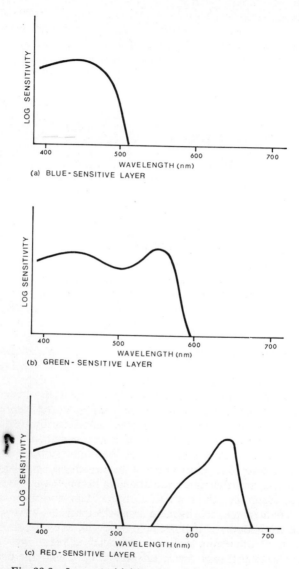

Fig. 28.2 – *Layer sensitivities of an elementary tripack film*

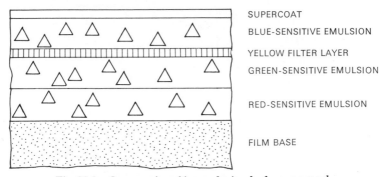

SUPERCOAT

BLUE-SENSITIVE EMULSION

YELLOW FILTER LAYER

GREEN-SENSITIVE EMULSION

RED-SENSITIVE EMULSION

FILM BASE

Fig. 28.3 – Cross-section of integral tripack of camera speed

emulsion we shall be concerned especially with the location of colour formers in chromogenic development.

Location of colour formers
It is required that the blue, green and red light records shall be composed of yellow, magenta and cyan dyes respectively. This distribution of dyes is achieved by presenting colour formers to developer oxidation products in a selective manner. Thus the oxidation products of development of the blue-recording emulsion are allowed to react only with a yellow-forming coupler. The coupler may be located either in solution in the colour developer, or it may be introduced into the emulsion during manufacture of the film.

Developer-soluble couplers can be used only when a single dye is to be formed in a colour development stage. Three colour developers are needed for a tripack and only one emulsion must be rendered developable before each colour development, if separation of the colour records is to be achieved. These conditions can be satisfied only in certain reversal processes which we shall consider later.

Couplers incorporated in the emulsions are used to form all three image dyes in one colour development step. In this case only the appropriate dye-forming couplers may be permitted in an emulsion layer if separation of the colour records is to be adequate. The colour formers therefore have to be immobilised to prevent diffusion of the couplers from layer to layer during manufacture or later.

Two main methods of immobilising couplers have been adopted. The method adopted by Agfa has been to link the otherwise mobile coupler with a long chemically inert chain. This chain interacts with gelatin in such a way that the molecule is effectively anchored in the

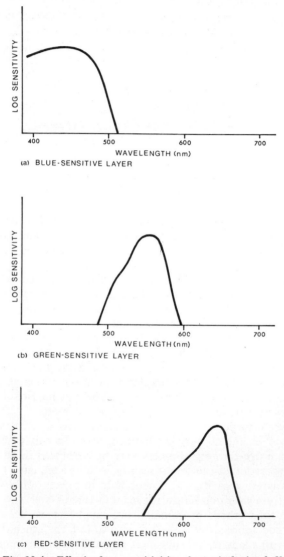

Fig. 28.4 – Effective layer sensitivities of a typical tripack film

layer and is described as being *substantive* to gelatin. Processes employing this type of immobilised coupler are referred to as *substantive processes*. Processes employing developer-soluble couplers are often called *non-substantive processes*.

The second immobilising method is due to Eastman Kodak and employs shorter chemically inert chains linked to the otherwise mobile coupler. The inert chains are selected for oil solubility and render the entire molecule soluble in oily solvents. A solution of such a coupler is made in an oily solvent and the solution dispersed as minute droplets in the emulsion, before coating. The coupler is very insoluble in water and the oily droplets are immobile in gelatin, so that the coupler is unable to diffuse out of the emulsion layer in which it is coated. Processes of the *oil-dispersed coupler* type are also sometimes loosely called substantive processes.

Colour processing
We have already encountered a number of processing steps which are used in colour processing. Before examining the applications of such steps we will summarise the functions of processing solutions commonly encountered in colour processes (Table 28.1).

Solution	Function
Black-and-white developer	Develops a metallic silver image.
Colour developer	Develops dye images together with metallic silver.
Clearing bath	Acid. Stops development, prevents subsequent stain formation in bleach bath.
Fix	Dissolves silver halide present after required development has taken place.
Stop-fix	Stops development as well as removing silver halide.
Bleach bath	Bleaches a metallic silver image, usually by oxidation and rehalogenation to silver halide.
Bleach-fix	Bleaches the metallic silver image and fixes the silver salts formed. Leaves only the dye image required.
Stabiliser	Improves the stability of dye images, may also contain wetting agent and hardener for hot glazed colour papers.
Hardener	Hardens the gelatin to resist damage in subsequent processing stages.

Table 28.1 – The primary functions of solutions commonly used in colour processes

The major differences between black-and-white and colour processing arise because of the need to generate precisely the required amounts of the image dyes in all three layers. If this is not achieved then objectionable colour effects tend to occur: either largely independent of density level – resulting in a uniform colour cast over most of the tone scale – or, if density-dependent, showing a change in colour balance with density level. The former case corresponds to a speed imbalance of the three layers and is illustrated in Figure 28.5b, while the latter corresponds to a contrast mismatch and is illustrated in Figure 28.5c.

The processing conditions under which a tripack film will give correct values of speed and contrast for all three layers are very limited and are generally specified very closely by the film manufacturer. The specifications usually include processing times and temperatures, as well as the method and timing of agitation in processing solutions. In addition, such factors as rate of flow of wash water may also be specified. It is important to realise that any departure from the exact processing specifications laid down by the film manufacturer is likely to lead to a lower quality result. Where manufacturers suggest process variations in order to modify a property, speed for instance, there is often a penalty to be paid in terms of some other property, such as graininess.

We will now consider how solutions of the types shown in Table 28.1 are used in colour processes. We shall start by examining colour reversal processing.

Reversal process
As already described, there are two main types of colour reversal process, the developer-soluble coupler type and that with couplers incorporated in the emulsions. The Kodachrome process is of the former (non-substantive) type, the couplers being present in the colour developer solutions. It is illustrated schematically in Figure 28.6.

The first solution is an active black-and-white developer in which silver halide grains bearing the latent image are developed to metallic silver – a black-and-white negative image. It is then necessary to form the required dye images by colour development of the residual silver halide grains.

In order to develop cyan dye where red sensitive grains were *not* rendered developable by the camera exposure, all that is needed is to expose the film fully to red light, and to develop the fogged red-sensitive grains in a cyan-forming developer. The exposure is most efficient when unscreened by developed silver and is therefore made through the back of the film to avoid screening by the upper two emulsion layers.

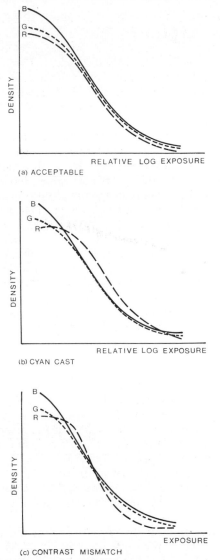

Fig. 28.5 – Characteristic curves of colour reversal films

The blue-sensitive layer is then exposed to blue light through the front of the film and developed in a yellow-forming developer. The green-sensitive layer may then be fogged by an intense white or green

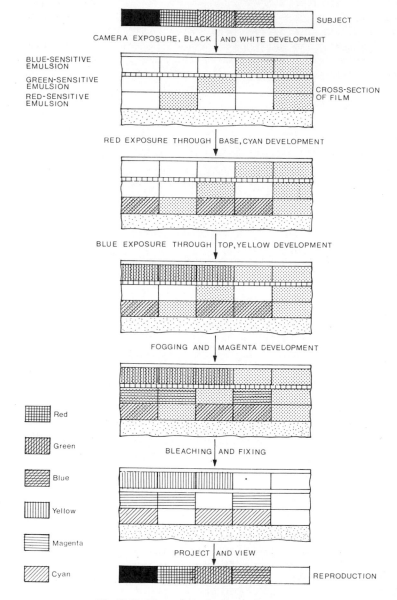

Fig.28.6 – Non-substantive reversal processing

exposure, but in practice it is often preferable to use a chemical fogging agent in the magenta colour developer. In either case the remaining silver halide grains are developed to yield a magenta dye.

At this stage in the process there are three positive dye images together with silver resulting from the complete development of the silver halide emulsions. The developed silver is quite dense and would make viewing of the dye images impractical.

The silver has to be removed by a bleach bath followed by a fix. The bleach bath is usually of the ferricyanide-bromide type and forms silver bromide from the silver metal. The yellow filter layer is also usually discharged during bleaching. The silver bromide may then

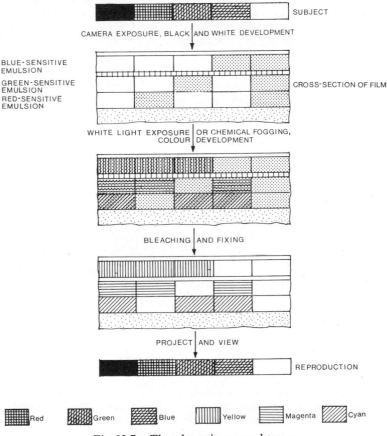

Fig. 28.7 – *The substantive reversal process*

be removed in a conventional fixing solution leaving only the required dye images present in the gelatin.

In addition to the processing steps outlined there are likely to be intermediate rinses and washes and other baths for special purposes. The apparent simplicity of putting soluble couplers in colour developers is thus offset by the complexity of such a non-substantive process which effectively prohibits user processing.

Reversal films incorporating couplers in the emulsion are simpler to process, and in many cases may be processed by the user. A substantive reversal process is shown in Figure 28.7, and commences with black-and-white development. After the first developer the film is fogged with white light before colour development, or chemically in the colour developer itself. The fogged silver halide grains are then colour developed to yield positive dye images together with metallic silver. The appropriate dye colours are ensured by the location of the yellow-forming coupler only within the blue-recording layer, the magenta-forming coupler only within the green-recording layer, and the cyan-forming coupler only within the red-recording layer. Bleaching and fixing are then carried out in order to leave only the image dyes in the gelatin layers.

	Step	Temp. (°C)	Time (mins.)
1	First developer	$24\pm\frac{1}{4}$	10
2	Rinse in running water	23–25	1
3	Hardener	23–25	3
4	Wash in running water	23–25	3
5	Reversal exposure to photoflood – drain for 60 seconds		1
6	Colour developer	23–25	15
7	Wash in running water	23–25	5
8	Clearing bath	23–25	5
9	Rinse in running water	23–25	1
10	Bleach	23–25	8
11	Rinse in running water	23–25	1
12	Fixing bath	23–25	4
13	Wash in running water	23–25	8
14	Stabilizer	23–25	1
15	Dry	$\leqslant 43$	

Steps 1–3 take place in the dark, 4 onwards in the light.
Total time, steps 1–14 inclusive, 66 minutes.
Agitation is essential in all steps other than washes and reversal exposure, and the agitation procedure is specified by the manufacturer.

Table 28.2 – Kodak Ektachrome E3 process

An example of a Kodak reversal processing procedure, the Ekta-chrome E3 process, is included as illustration (Table 28.2). The colour couplers are present in oil dispersions within the emulsions of Ektachrome film.

Negative-positive process

The negative-positive process is analogous to the conventional black-and-white process in that a negative record is made by camera exposure followed by processing. This record is not intended for viewing but is used to produce a usable positive by a further exposure and processing procedure.

Since information about the blue, green and red light contents of the camera image is to be available at the printing stage it is customary to use the blue-, green- and red-sensitive layers of the colour negative film to generate yellow, magenta and cyan image dyes respectively. Metallic silver is of course generated at the same time and is removed by bleaching and fixing operations. The remaining dye images form the colour negative record, the colours formed being complementary to to those of the subject of the photograph. The production of a colour negative record is illustrated in Figure 28.8a.

If integral masking is employed in the colour negative then low-contrast positive masks may be formed at the development stage if coloured couplers are used. If some other technique of mask production is used, it may take place in the developer, or at some later stage, depending upon the chemistry involved.

The colour negative produced is then the subject of the printing stage. In principle, the negative is printed onto a second integral tripack which is processed in similar fashion to a colour negative. The production of a positive print is shown in Figure 28.8b as the preparation of a reproduction of the subject of the negative exposure.

Colour printing materials have similar characteristic curves to those of black-and-white print materials, because the tone reproduction requirements are quite similar. Thus, the colour negative film may have characteristic curves similar to those shown in Figure 28.9a, a motion picture release positive film being shown in Figure 28.9b and a typical printing paper in Figure 28.9c. The negative illustrated is masked giving an overall colour cast, and this results in a vertical displacement of the blue and green filter density curves compared with the red curve.

The higher blue and green densities of colour negatives are compensated by manufacturing colour print materials with correspondingly

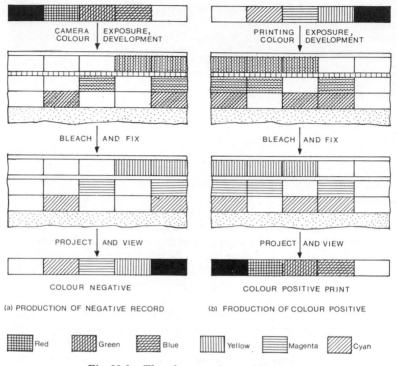

Fig. 28.8 – The colour negative–positive process

higher blue and green sensitivities than red sensitivity. The printing operation allows manipulation of the overall colour of the reproduction, by modification of the quantities of blue, green and red light allowed to reach the print material from the negative. This may be achieved by separate additive exposures through blue, green and red filters ("tricolour printing"), or by making one exposure through appropriate dilute subtractive filters – yellow, magenta or cyan ("white-light printing"). This control of colour-balance being easy to achieve, it is not so important that negative and print materials shall possess standard speed-balances as it is that reversal materials shall. No colour correction of a reversal transparency is usually possible after the taking stage whereas in the negative-positive process adjustment of colour balance is a usual procedure at the printing stage.

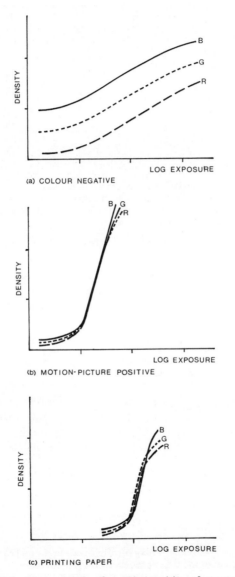

Fig.28.9 – Characteristics of negative-positive colour materials

Typical colour negative and colour paper processes are shown in Tables 28.3 and 28.4.

Step	Temp. (°C)	Time (mins)
1 Colour developer	$24 \pm \frac{1}{4}$	8
2 Rinse in running water	23–25	$\frac{1}{2}$
3 Stop-fix	23–25	2
4 Wash in running water	23–25	2
5 Bleach	23–25	6
6 Wash in running water	23–25	2
7 Fix	23–25	2
8 Wash in running water	23–25	6
9 Stabilizer	23–25	1
10 Dry	$\leqslant 43$	

Steps 1–3 take place in the dark, the remainder in the light.
Total process time, steps 1–9 inclusive, 30 minutes.

Once again agitation procedures suitable for such a process are specified by the manufacturer, and are often critical.

Table 28.3 – Colour negative process

Two Kodak colour paper processes are given. One process using CP–5 chemicals operates at a high temperature and is rapid, using the Kodak drum processor and discarding solutions after use.

Step	CP–5 Chemicals Temp (°C)	Time (mins.)	Ektaprint C Chemicals Temp (°C)	Time (mins.)
1 Developer	$38 \pm \frac{1}{4}$	$2\frac{1}{2}$	$29\frac{1}{2} \pm \frac{1}{4}$	6
2 Wash	37–39	$\frac{1}{2}$	—	—
3 Stop-fix	37–39	$\frac{1}{2}$	$28\frac{1}{2}$–$30\frac{1}{2}$	2
4 Wash	37–39	$\frac{1}{2}$	$28\frac{1}{2}$–$30\frac{1}{2}$	2
5 Bleach	37–39	1	$28\frac{1}{2}$–$30\frac{1}{2}$	4
6 Wash	37–39	$\frac{1}{2}$	$28\frac{1}{2}$–$30\frac{1}{2}$	2
7 Formalin fix	37–39	$\frac{1}{2}$	$28\frac{1}{2}$–$30\frac{1}{2}$	4
8 Wash	37–39	$\frac{1}{2}$	$28\frac{1}{2}$–$30\frac{1}{2}$	4
9 Stabilizer	37–39	$\frac{1}{2}$	$28\frac{1}{2}$–$30\frac{1}{2}$	2
10 Dry	$\leqslant 82$		$\leqslant 82$	
Total time excluding drying:		7		26

After the stop-fix bath operations may be carried out in normal room light. Agitation is specified for the CP–5 process by the manufacturer.

Table 28.4 – Ektacolor Commercial Paper processes

The second process is less rapid, using Ektaprint C chemicals at a lower temperature, but makes replenishment of solutions possible.

The colour paper process selected depends on the number of prints to be made and the frequency of processing required.

Silver-dye-bleach process

The processes so far considered have relied on the formation of image dyes by colour development within the emulsions. There are, however, alternative approaches and one of these has been to destroy suitable dyes introduced into the emulsions at manufacture. In such processes a red exposure is arranged to lead to the destruction of a cyan dye, while a green exposure causes bleaching of a magenta dye and a blue exposure leads to the destruction of a yellow dye.

Commercial processes of this type have used the silver photographic image to bring about the chemical decomposition of dyes present in the emulsion layers. A current process which uses this mechanism is *Cibachrome*, a process for the production of positive prints from positive transparencies. In this system the print material is an integral tripack and is constructed as shown in Figure 28.10. The uppermost, blue-sensitive, emulsion contains a yellow dye. The green-sensitive layer contains a magenta dye, and the red-sensitive layer contains a cyan dye.

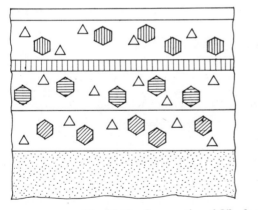

SUPERCOAT

BLUE-SENSITIVE EMULSION

YELLOW FILTER LAYER

GREEN-SENSITIVE EMULSION

RED-SENSITIVE EMULSION

REFLECTING BASE

Fig. 28.10 – Cross-section of Cibachrome material

Because of the high optical density of the dyes present in the emulsions, together with emulsion desensitization by some of the dyes, it is often necessary to use quite high speed emulsions in order to achieve printing exposures of a tolerable duration.

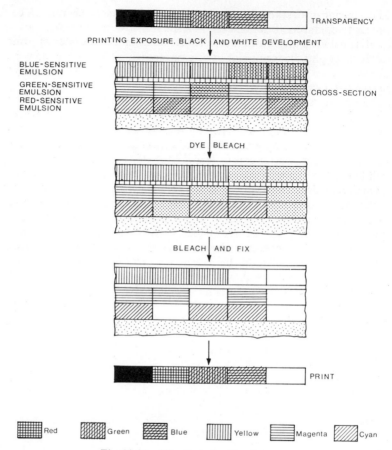

Fig. 28.11 – The silver-dye-bleach process

The processing of silver-dye-bleach materials follows the scheme illustrated in Figure 28.11. The initial step is the black-and-white development of emulsion grains rendered developable by the printing exposure. The silver image is then used to reduce the dyes present in the emulsions. This reaction may be summarized:

Dye + halogen acid + silver metal →

Reduced dye fragments + silver halide

It is arranged that the fragments resulting from the reduction of the dyes are colourless or soluble or both. Thus in the dye-bleach bath we have imagewise reduction of the dyes by metallic silver and corresponding oxidation of the silver. The reaction is extremely slow and a catalyst is necessary to obtain a satisfactory rate of bleaching. The catalyst may be incorporated in the silver-dye-bleach, or it may be carried over from solution in the black-and-white developer, within the emulsion layers.

Following the silver-dye-bleach excess silver may have to be removed by a conventional bleach bath. The silver halides formed in the bleaching operations are then fixed. The result is a positive dye record retained within the gelatin, as shown in Figure 28.11.

Major advantages claimed for the silver-dye-bleach process follow from the freedom to use compounds classed as azo dyes. These possess better spectral properties than the dyes formed by chromogenic development and are markedly less light-fugitive. The better spectral properties improve the saturation and lightness of image colours, while the improved light-fastness gives a much greater life for displayed prints, compared with those prepared by chromogenic processes.

Dye diffusion transfer

As an alternative to the chemical development or bleaching of dyes in order to form a colour image it is possible to use the development of a silver image to modify the mobility of suitable image dies. Such a method is used in the *Polacolor* system.

A negative film of three light-sensitive assemblies is coated in the conventional order with the red-sensitive emulsion next to the base, and the blue-sensitive emulsion farthest from the support. Each light-sensitive assembly consists of two layers, one of which contains a silver halide emulsion of appropriate sensitivity while the other, nearer the film base, contains a compound of an unusual

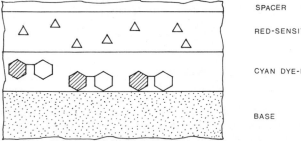

SPACER

RED-SENSITIVE EMULSION

CYAN DYE-DEVELOPER

BASE

Fig. 28.12 – Polacolor emulsion and dye-developer layer combination

nature. This compound has a molecular structure which comprises a black-and-white developing agent chemically linked by an inert chain to a dye. The construction of a Polacolor light-sensitive assembly is shown in Figure 28.12.

After exposure, the Polacolor film is processed within the camera to yield a positive colour reflection record. To achieve this, the film is pulled, together with a receiving material, between pressure rollers. The pressure rollers rupture a pod attached to the receiving layer and this releases a viscous alkali solution which is then spread between the negative film and the positive receiving layer.

The alkali solution penetrates the negative emulsions and activates the dye-developer molecules, rendering them soluble and thus mobile. The mobile dye-developer molecules are very active developing agents in alkaline solution, and on development taking place are once more rendered immobile. Dye developer molecules which diffuse out of of an emulsion-developer layer combination have to pass through a spacer layer. They are thus delayed so that by the time they reach another emulsion layer, development of that layer has taken place and they are unlikely to encounter developable silver halide. Under these circumstances the dye-developer molecules are free to diffuse out of the negative material and into the receiving material. The receiving material acts as a sink for dye-developer molecules and this encourages diffusion into the receiving layer. The structure of the receiving layer is shown in Figure 28.13 and the diffusion stage is shown in Figure 28.14.

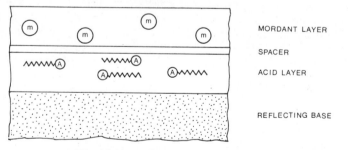

Fig. 28.13 – Polacolor receiving material

Dye-developer molecules entering the receiving layer encounter a mordant which immobilises the dye part of the molecule and therefore anchors the entire molecule. The alkali present in the processing solution diffuses slowly through the spacer layer in the receiving material and reaches the layer which contains large immobile organic acid

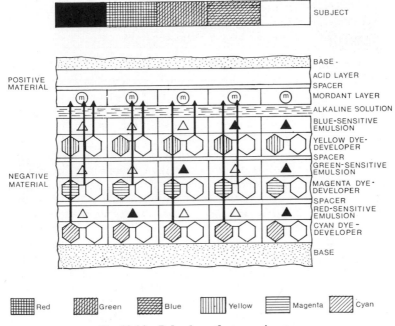

Fig. 28.14 – Polacolor – the processing stage

molecules. The alkali is neutralized by the acid with the evolution of water which swells the spacer layer and assists further penetration by alkali to the acid layer and consequent neutralization. After about one minute the reactions are completed and the reflection positive is peeled off the residual negative and is suitable for viewing. The positive image is illustrated in Figure 28.15.

The elegance and ingenuity of the process lie in the carrying out of the processing within the camera, and in leaving behind in the discarded negative unwanted silver and dye-developer. Note that any emulsion fog results in a lowering of the dye density in the positive; the stain is not increased.

Important chemistry

For those readers with some chemical knowledge there follows a short review of chemical formulae of some compounds and reactions important in colour image formation.

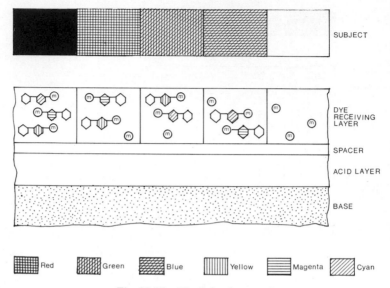

| Red | Green | Blue | Yellow | Magenta | Cyan |

Fig. 28.15 – The Polacolor record

Chromogenic processes

The colour forming reaction takes place between oxidised colour developer and suitable colour formers. Colour developing agents of practical importance possess the general formula shown in Figure 28.16. Such developing agents are usually supplied as salts of acids.
Fig. 28.16

Colour formers usually contain an active methylene or methine group activated by a group or groups adjacent to the active site, or linked by a conjugated chain. Generally, cyclic couplers require one activating group while open chain couplers require two such groups. Examples of colour couplers are shown in Figure 28.17 in which (a) is

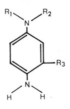

R_1 ethyl
R_2 ethyl, hydroxyethyl or β-methylsulphonamidoethyl
R_3 hydrogen or methyl

Fig. 28.16 – General formula of common colour developing agents

a yellow-forming coupler, (b) is a magenta-forming coupler, and (c) is cyan-forming; all three are developer soluble.

(a) 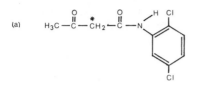   ACETOACET-2,5-DICHLOROANILIDE

(b) 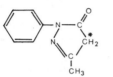   3-METHYL-1-PHENYLPYRAZOL-5-ONE

(c) 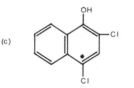   2,4-DICHLORO-1-NAPHTHOL

* Indicates the site of coupling

Fig. 28.17 – Simple developer–soluble colour couplers

The coupling reaction has the stoichiometry:

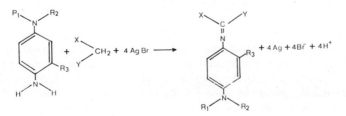

unless the coupling position is occupied by an electronegative substituent, when a useful change in stoichiometry is observed:

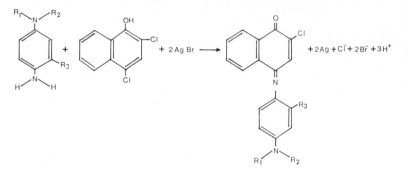

Only two silver ions are then reduced to yield one molecule of developed dye, whereas without the electronegative substituent four
silver ions were required.

Substitution at the site of coupling is made use of in methods of
colour masking using coloured couplers. The coloured moiety is
linked to the coupling position of the coupler and is discharged on dye
formation:

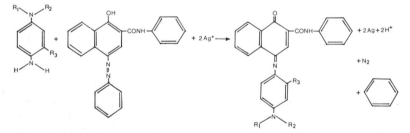

In this case an azo dye moiety is displaced from the 4-position of the
colour former on coupling.

Other substitutents in colour former molecules are added to influence solubility and mobility in the emulsion. Examples of differently
immobilised cyan-forming couplers are shown in Figure 28.18. In the
case (a) we have a $-C_{18}H_{37}$ anchoring group which renders the
coupler substantive to gelatin, and in order to make the coupler water-
soluble for coating purposes the $-SO_3Na$ group is substituted into
the 4-position. In (b) the coupler is made suitable for oil dispersion by
the $-C_5H_{11}$ group, no water solubilisation is required or desired when
oil dispersion is intended.

The silver-dye-bleach process
This process is usually operated with azo dyes and these are characterised by the azo linkage:

$$- N = N -$$

These dyes may be given the general formula:

$$R_1 - N = N - R_2$$

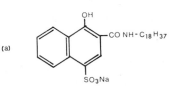

(a)

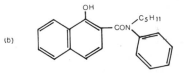

(b)

Fig. 28.18 – Immobilised colour couplers

The overall dye-bleach reaction may be represented by the stoichiometric equation:

$$R_1 - N = N - R_2 + 4H^+ + 4Ag \longrightarrow R_1NH_2 + R_2NH_2 + 4Ag^+$$

It will be seen that a low pH favours this reaction and consequently the silver-dye-bleach bath is usually strongly acid and operates at a pH between 0 and 1. This pH is conveniently achieved by the use of a halogen acid which will also withdraw silver ions formed by dye bleaching, and hence favour the reaction. The concentration of *free silver ion* may also be kept to a minimum by the formation of a soluble complex of high stability. A suitable complexing agent is thiourea, and the reaction employing thiourea may be represented:

$$R_1N = NR_2 + 4H^+ + 4\,Ag + 12\,S = C \begin{array}{c} \diagup NH_2 \\ \diagdown NH_2 \end{array} \longrightarrow$$

$$R_1NH_2 + R_2NH_2 + 4 \left[Ag(S = C \begin{array}{c} \diagup NH_2 \\ \diagdown NH_2 \end{array})_3 \right] +$$

The dye-bleach reaction as shown is very slow even at very low pH values and at very low concentrations of free silver ions. It is necessary to employ a catalyst to speed up the reaction, and the useful compounds contain this structural group:

Examples of compounds used as catalysts are shown in Figure 28.19.

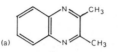

2,3-DIMETHYLQUINOXALINE

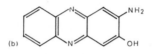

2-HYDROXY-3-AMINOPHENAZINE

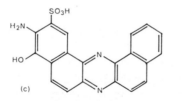

3-HYDROXY-4-AMINO-NAPHTHAZINE-5-SULPHONIC ACID

Fig 28.19 – Silver-dye-bleach catalysts

Examples (a) and (b) are catalysts which have been used dissolved in the bleach bath, while (c) represents a catalyst which is dissolved in the developer and carried into the bleach in small quantities by the emulsion layers.

According to L. F. A. Mason, at the pH of the bleach bath such catalysts become protonated:

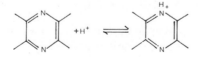

and the protonated catalyst, catH^+, acts as a redox intermediate:

$$Ag + cat\,H^+ \rightleftharpoons Ag^+ + cat\,H^+$$

oxidizing a silver atom and gaining an electron to form a free radical. The free radicals formed in this way are able to attack the azo linkages of the dyestuff present, and destruction of the dye results from stepwise attack summed up in the equation:

$$4\,catH^+ + R_1N = NR_2 \rightarrow 4\,cat + R_1NH_2 + R_2NH_2$$

Examples of azo dyes suitable for the silver-dye-bleach process are shown in Figure 28.20 in which (a) represents a yellow dye, (b) a magenta dye and (c) represents a cyan dye. It should be noted that for dyes to be used in the silver-dye-bleach process they must be substantive to the appropriate emulsion layer, and the amine breakdown products should be soluble enough to wash out of the emulsion in the bleach bath or at a later stage. This latter property is desirable in order to reduce stain, especially on keeping.

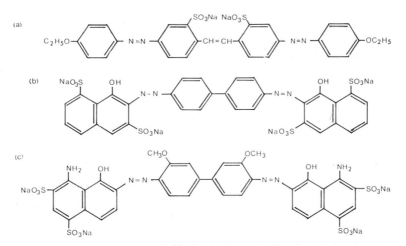

Fig. 28.20 – *Dyes suitable for the silver-dye-bleach process:*
(a) yellow (b) magenta (c) cyan

Dye diffusion transfer

The Polacolor process depends for its success on the novel dye-developer compounds incorporated in the negative material. The changes in mobility of these compounds already referred to arise from the behaviour of developing agents of the substituted hydroquinone type:

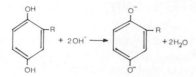

The neutral molecule is insoluble, and hence immobile, in acid conditions and shows *no* developing activity; but in alkali the developing moiety deprotonates to form the soluble and mobile developer anion. This anion is an active developer and readily reduces exposed silver halide to metallic silver with the formation of an uncharged quinone.

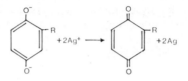

The quinone is almost insoluble, and thus immobile, and possesses no photographic activity.

Thus activation of the dye-developer by alkali yields a mobile anionic molecule which remains mobile so long as the solution is sufficiently alkaline and development does not take place.

The dye moiety may be of the azo type and attached to the developer moiety by an inert chain. The dye-developer molecules may be of the type:

where –X– constitutes the inert chain. Polaroid themselves have described linking chains of the type:

$$- S (CH_2)n -$$

where the inert link is the sulphur linked hydrocarbon chain. A dye-developer constructed in this way could possess the general formula:

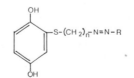

APPENDIX

Processing Formulae

THE following formulae are those published by Ilford Ltd. and are broadly similar to those of other manufacturers. They are grouped under the following headings:

Developers
Fixers and stop bath
Reducers
Intensifiers
Toners

Making up solutions

All quantities are given in SI (metric) units; conversions between SI units and avoirdupois (Imperial) units are given on page 550.

Dissolve the chemicals in the order given, using about three-quarters of the total volume of water required. This water should be hot, at about 50°C, and then cold water should be added to make up the full amount.

Substitution of chemicals

In formulae containing sodium sulphite, the quantities given are for sodium sulphite, anhydrous. If sodium sulphite, crystalline is used the quantities given must be doubled.

In formulae containing sodium carbonate, the quantities given are for sodium carbonate, anhydrous. If sodium carbonate, crystalline (decahydrate) is used the quantities given must be multiplied by two and three-quarters. If sodium carbonate, monohydrate is used the quantities given must be multiplied by one and a quarter.

In formulae containing sodium thiosulphate (hypo), the quantities given are for sodium thiosulphate, crystalline. If sodium thiosulphate, anhydrous, is used the quantities given must be multiplied by five-eighths.

In most P.Q. formulae, Ilford IBT Restrainer solution is specified. If this is not available, an alternative restrainer may be made by dissolving 10 grammes of benzotriazole in 1 litre of 1 per cent. sodium carbonate (anhydrous) solution.

DEVELOPERS

ID-2 M.Q. Developer

A general-purpose M.Q. developer for films and plates. Also recommended for the development of high-contrast graphic arts films and plates, when a non-caustic developer is required.

STOCK SOLUTION

Metol	2	g
Sodium sulphite, anhyd.	75	g
Hydroquinone	8	g
Sodium carbonate, anhyd.	37·5	g
Potassium bromide	2	g
Water to make	1	litre

WORKING STRENGTH

For normal use
    Dish: Dilute 1 part with 2 parts water.
    Tank: Dilute 1 part with 5 parts water.

For line and screen work (high contrast)
    Use in dish at stock solution strength.

ID-11 Fine Grain Developer

An M.Q. borax developer for films and plates. Gives grain fine enough for all normal requirements without loss of emulsion speed.

Metol	2	g
Soldium sulphite, anhyd.	100	g
Hydroquinone	5	g
Borax	2	g
Water to make	1	litre

    Use without dilution in dish or tank.

Replenisher for ID-11 Developer

A replenisher designed to maintain the activity of ID-11 developer, and thus prolong its life.

Metol	3	g
Sodium sulphite, anhyd.	100	g
Hydroquinone	7·5	g
Borax	20	g
Water to make	1	litre

    Add to the developer tank as required to maintain the level of the solution. Under normal working conditions, where the tank is in regular use, a total quantity of replenisher equal to that of the original developer may be added before discarding the developing solution.

ID-13 Hydroquinone-caustic Developer

For the dish development of high-contrast graphic arts films and plates, when maximum contrast is required. Also recommended for the development of certain special plates used for scientific purposes, when maximum contrast is required.

STOCK SOLUTION A

Hydroquinone	25 g
Potassium metabisulphite	25 g
Potassium bromide	25 g
Water to make	1 litre

STOCK SOLUTION B

Potassium hydroxide (caustic potash)	50 g
Water to make	1 litre

WORKING STRENGTH

Dish: Mix equal parts of A and B immediately before use.

ID-20 M.Q. Developer

An M.Q. formula for enlarging papers.

STOCK SOLUTION

Metol	3 g
Sodium sulphite, anhyd.	50 g
Hydroquinone	12 g
Sodium carbonate, anhyd.	60 g
Potassium bromide	4 g
Water to make	1 litre

WORKING STRENGTH

For Normal Use

Dilute 1 part with 3 parts water.

For Press Use

Dilute 1 part with 1 part water.

ID-36 M.Q. Developer

A universal M.Q. developer for films, plates and papers.
Especially recommended for contact papers and lantern plates.

STOCK SOLUTION

Metol	3 g
Sodium sulphite, anhyd.	50 g
Hydroquinone	12·5 g
Sodium carbonate, anhyd.	72 g
Potassium bromide	0·75 g
Water to make	1 litre

WORKING STRENGTH

Films and Plates
Dish: Dilute 1 part with 3 parts water.
Tank: Dilute 1 part with 7 parts water.

Contact Papers and Lantern Plates
Dilute 1 part with 1 part water.

Enlarging and Rollhead Papers
Dilute 1 part with 3 parts water.

ID-62 Phenidone-hydroquinone Developer

A universal P.Q. formula for films, plates and papers.

STOCK SOLUTION

Sodium sulphite, anhyd.	50	g
Sodium carbonate, anhyd.	60	g
Hydroquinone	12	g
Phenidone	0·5	g
Potassium bromide	2	g
IBT Restrainer, soln.	20	ml
Water to make	1	litre

WORKING STRENGTH

Films and Plates
Dish: Dilute 1 part stock solution with 3 parts water.
Tank: Dilute 1 part stock solution with 7 parts water.

Contact Papers and Lantern Plates
Dilute 1 part stock solution with 1 part water.

Enlarging and Rollhead Papers
Dilute 1 part stock solution with 3 parts water.

ID-67 Phenidone-hydroquinone Developer

A general-purpose P.Q. formula for roll films, flat films and plates.

STOCK SOLUTION

Sodium sulphite, anhyd.	75	g
Sodium carbonate, anhyd.	37·5	g
Hydroquinone	8	g
Phenidone	0·25	g
Potassium bromide	2	g
IBT Restrainer, soln.	15	ml
Water to make	1	litre

WORKING STRENGTH

Dish: Dilute 1 part stock solution with 2 parts water.
Tank: Dilute 1 part stock solution with 5 parts water.

ID-68 Fine Grain Developer

A P.Q. borax formula for films and plates. Gives grain fine enough for all normal requirements without loss of emulsion speed.

Sodium sulphite, anhyd.	85	g
Hydroquinone	5	g
Borax	7	g
Boric acid	2	g
Potassium bromide	1	g
Phenidone	0·13	g
Water to make	1	litre

Use without dilution in dish or tank.

Replenisher for ID-68 Developer

A replenisher formula designed to maintain the activity of ID-68 developer, and thus prolong its life.

Sodium sulphite, anhyd.	85	g
Hydroquinone	8	g
Borax	10	g
Phenidone	0·22	g
Water to make	1	litre

Add to the developer tank as required to maintain the level of the solution. Under normal working conditions, where the tank is in regular use, a total quantity of replenisher equal to that of the original developer may be added before discarding the developing solution.

FIXERS AND STOP BATH

IF-2 Acid-hypo Fixer

A non-hardening acid fixing bath for films, plates and papers.

STOCK SOLUTION

Sodium thiosulphate (hypo), cryst.	200	g
Potaassium metabisulphite	12·5	g
Water to make	1	litre

WORKING STRENGTH

Films and Plates: Use undiluted. Fix for 10 to 20 minutes.

Papers: Dilute with an equal quantity of water. Fix for 5 to 10 minutes.

Note. For more rapid fixing of films and plates the quantities of hypo and metabisulphite in this formula may be doubled.

IF-13 Potassium Alum Acid Hardener-Fixer

For papers.

STOCK HARDENING SOLUTION

Sodium sulphite, anhyd.	50 g
Acetic acid, glacial	75 ml
Potassium alum, cryst.	100 g
Water to make	1 litre

Dissolve the sulphite in 200 ml of warm water, allow to cool and add the acetic acid slowly, stirring all the time. Dissolve the alum in 600 ml of hot water, allow to cool to below 21°C and add to the sulphite-acid solution. Finally, make up to 1 litre with cold water.

WORKING SOLUTION

Sodium thiosulphate (hypo), cryst.	200 g
Stock hardening solution (as above)	125 ml
Water to make	1 litre

Dissolve the hypo in 500 ml of warm water and to this when cold add the stock hardening solution and cold water to make up to 1 litre.

IF-15 Potassium Alum Acid Hardener-Fixer

For films and plates.

Sodium thiosulphate (hypo), cryst.	320 g
Sodium sulphite, anhyd.	30 g
Boric acid, cryst.	10 g
Acetic acid, glacial	18 ml
Potassium alum, cryst.	25 g
Water to make	1 litre

Dissolve the hypo in 500 ml of hot water and when this solution is cool add the sulphite. Dissolve the boric acid, acetic acid and alum in 150 ml of hot water, allow to cool to below 21°C and slowly pour into the sulphite-hypo solution. Finally, make up to 1 litre with cold water. To obtain full hardening, films should be allowed to remain in the bath for 5 to 10 minutes.

IS-1 Acetic Acid Stop Bath

For films, plates and papers.

Acetic acid, glacial	17 ml
Water to make	1 litre

Films, plates or papers should be immersed in the bath for about 5 seconds, and should be kept moving.

Note. This stop bath should be replaced when its pH reaches 5·8. This may be determined by using BDH Narrow Range Indicator Paper 5570.

REDUCERS

IR-1 Ferricyanide-hypo ("Farmer's") Reducer

A subtractive reducer, for clearing shadow areas in negatives, and for brightening highlights of prints.

SOLUTION A

Potassium ferricyanide	100 g
Water to make	1 litre

SOLUTION B

Sodium thiosulphate (hypo), cryst.	200 g
Water to make	1 litre

For use, add to Solution B just sufficient of Solution A to colour the mixture pale yellow (e.g., 10 ml of A per 200 ml of B). This should be used immediately after mixing. The process of reduction should be carefully watched and the negative washed thoroughly as soon as it has been reduced sufficiently. The energy of reduction can be controlled by varying the amount of Solution A in the mixture.

IR-2 Persulphate Reducer

A super-proportional reducer, for great reduction of negative contrast.

Ammonium persulphate	25 g
Water to make	1 litre

It is important that the water used for making up this bath should be free of dissolved chlorides; distilled water is recommended.

One or two drops of sulphuric acid should be added to induce regularity of action. When reduction has gone nearly but not quite far enough, pour off the reducer and flood the negative with a 5 per cent. solution of sodium sulphite to arrest further action. Wash the negative thoroughly before drying.

Note. This reducer is ineffective with some modern high-speed emulsions. If it fails, IR-3 should be tried.

IR-3 Permanganate-persulphate Reducer

A proportional reducer for lowering negative contrast.

SOLUTION A

Sulphuric acid, conc.	1·5	ml
Potassium permanganate	0·25 g	
Water to make	1	litre

SOLUTION B

Ammonium persulphate	25	g
Water to make	1	litre

Caution. When making up solution A, the acid must be added to the water, drop by drop, and not the water to the acid. Adding water to sulphuric acid is highly dangerous. The permanganate should be added last.

It is important that the water used for both solutions should be free of dissolved chlorides; distilled water is recommended.

For use, mix 1 part of A with 3 parts of B. When reduction has gone far enough, pour off the reducer and flood the negative with a 1 per cent. solution of sodium bisulphite to clear it. Wash the negative thoroughly before drying.

Ilford IR-4 Iodine Reducer

For local or general reduction of prints.

STOCK SOLUTION

Potassium iodide	16 g
Iodine	4 g
Water to make	1 litre

WORKING STRENGTH

For use, dilute 1 part stock solution with 19 parts water. After reduction, rinse and re-fix in a 20 per cent. plain hypo bath. Wash the print thoroughly before drying.

IR-5 Iodine-cyanide Reducer

For local or general reduction of negatives and prints.

STOCK SOLUTION A

Potassium iodide	25 g
Iodine	4 g
Water to make	1 litre

STOCK SOLUTION B

Potassium cyanide	8 g
Water to make	1 litre

For use, mix 1 part A, 1 part B and 18 parts water.

Caution. Potassium cyanide is a very strong poison and must be handled with extreme care.

INTENSIFIERS

IIn-3 Chromium Intensifier

For controlled intensification of negatives. This intensifier is not liable to produce stains.

BICHROMATE STOCK SOLUTION

Potassium bichromate	100 g
Water to make	1 litre

This solution keeps indefinitely.

BLEACHING SOLUTION A

Bichromate stock solution (as above)	100 ml
Hydrochloric acid, conc.	2·5 ml
Water to make	1 litre

BLEACHING SOLUTION B

Bichromate stock solution (as above)	100 ml
Hydrochloric acid, conc.	12·5 ml
Water to make	1 litre

Bleaching Solution A gives more intensification than Solution B. Whichever solution is selected should be freshly mixed. Immerse the washed negative in the bleaching solution selected until it is completely bleached, then wash until the yellow stain is removed and re-develop, by white light, or after exposure to light, in an M.Q. or P.Q. developer. Wash the negative thoroughly before drying.

IIn-4 Monckhoven's Intensifier

For use when a great increase in contrast is required.

BLEACHING SOLUTION

Mercuric chloride (corrosive sublimate)	25 g
Potassium bromide	25 g
Water to make	1 litre

DARKENING SOLUTION

Potassium cyanide	14 g
Silver nitrate	22 g
Water to make	1 litre

Dissolve the cyanide and silver nitrate in separate lots of water and gradually add the silver nitrate solution to the cyanide, with constant stirring, until a permanent precipitate is just produced. Allow the mixture to stand for a short time and then filter it. After thoroughly washing the negative, immerse it in the bleaching solution until the image is white throughout. Wash in running water for 20 minutes and then immerse in the darkening solution until black. Wash the negative thoroughly before drying. If, after intensification, the negative is too dense it can be reduced with a 5 per cent. solution of hypo.

Caution. Mercuric chloride is a poison. Potassium cyanide is a very strong poison and must be handled with extreme care.

IIn-5 Uranium Intensifier

For considerable intensification of negatives.

STOCK SOLUTION A

Uranium nitrate	25 g
Water to make	1 litre

STOCK SOLUTION B

Potassium ferricyanide	25 g
Water to make	1 litre

For use, mix 4 parts A, 4 parts B and 1 part acetic acid, glacial. After immersing negative in intensifier, remove the yellow stain remaining by rinsing in water containing a trace of acetic acid. Wash the negative thoroughly before drying.

If required, the intensification can be removed with a weak solution of sodium carbonate.

Intensification by this process is of limited permanence.

TONERS

IT-1 Sulphide Toner

For sepia tones.

STOCK FERRICYANIDE SOLUTION

Potassium ferricyanide	100 g
Potassium bromide	100 g
Water to make	1 litre

For use, dilute 1 part with 9 parts water.

STOCK SULPHIDE SOLUTION

Sodium sulphide	50 g
Water to make	1 litre

For use, dilute 1 part with 9 parts water.

Prints should be fully developed. After the prints have been fixed and *thoroughly* washed, immerse them in the ferricyanide solution until the image is bleached. Then wash them for 10 minutes and place them in the sulphide solution, in which they will acquire a rich sepia colour. After darkening, wash prints for half-an-hour. Warmer tones can be produced by reducing the potassium bromide in the stock ferricyanide solution to one-quarter of the figure given. Colder tones can be obtained by immersing the washed black-and-white prints for 5 minutes in the sulphide bath *before* bleaching. Prints are then washed, bleached and darkened in the usual way.

IT-2 Hypo-alum Toner

For purplish-sepia tones.

Sodium thiosulphate (hypo), cryst.	150 g
Potassijm alum, cryst.	25 g
Water to make	1 litre

First dissolve the hypo in hot water, then add the alum a little at a time.

Until ripened, the bath has a reducing action; ripening is best done by immersing some waste prints or by adding to every 1 litre of the bath 0·14 gramme of silver nitrate dissolved in a little water to which is added just sufficient strong ammonia drop by drop, to re-dissolve the precipitate formed. This bath lasts for years and improves on keeping; it should be kept up to bulk by adding freshly made solution. The prints (which should be developed a little further than for black-and-white) are toned at about 50°C for about 10 minutes. At lower temperatures toning is unduly prolonged; higher temperatures give colder tones. Finally, wash the prints thoroughly and swab with a tuft of cotton wool. This process is suitable for bulk work. For warmer tones, add 1 gramme of potassium iodide to every 1 litre of the toning bath.

Dissolve the sulphide and warm the solution before adding the selenium; continue heating until the latter is completely dissolved. For use, dilute 1 part with 10 parts water.

Tone the prints for 2 to 3 minutes, keeping them moving in the bath. Wash the prints thoroughly before drying.

IT-6 Ferricyanide-iron Toner

For blue tones.

STOCK FERRICYANIDE SOLUTION

Potassium ferricyanide	2 g
Sulphuric acid, conc.	4 ml
Water to make	1 litre

First add the acid to the water, slowly; then dissolve the ferricyanide in the diluted acid.

STOCK IRON SOLUTION

Ferric ammonium citrate	2 g
Sulphuric acid, conc.	4 ml.
Water to make	1 litre

First add the acid to the water, slowly; then dissolve the ferric ammonium citrate in the diluted acid. For use, mix equal parts of of the two solutions just before using.

Caution. When making up both solutions the acid must be added to the water, drop by drop, and not the water to the acid. Adding water to sulphuric acid is highly dangerous.

The prints, which should be a little lighter than they are required to be when finished, must be thoroughly washed before toning. They should be immersed until the desired tone is obtained and then washed until the yellow stain disappears from the whites. Bleaching of the blue image, which may occur on washing, may be prevented by washing in very slightly acid water.

Conversion from SI to British Units

Length

$$1m \quad = \quad 1\cdot094\,\text{yd}$$
$$\quad = \quad 3\cdot281\,\text{ft}$$
$$1mm \quad = \quad 0\cdot039\,\text{in}$$
$$1\mu m \quad = \quad 39\cdot370\mu\text{in}$$
$$1\,\text{nm} \quad = \quad 10\text{Å (angstrom)}$$

Area

$$1\,m^2 \quad = \quad 1\cdot196\,\text{yd}^2$$

Capacity

$$1\,\text{l (litre)} \quad = \quad 0.220\,\text{gal (UK unit)}$$
$$1\,\text{l (litre)} \quad = \quad 0\cdot264\,\text{gal (US unit)}$$
$$1\,\text{ml} \quad = \quad 0\cdot035\,\text{fl oz (UK unit)}$$
$$1\,\text{ml} \quad = \quad 0\cdot034\,\text{fl oz (US unit)}$$

Velocity

$$1\,\text{km/h} \quad = \quad 0\cdot621\,\text{mile/h}$$
$$1\,\text{m/s} \quad = \quad 3\cdot281\,\text{ft/s}$$

Luminance

$1\,cd/m^2$ (candela per square metre) $\quad = \quad 0\cdot292$ foot-lamberts

Illumination

$1\,\text{lx (lux)} \quad = \quad 0\cdot093$ lumens per square foot (foot-candles)

Temperature

To convert temperatures in degrees Celsius (centigrade) to degrees Fahrenheit multiply the former by $\frac{9}{5}$ and then add 32.

Logarithms

When a number is multiplied by itself, the result is called the square, or second power of the number. Thus, 4 is called the square of 2, since $2 \times 2 = 4$. The square of 2 is usually written 2^2, the small figure ^{2} – called an index – indicating how many factors, each equal to the given number, are to be multiplied together. Thus:

$$2^3 = 2 \times 2 \times 2 \qquad = 8$$
$$2^4 = 2 \times 2 \times 2 \times 2 \quad = 16$$
$$2^5 = 2 \times 2 \times 2 \times 2 \times 2 = 32 \quad \text{etc.}$$

8 is called the third power of 2, 16 the fourth power, 32 the fifth power etc.

If we add the indices of two powers of the same number we obtain the index of their product. In this way, we can perform multiplication by the usually simpler method of addition. Thus:

$$2^2 \times 2^3 = 2^{2+3} = 2^5$$

Similarly, we can divide any power of a number by another power of the same number by subtracting the index of the latter power from the index of the former. Thus:

$$\frac{2^5}{2^3} = 2^{5-3} = 2^2$$

In these examples we have used only powers of 2, but powers of other numbers can be used to perform multiplication and division in the same way. Thus:

$$5^3 \times 5^2 = 5^{3+2} = 5^5$$
$$\text{and} \quad \frac{10^4}{10^2} = 10^{4-2} = 10^2$$

When indices of powers of 10 are used, as in the last example, they are called *common logarithms*. Every number can be expressed as some power of 10, and tables giving the common logarithms of all numbers have been prepared and their use saves much time in multiplication and division. Common logarithms – usually contracted simply to logarithms – are sometimes distinguished by the prefix "$\log_{10}$".

The logarithms of most numbers are not whole numbers, but fractions. Thus, the logarithm of 2 is $0 \cdot 3010$. It may not be easy to understand the meaning of this (i.e., that $2 = 10^{0 \cdot 3010}$), but there need be no difficulty in appreciating that fractional indices can be used to perform multiplication and division in the same way as integral ones. Thus:

$$2 \times 2 = 10^{0.3010+0.3010} = 10^{0.6020}$$

and 0·6020 is the logarithm of 4. (For certain photographic purposes it is convenient to remember that the logarithm of 2 is almost exactly 0·3).

This example, while illustrating the fact that fractional indices may be added to perform multiplication, does not well illustrate the (convenience) afforded by logarithms; in this instance they appear, in fact, to complicate the multiplication rather than to simplify it. When, however, we come to a problem such as multiplying 2·863 by 1·586, the value of logarithms is readily apparent. For:

$$\log 2{\cdot}863 = 0{\cdot}4569 \quad \text{(from table of}$$
$$\log 1{\cdot}586 = 0{\cdot}2004 \quad \text{logarithms)}$$
$$\text{Sum} = \overline{0{\cdot}6573}$$

and the number whose logarithm is 0·6573 is 4·542, which is the result required.

Tables of logarithms and detailed instructions for their use will be found in a number of textbooks and mathematical tables, as, for instance, *Logarithmic and Other Tables for Schools*, by Frank Castle (Macmillan). A table of two-figure logarithms is given on the next page.

Logarithmic scales

In photographic sensitometry, a logarithmic (log) exposure scale is almost invariably used, for reasons explained in Chapter 15. The relation between an arithmetical and a logarithmic exposure scale is illustrated by the figure below, where the increased space given to low values of exposure by the logarithmic scale will be noted.

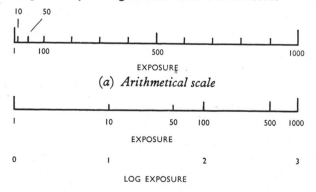

(a) *Arithmetical scale*

(b) *Logarithmic scale covering same range*

Two-figure logarithms

The following table of logarithms has proved useful in practical problems involving exposure and density. The table is confined to two-figure logarithms, as these give sufficient accuracy for most photographic purposes.

Logarithm	Number	Logarithm	Number	Logarithm	Number
·00	1·0	·35	2·2	·70	5·0
·01	1·0	·36	2·3	·71	5·1
·02	1·0	·37	2·3	·72	5·2
·03	1·1	·38	2·4	·73	5·4
·04	1·1	·39	2·5	·74	5·5
·05	1·1	·40	2·5	·75	5·6
·06	1·1	·41	2·6	·76	5·8
·07	1·2	·42	2·6	·77	5·9
·08	1·2	·43	2·7	·78	6·0
·09	1·2	·44	2·8	·79	6·2
·10	1·3	·45	2·8	·80	6·3
·11	1·3	·46	2·9	·81	6·5
·12	1·3	·47	3·0	·82	6·6
·13	1·3	·48	3·0	·83	6·8
·14	1·4	·49	3·1	·84	6·9
·15	1·4	·50	3·2	·85	7·1
·16	1·4	·51	3·2	·86	7·2
·17	1·5	·52	3·3	·87	7·4
·18	1·5	·53	3·4	·88	7·6
·19	1·5	·54	3·5	·89	7·8
·20	1·6	·55	3·5	·90	7·9
·21	1·6	·56	3·6	·91	8·1
·22	1·7	·57	3·7	·92	8·3
·23	1·7	·58	3·8	·93	8·5
·24	1·7	·59	3·9	·94	8·7
·25	1·8	·60	4·0	·95	8·9
·26	1·8	·61	4·1	·96	9·1
·27	1·9	·62	4·2	·97	9·3
·28	1·9	·63	4·3	·98	9·6
·29	2·0	·64	4·4	·99	9·8
·30	2·0	·65	4·5	1·00	10·0
·31	2·0	·66	4·6	2·00	100·0
·32	2·1	·67	4·7	3·00	1000·0
·33	2·1	·68	4·8		
·34	2·2	·69	4·9		

Trigonometrical Ratios

Sine, cosine, tangent etc.

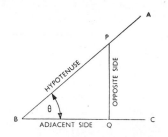

ABC contains an acute angle θ. From a point P on AB, a line PQ is drawn perpendicular to BC. Then, the ratios PQ/BP, BQ/BP and PQ/BQ are called respectively the *sine, cosine* and *tangent* of the angle θ. These terms are usually abbreviated to *sin, cos* and *tan.* Thus:

$$\sin \theta = \frac{PQ}{BP} = \frac{\text{opposite side}}{\text{hypotenuse}}$$

$$\cos \theta = \frac{BQ}{BP} = \frac{\text{adjacent side}}{\text{hypotenuse}}$$

$$\tan \theta = \frac{PQ}{BQ} = \frac{\text{opposite side}}{\text{adjacent side}}$$

Three other less widely used ratios are the *cosecant* (*cosec*), *secant* (*sec*) and *cotangent* (*cot*) of an angle, where:

$$\text{cosec } \theta = \frac{1}{\sin \theta} = \frac{BP}{PQ} = \frac{\text{hypotenuse}}{\text{opposite side}}$$

$$\sec \theta = \frac{1}{\cos \theta} = \frac{BP}{BQ} = \frac{\text{hypotenuse}}{\text{adjacent side}}$$

$$\cot \theta = \frac{1}{\tan \theta} = \frac{BQ}{PQ} = \frac{\text{adjacent side}}{\text{opposite side}}$$

The values of the trigonometrical ratios (sine, cosine, tangent, cosecant, secant and cotangent) of angles from 0 to 90° are published in mathematical tables, as, for instance, *Logarithmic and Other Tables for Schools*, by Frank Castle (Macmillan).

Radians

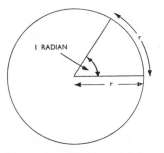

If an arc equal in length to the radius be measured along the circumference of a circle (see figure), the angle subtended at the centre by the arc is said to be a *radian*. This angle, which is equal to about 57° 18′, is another unit used in trigonometry.

The pH Scale

Every aqueous solution contains hydrogen and hydroxyl ions (charged atoms or groups of atoms). In a neutral solution, such as pure water, the two types of ions are present in equal concentrations of 10^{-7} g. ions per litre. In an acid solution there is an excess of hydrogen ions over hydroxyl ions, and in an alkaline solution an excess of hydroxyl ions over hydrogen ions, but the product of the two concentrations remains at 10^{-14}, as in pure water.

The degree of acidity or alkalinity of a solution is related to the relative concentrations of the two ions, and for this purpose the *pH scale* is used, where:

$$pH = \log_{10} \left(\frac{1}{\text{hydrogen ion concentration}} \right)$$

On this scale, pure water – a neutral solution – has a pH of 7. An acid solution has a pH below 7, and an alkaline solution a pH above 7. The greater the amount by which the pH of a solution differs from 7, the greater is its acidity or alkalinity. The limits of the scale are 0 and 14. It will be appreciated that, since the pH scale is logarithmic, quite small changes in pH may indicate significant changes in the activity of a solution.

pH can be determined precisely only by electrometric means, using an instrument known as a *pH meter*. For many photographic purposes, however, the pH of a solution may be determined with sufficient accuracy by means of *indicator papers* – strips of paper impregnated with substances which change colour according to the degree of acidity or alkalinity of the solution. There are papers suited to most parts of the pH scale.

Some Outstanding Dates and Names
in the Early History of Photography

1725 J. H. Schulze

Established light sensitivity of silver nitrate. Produced images by allowing sun's rays to fall on flask containing a mixture of chalk, silver and nitric acid, around which stencils of opaque paper were pasted.

1777 C. W. Scheele

Noted that blue and violet light is much more active in darkening silver chloride than red or orange.

1802 T. Wedgwood and (Sir) H. Davy

Printing of silhouettes by contact on paper or leather sensitised with silver nitrate. No fixation. First light-sensitive surface attached to a support. Material found to be too slow to record images produced in camera obscura.

1812 W. H. Wollaston

Meniscus lens ("landscape lens") for camera obscura. (The camera obscura using a pinhole was known at least as early as the eleventh century; with convex lens as early as the sixteenth century.)

1819 (Sir) J. F. W. Herschel

Discovery of thiosulphates (hypo) and their property of dissolving silver halides.

1816 J. N. Niépce

Obtained negative record of camera obscura image on paper sensitised with silver chloride. Partial fixation with nitric acid. Unable to print through negative to obtain a positive.

1822 J. N. Niépce

Permanent copy of engraving by contact printing on to a glass plate sensitised with bitumen of Judæa. The bitumen, normally soluble in lavender oil, became insoluble in this oil on exposure to light. In the following years, Niépce used zinc and pewter plates which, after the image had been perpetuated, were etched in weak acid to form printing plates. Process named "heliography".

1826 J. N. Niépce
First permanent photographs from nature. Bitumen process on pewter plate, giving a direct positive picture.

1828 C. and V. Chevalier
Achromatized landscape lens for use on camera obscura.

1829 L. J. M. Daguerre and J. N. Niépce
Joined articles of partnership. (J. N. Niépce died in **1833**; his son Isidore Niépce then took his place as Daguerre's partner.)

1835 W. H. Fox Talbot
Photogenic drawings. Negative prints on print-out paper sensitised with common salt and silver nitrate, forming silver chloride. Fixation with potassium iodide or by prolonged washing in salt water. Print-out exposure by contact or in the camera obscura. Right-reading positives obtained by contact printing from the negatives.

1837 L. J. M. Daguerre
First successful Daguerrotype. Employed silvered copper plate sensitised with iodine vapour, which formed layer of silver iodide. Development of the latent image by mercury vapour. Fixation with common salt. Image laterally reversed.

1837 J. B. Reade
Photomicrographs with solar microscope. Paper sensitised with solutions of common salt and silver nitrate, producing silver chloride. This was washed over with gallic acid immediately before and during the exposure. Fixation with hypo. (Reade did not realise that he was developing a latent image.)

1839 F. D. Arago
Announced Daguerre's discovery to the Academy of Science, Paris, 7th January.

1839 M. Faraday
Showed Fox Talbot's photogenic drawings and gave the first public description of the process at a meeting of the Royal Institution, London, 25th January.

1839 W. H. Fox Talbot
Disclosed working details of photogenic drawings to the Royal Society, London, 21st February.

1839   F. D. Arago
Made public, on the instructions of the French Government, the working details of the Daguerrotype process, at a joint meeting of Academies of Science and Fine Arts, Paris, 19th August.

1839   (Sir) J. F. W. Herschel
Use of the words "photography", "negative" and "positive". Suggested to Fox Talbot the use of hypo as fixing agent.

1840   J. Petzval
Designed first lens of sufficiently high aperture for portraiture. First lens to be mathematically computed. Manufactured by Voigtländer.

1840   J. W. Goddard
Increased the speed of Daguerrotype plates by fuming the iodized plate with bromine.

1840   H. L. Fizeau
Tones of Daguerrotype images softened and enriched by gold toning.

1840   W. H. Fox Talbot
Discovery of the possibility of the development of the latent image by gallic acid.

1841   W. H. Fox Talbot
Calotype process (later named Talbotype process). Negative prints on silver iodide paper bathed in silver nitrate and gallic acid. Development of the latent image by bathing in the same solution. Fixation with potassium bromide; later with hypo. Positives obtained by contact printing from the negatives on to silver chloride paper.

1847   C. F. A. Niépce de Saint Victor
Negatives on glass. Albumen process. Printed more rapidly than paper negatives and gave clearer prints.

1850   L. D. Blanquart-Evrard
Albumen paper for printing of positives from negatives. Recorded more detail than Fox Talbot's salted paper and became almost universal method of print-making for remainder of century.

1851   F. Scott Archer
Wet collodion process. Glass coated with collodion in which potassium iodide was dissolved, dipped in silver nitrate solution and exposed while wet. Development of latent image with pyrogallic acid or ferrous sulphate. Fixation with hypo or potassium cyanide.

1861 J. Clerk Maxwell
Demonstrated three-colour separation and additive synthesis.

1864 (Sir) J. W. Swan
Introduced carbon tissue commercially and thus first made carbon printing really practicable.

1866 J. H. Dallmeyer, H. A. Steinheil
Introduced, independently, the rapid rectilinear lens.

1868 L. Ducos du Hauron
Proposed various methods of three-colour photography, including subtractive colour synthesis.

1871 R. L. Maddox
Gelatin dry plates. At first, positive-type plates for physical development only.

1873 H. W. Vogel
Discovery of colour sensitisation by dyes.

1880 (Sir) W. de W. Abney
First use of hydroquinone as a developer.

1882 J. Clayton and P. A. Attout
First gelatin colour-sensitive plates (isochromatic).

1883 Howard E. Farmer
"Farmer's" reducer (ferricyanide-hypo).

1887 H. Goodwin
Applied for patent (granted in 1898) for the manufacture of sensitive material on a celluloid base.

1888 G. Eastman
First roll film camera. Employed paper with an emulsion which could be stripped after processing, for printing purposes.

1890 P. Rudolph and E. Abbe
Anastigmatic lenses. Manufactured by Zeiss.

1890 F. Hurter and V. C. Driffield
Scientific study of the behaviour of photographic materials (sensitometry).

1891   A. Bogisch
First use of metol as a developer (introduced by Hauff).

1893   H. D. Taylor
Cooke triplet – an anastigmatic lens with only three elements. Manufactured by Taylor, Taylor and Hobson.

1893   L. Baekeland
Unwashed paper emulsions ("gaslight" paper.)

British Standards on Photography

Many aspects of photography are the subjects of British Standards. Details of some photographic standards of general interest are given below. These particulars are reprinted by kind permission from the British Standards Yearbook: A Sectional List of British Standards on Cinematography and Photography is available free of charge from the British Standards Institution, Sales Branch, 101–113 Pentonville Road, London, N.1.

Cameras, lenses and shutters

BS. 1019 : 1963 Photographic lenses. Definitions, methods and accuracy of marking

Defines the parts of a photographic lens, focal length and associated quantities, and the aperture and related quantities. Marking requirements, accuracy of markings and sequence of markings are specified. Appendices are provided covering the methods of measurement of focal length and of effective aperture and aperture ratio.

BS. 1618 : 1961 Dimensions of lenses and lens attachments for still cameras

Provides a range of front lens barrel diameters from 21 to 100 mm. and specifies the appropriate lengths of bearing surface for push-on lens attachments, e.g. hoods and filters.

BS. 1613 : 1961 Determining the resolving power of lenses for cameras

Provides a method of determining the resolving power of process, general purpose (including cinematograph taking lenses), air camera and copying lenses under appropriate conditions.

BS. 3824 : 1964 Colour transmission of photographic lenses

Requirements for a standard colour contribution for lenses.

BS. 1592 : 1958 Camera shutters

Applies to shutters for still-cameras, not for cine-cameras, and in particular to front shutters and focal-plane shutters. For each of these types of shutter the standard gives a series of definitions and prescribes the exposure-time markings and performance requirements. Limits for the effect of humidity and temperature on performance are laid down. Synchro-flash mechanisms and cable-release sockets are standardised, and recommended methods of testing shutters are given in appendices.

BS. 1487 : 1948 Picture sizes and location of rear windows of film cameras
Specifies the dimensions of picture sizes for film cameras and the dimensions required to locate the rear window for each picture size. It also gives the appropriate British Standard spool size or cassette reference for each type of film and includes a table showing British Standard sizes for backing paper and spools, with manufacturer's present references.

Sizes of sensitised materials

BS. 1772 : 1951 Sizes of photographic sheet-film other than x-ray film
Establishes a series of nominal sizes in both British and metric measure, ranging from $2\frac{1}{4}$ in. $\times 3\frac{1}{4}$ in. to 30 in. $\times$ 40 in. The appropriate cutting sizes and tolerances on the length, width and squareness are laid down. The method of notching the film to indicate the emulsion side is given, and the manner in which the nominal size is to be marked on the packaged film is also specified.

BS. 1491 : 1970 Dimensions of 127, 120 and 620 roll film, backing paper and film spools
Specifies dimensions of roll film, backing paper and film spools as well as the dimensions of the printing of the various series of numbers on the backing paper for purposes of correct location in rear windows of standard cameras.

BS. 3368 : 1961 Identification of exposed colour roll film
Specifies means of identification of the two main types of colour roll film (for still cameras) by suitable markings on the end of the backing paper visible after the film has been used in the camera.

BS. 1879 : 1952 Dimensions of 35 mm. film for miniature cameras
Relates to the dimensions of 35-mm. film for loading into cassettes to be used in miniature cameras. It specifies the essential dimensions

relating to the overall length of the film, and the width and length of the tongue, for 36 and 20 exposures of a picture size of 24 mm. × 36 mm.

BS. 3540 : 1962   The identification of the emulsion side of edge-marked roll film for still picture cameras

Specifies a means of identifying the emulsion side of roll film and 35 mm. film for still picture cameras, which carries edge markings. The disposition of these edge markings (letters, figures or arrows) provides an easy means for identifying the two sides of the film.

BS. 1406 : 1960   Sizes of sensitised photographic plates

Specifies the nominal sizes, cutting sizes, thicknesses and squareness of sensitized photographic plates except those intended for photogrammetry.

BS. 1112 : 1962   Sizes of photographic paper for general use

Gives dimensions and tolerances for paper in sheet and roll form and also postcard material. A supplementary table gives details of papers intended for export purposes. A quantity packing system and identification scheme for contrast gradation are also included.

BS. 3545 : 1962   Thickness of photographic papers

Covers a series of eight group designations for the bulking (average) thickness of sensitised photographic paper which has not been subject to further photographic treatment after manufacture. An appendix provides a method for determining the bulking thickness per sheet.

Film speed and exposure

BS. 1380 : Part 1 : 1962   Method for determining the speed of sensitised photographic materials: negative monochrome material for use in daylight

Lays down the method of determining the photographic speed of negative monochrome sensitised materials for use in daylight and provides a table of British Standard arithmetical speeds. An appendix is provided dealing with the log base 2 speed of photographic material and an additive system of photographic exposure. A further appendix provides a comparative table of the new British Standard arithmetical speeds and the corresponding adjusted British Standard logarithmic (base 10) speeds which are now obsolescent.

BS. 1380 : Part 2: 1963   Method for determining the speed of sensitised photographic materials: reversal colour film for still and cine photography

Provides a method of determining the photographic speed (arithmetical) of reversal colour film for still and cine photography. An appendix introduces the concept of log base 2 speeds and describes the Additive system of Photographic Exposure (APEX).

BS. 1383 : 1966   Photo-electric exposure meters

Requirements for exposure meters of both the reflected light type and the incident light type; methods of test covering acceptance characteristics and calibration procedures.

BS. 1437 : 1948   Methods of determining filter factors of photographic negative materials

Prescribes methods of determining filter factors for photographic negative materials, according to the type of use. It includes a description of the standard light source to be used for this purpose.

Processing equipment

BS. 1378 : 1947   Dishes for photographic processing

Provides eight standard sizes of dish to cover work up to 20×24 in. and specifies the shape and dimensions of the dishes, and essential features of design.

BS. 2476 : 1954   Dimensions of photographic processing tanks

Specifies the nominal rated capacity, maximum size of sensitised material and minimum internal dimensions of photographic processing tanks, dental x-ray film tanks and finisher tanks. Diagrams are included showing the location of the dimensions of galleries and of bung holes where applicable. Reference numbers are specified for each tank type.

BS. 1379 : 1947   Bite of film clips

Covers clips used to hold photographic film during processing, and prescribes the maximum permissible projection inwards from the edge of a film for any part of the clip that could touch the film during normal manipulation.

BS. 2753 : 1956 Dimensions of processing hangers for sensitised material

Specifies the essential dimensions of hangers for sensitised material of sizes up to 14×17 in., for use in processing tanks conforming to *BS. 2476*. Four standard types of hanger are recognized and the essential features of construction and design are indicated. Certain chemical requirements are included for the materials of which the hangers are made, and surface finish requirements are also stated.

Slides, filmstrips and still projectors

BS. 1917 : 1968 Slides and filmstrips
Specifies details for 5 × 5 cm and 7 × 7 cm slides as well as filmstrips.

BS. 2698 : 1960 Containers and notes for filmstrips
Specifies dimensions and certain other details for unit containers and details of labelling and identification marking. Also specifies page size, cover and binding edge of filmstrip notes. Examples of outer containers are illustrated.

BS. 1915 : 1968 Still projectors
Design and performance requirements for slide (5 × 5 cm and 7 × 7 cm), film (35 mm) and combined slide and film strip projectors. Appendix gives electrical and safety requirements and methods of test. Methods for measurement of performance are given in BS. 4120.

BS. 4120 : 1968 Methods of measurement of performance of still projectors
General conditions of test. Test methods for determining accuracy of location of the pictures projected on the screen, resolving power, uniformity of illumination, temperature rise of slide, distance between lens and screen for a 1 metre wide picture, light output and working temperature of casing. Annex A gives outline of Consumer Council's informative labelling (Teltag) scheme for still projectors and Annex B the use and care instructions required by the scheme.

Miscellaneous

BS. 1496 : 1948 Photographic safelight screens and housings
Specifies dimensions for rectangular safelight screens and housings, to provide for interchangeability.

B.S. 1384 : 1947   Measurement of photographic transmission density

Classifies the various types of diffuse transmission density and defines three fundamental types, diffuse density, doubly-diffuse density, and specular density. The standard then specifies diffuse density in further detail, distinguishing two main groups, British Standard diffuse visual density and British Standard diffuse printing density. Three methods for determining British Standard diffuse density are fully described, as a basis for the calibration of densitometers.

B.S. 1359 : 1947   Photographic conversion tables

Provides conversion factors and tables for metric and imperial weights and measures, for use in packaging and using photographic chemicals. The standard includes conversion tables and factors for American measures and compound conversion factors.

B.S. 2833 : 1968   Schedule of expendable photographic flash bulbs

Classification into five classes according to luminous flux/time or luminous intensity/time characteristics. Specifies the type of caps and bases and maximum dimensions of bulbs and cube. Applies to clear and blue flash bulbs.

B.S. 4095 : 1966   Method for determination of photographic flash numbers

Definitions and procedure for class M flash bulbs or electronic flash tubes concentrated by means of a reflector with a minimum angle of 25°.

B.S. 4329 : 1968   Flash apparatus using expendable photographic flash bulbs

Gives performance and constructional requirements as a guide to manufacturers for development and manufacture of flash apparatus using expendable bulbs. Includes details of the camera shoe, which complies with ISO Recommendation R 518.

B.S. 3337 : 1961   Dimensions of plug part and lampholder for capless photo-flash lamps

Specifies the principal dimensions for the plug part and lampholder of capless photo-flash lamps. Dimensions for recommended gauges are also given in an appendix.

BS. 3205 : 1969   Photographic electronic flash equipment

Describes performance in terms of number of flashes (for battery-operated equipment), charging time and stored energy. Gives specific electrical safety requirements for flash tubes operating above and below 600V, and for the trigger circuit, together with extensive general requirements for the equipment as a whole in an appendix. Includes constructional details for charge indicator, camera shoe, electrical and battery connections and battery compartment. Lists information to be supplied with equipment and marking requirements.

BS. 1153 : 1955   Recommendations for the storage of microfilm

Applies to microfilms, made of a film base, which comply with the burning test requirements of *BS. 850,* and which have a nitrate nitrogen content not exceeding 0·15 per cent. Storage conditions relating to processing, protection from fire and water, chemical contamination, temperature, relative humidity, air conditioning and other hazards of storage are given. Containers, film removal and viewing and conditions for transportion are also dealt with. Methods of testing for residual thiosulphate and for injurious residual silver are given in the appendices.

ALPHABETICAL

INDEX

* To the text – excluding the Appendix